Texas Student Edition

SpringBoard®
Mathematics

Course 3

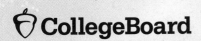
CollegeBoard

About the College Board

The College Board is a mission-driven not-for-profit organization that connects students to college success and opportunity. Founded in 1900, the College Board was created to expand access to higher education. Today, the membership association is made up of over 6,000 of the world's leading educational institutions and is dedicated to promoting excellence and equity in education. Each year, the College Board helps more than seven million students prepare for a successful transition to college through programs and services in college readiness and college success—including the SAT® and the Advanced Placement Program®. The organization also serves the education community through research and advocacy on behalf of students, educators, and schools.

For further information, visit www.collegeboard.org.

ISBN: 1-4573-0122-9
ISBN: 978-1-4573-0122-3

5 6 7 8 9   19 20 21 22
Printed in the United States of America

Acknowledgments

The College Board gratefully acknowledges the outstanding work of the classroom teachers and writers who have been integral to the development of this revised program. The end product is testimony to their expertise, understanding of student learning needs, and dedication to rigorous but accessible mathematics instruction.

Michael Allwood
Brunswick School
Greenwich, Connecticut

Floyd Bullard
North Carolina School of Science and Mathematics
Durham, North Carolina

Marcia Chumas
East Mecklenburg High School
Charlotte, North Carolina

Kathy Fritz
Plano Independent School District
Plano, Texas

Shawn Harris
Ronan Middle School
Ronan, Montana

Marie Humphrey
David W. Butler High School
Charlotte,
North Carolina

Brian Kotz
Montgomery College
Monrovia, Maryland

Chris Olsen
Prairie Lutheran School
Cedar Rapids, Iowa

Dr. Roxy Peck
California Polytechnic Institute
San Luis Obispo, California

Katie Sheets
Harrisburg School
Harrisburg,
South Dakota

Andrea Sukow
Mathematics Consultant
Nashville, Tennessee

Stephanie Tate
Hillsborough School District
Tampa, Florida

SpringBoard Mathematics Product Development

Betty Barnett
Executive Director
Content Development

John Nelson
Mathematics Editor

Allen M. D. von Pallandt, Ph.D.
Senior Director
Mathematics Content Development

Judy Windle
Senior Math Instructional Specialist

Acknowledgments *continued*

Research and Planning Advisors

We also wish to thank the members of our SpringBoard Advisory Council and the many educators who gave generously of their time and their ideas as we conducted research for both the print and online programs. Your suggestions and reactions to ideas helped immeasurably as we planned the revisions. We gratefully acknowledge the teachers and administrators in the following districts.

ABC Unified
Cerritos, California

Albuquerque Public Schools
Albuquerque, New Mexico

Amarillo School District
Amarillo, Texas

Baltimore County Public Schools
Baltimore, Maryland

Bellevue School District 405
Bellevue, Washington

Charlotte Mecklenburg Schools
Charlotte, North Carolina

Clark County School District
Las Vegas, Nevada

Cypress Fairbanks ISD
Houston, Texas

District School Board of
Collier County
Collier County, Florida

Denver Public Schools
Denver, Colorado

Frisco ISD
Frisco, Texas

Gilbert Unified School District
Gilbert, Arizona

Grand Prairie ISD
Grand Prairie, Texas

Hillsborough County Public
Schools
Tampa, Florida

Houston Independent School
District
Houston, Texas

Hobbs Municipal Schools
Hobbs, New Mexico

Irving Independent School
District
Irving, Texas

Kenton County School District
Fort Wright, Kentucky

Lee County Public Schools
Fort Myers, Florida

Newton County Schools
Covington, Georgia

Noblesville Schools
Noblesville, Indiana

Oakland Unified School District
Oakland, California

Orange County Public Schools
Orlando, Florida

School District of Palm Beach
County
Palm Beach, Florida

Peninsula School District
Gig Harbor, Washington

Polk County Public Schools
Bartow, Florida

Quakertown Community School
District
Quakertown, Pennsylvania

Rio Rancho Public Schools
Rio Rancho, New Mexico

Ronan School District
Ronan, Montana

St. Vrain Valley School District
Longmont, Colorado

Scottsdale Public Schools
Phoenix, Arizona

Seminole County Public Schools
Sanford, Florida

Southwest ISD
San Antonio, Texas

Spokane Public Schools
Spokane, Washington

Volusia County Schools
DeLand, Florida

Contents

Contents *continued*

Contents *continued*

Contents *continued*

To the Student

Welcome to the SpringBoard program. We hope you will discover how SpringBoard can help you achieve high academic standards, reach your learning goals, and prepare for success in future mathematics studies.

The program has been created with you in mind: the content you need to learn, the tools to help you learn, and the critical thinking skills that help you build confidence in your own knowledge of mathematics. The College Board publishes the SpringBoard program. It also publishes the PSAT/NMSQT, the SAT, and the Advanced Placement exams—all exams that you are likely to encounter in your student years. Preparing you to perform well on those exams and to develop the mathematics skills needed for high school success is the primary purpose of this program.

Standards-Based Mathematics Learning

Knowledge of mathematics helps prepare you for future success in college, in work, and in your personal life. We all encounter some form of mathematics daily, from calculating the cost of groceries to determining the cost of materials and labor needed to build a new road. The SpringBoard program is based on learning standards that identify the mathematics skills and knowledge that you should master to succeed in high school and in future college-level work. In this course, the standards follow these broad areas of mathematics knowledge:

- Mathematical process standards
- Number and operations
- Proportionality
- Expressions, equations, and relationships
- Measurement and data
- Personal financial literacy

Mathematical process standards guide your study of mathematics. They are actions you take to help you understand mathematical concepts rather than just mathematical procedures. For example, the mathematical process standards suggest the following:

- Connect mathematics concepts to everyday life and situations around you.
- Use models to solve problems and to justify solutions and their reasonableness.
- Choose tools, such as number lines, protractors, technology, or paper and pencil to help you solve problems.
- Communicate what you are learning both orally and in writing.
- Create and use representations to communicate mathematical ideas.
- Analyze mathematical relationships to connect ideas.
- Learn and use precise mathematical language in both written and oral communication.

In the middle school years, your study of mathematics begins with a basic understanding of fractions and the operations performed with them. Your study continues with the development of a deep understanding of the rational numbers, their different representations, and the connections between these numbers and other number systems and operations. You will need a broad understanding of addition, subtraction, and multiplication with rational numbers, along with computational fluency with whole-number operations.

As you continue your studies, you will examine ratios and rates, which will allow you to make comparisons between numbers. Ratios and rates represent proportionality. Understanding the concept of proportionality is critical to future success in your study of algebra and the rest of the high school mathematics curriculum.

See pages xiii–xvi for a complete list of the Texas Essential Knowledge and Skills for this course.

Strategies for Learning Mathematics

Some tools to help you learn are built into every activity. At the beginning of each activity, you will see suggested learning strategies. Each of these strategies is explained in full in the Resources section of your book. As you learn to use each strategy, you'll have the opportunity to decide which strategies work best for you. Suggested learning strategies include:

- Reading strategies, which help you learn to look at problem descriptions in different ways, from marking the text to highlight key information to turning problem information into questions that help you break the problem down into its separate parts.
- Writing strategies, which help you focus on your purpose for writing and what you're writing about.
- Problem-solving strategies, which give you multiple ways to approach the problem, from learning to identify the tasks within a problem to looking for patterns or working backward to see how the problem is set up.
- Collaborative strategies, which you'll use with your classmates to explore concepts and problems in group discussions and working with partners.

Building Mathematics Knowledge and Skills

Whether it is mathematics or sports or cooking, one way we learn something really well is by practice and repetition. To help you learn mathematics, the SpringBoard program is built around problem solving, reasoning and justification, communication, connections between concepts and ideas, and visual representation of mathematical concepts.

Problem Solving Many of the problems in this book are based on real-life situations that require you to *analyze* the situation and the information in the problem, *make decisions, determine the strategies* you'll use to solve the problem, and *justify* your solution. Having a real-world focus helps you see how mathematics is used in everyday life.

Reasoning and Justification One part of learning mathematics, or any subject, is learning not only how to solve problems but also why you solved them the way you did. You will have many opportunities to predict possible solutions and then to verify solutions. You will be asked to explain the reasoning behind how you solved the problem, the mathematics concepts involved, and why your approach was appropriate for solving the problem.

Communication When learning a language, saying words out loud helps you learn to pronounce the words and to remember them. Communicating about mathematics, orally and in writing, with your classmates and teachers helps you organize your learning and explain mathematics concepts and problem-solving strategies more precisely. Sharing your ideas and thoughts allows you and your classmates to build on each other's ideas and expand your own understanding.

Mathematics Connections As you study mathematics, you will learn many different concepts and ways of solving problems. Reading the problem descriptions will take you into the real-life applications of mathematics. As you develop your mathematics knowledge, you will see the many connections between mathematics concepts and between mathematics and your own life.

Representations Artists create representations through drawings and paintings. In mathematics, representations can take many forms, such as numeric, verbal, graphic, or symbolic. In this course, you are encouraged to use representations to organize problem information, present possible solutions, and communicate your reasoning. Creating representations is a tool you can use to gain understanding of concepts and communicate that understanding to others.

We hope you enjoy your study of mathematics using the SpringBoard program. We, the writers, are all classroom teachers, and we created this program because we love mathematics. We wanted to inspire you to learn mathematics *and* build confidence that you can be successful in your math studies and in using mathematics in daily life.

Texas Essential Knowledge and Skills
Grade 8

8.1 Mathematical process standards. The student uses mathematical processes to acquire and demonstrate mathematical understanding. The student is expected to:

8.1.A apply mathematics to problems arising in everyday life, society, and the workplace;

8.1.B use a problem-solving model that incorporates analyzing given information, formulating a plan or strategy, determining a solution, justifying the solution, and evaluating the problem-solving process and the reasonableness of the solution;

8.1.C select tools, including real objects, manipulatives, paper and pencil, and technology as appropriate, and techniques, including mental math, estimation, and number sense as appropriate, to solve problems;

8.1.D communicate mathematical ideas, reasoning, and their implications using multiple representations, including symbols, diagrams, graphs, and language as appropriate;

8.1.E create and use representations to organize, record, and communicate mathematical ideas;

8.1.F analyze mathematical relationships to connect and communicate mathematical ideas; and

8.1.G display, explain, and justify mathematical ideas and arguments using precise mathematical language in written or oral communication.

8.2 Number and operations. The student applies mathematical process standards to represent and use real numbers in a variety of forms. The student is expected to:

8.2.A extend previous knowledge of sets and subsets using a visual representation to describe relationships between sets of real numbers;

8.2.B approximate the value of an irrational number, including π and square roots of numbers less than 225, and locate that rational number approximation on a number line;

8.2.C convert between standard decimal notation and scientific notation; and

8.2.D order a set of real numbers arising from mathematical and real-world contexts.

8.3 Proportionality. The student applies mathematical process standards to use proportional relationships to describe dilations. The student is expected to:

8.3.A generalize that the ratio of corresponding sides of similar shapes are proportional, including a shape and its dilation;

8.3.B compare and contrast the attributes of a shape and its dilation(s) on a coordinate plane; and

8.3.C use an algebraic representation to explain the effect of a given positive rational scale factor applied to two-dimensional figures on a coordinate plane with the origin as the center of dilation.

8.4 Proportionality. The student applies mathematical process standards to explain proportional and non-proportional relationships involving slope. The student is expected to:

8.4.A use similar right triangles to develop an understanding that slope, m, given as the rate comparing the change in y-values to the change in x-values, $(y_2 - y_1)/(x_2 - x_1)$, is the same for any two points (x_1, y_1) and (x_2, y_2) on the same line;

8.4.B graph proportional relationships, interpreting the unit rate as the slope of the line that models the relationship; and

8.4.C use data from a table or graph to determine the rate of change or slope and y-intercept in mathematical and real-world problems.

8.5 Proportionality. The student applies mathematical process standards to use proportional and non-proportional relationships to develop foundational concepts of functions. The student is expected to:

8.5.A represent linear proportional situations with tables, graphs, and equations in the form of $y = kx$;

8.5.B represent linear non-proportional situations with tables, graphs, and equations in the form of $y = mx + b$, where $b \neq 0$;

8.5.C contrast bivariate sets of data that suggest a linear relationship with bivariate sets of data that do not suggest a linear relationship from a graphical representation;

8.5.D use a trend line that approximates the linear relationship between bivariate sets of data to make predictions;

8.5.E solve problems involving direct variation;

8.5.F distinguish between proportional and non-proportional situations using tables, graphs, and equations in the form $y = kx$ or $y = mx + b$, where $b \neq 0$;

8.5.G identify functions using sets of ordered pairs, tables, mappings, and graphs;

8.5.H identify examples of proportional and non-proportional functions that arise from mathematical and real-world problems; and

8.5.I write an equation in the form $y = mx + b$ to model a linear relationship between two quantities using verbal, numerical, tabular, and graphical representations.

8.6 Expressions, equations, and relationships.
The student applies mathematical process standards to develop mathematical relationships and make connections to geometric formulas. The student is expected to:

8.6.A describe the volume formula $V = Bh$ of a cylinder in terms of its base area and its height;

8.6.B model the relationship between the volume of a cylinder and a cone having both congruent bases and heights and connect that relationship to the formulas; and

8.6.C use models and diagrams to explain the Pythagorean theorem.

8.7 Expressions, equations, and relationships.
The student applies mathematical process standards to use geometry to solve problems. The student is expected to:

8.7.A solve problems involving the volume of cylinders, cones, and spheres;

8.7.B use previous knowledge of surface area to make connections to the formulas for lateral and total surface area and determine solutions for problems involving rectangular prisms, triangular prisms, and cylinders;

8.7.C use the Pythagorean Theorem and its converse to solve problems; and

8.7.D determine the distance between two points on a coordinate plane using the Pythagorean Theorem.

8.8 Expressions, equations, and relationships.
The student applies mathematical process standards to use one-variable equations or inequalities in problem situations. The student is expected to:

8.8.A write one-variable equations or inequalities with variables on both sides that represent problems using rational number coefficients and constants;

8.8.B write a corresponding real-world problem when given a one-variable equation or inequality with variables on both sides of the equal sign using rational number coefficients and constants;

8.8.C model and solve one-variable equations with variables on both sides of the equal sign that represent mathematical and real-world problems using rational number coefficients and constants; and

8.8.D use informal arguments to establish facts about the angle sum and exterior angle of triangles, the angles created when parallel lines are cut by a transversal, and the angle-angle criterion for similarity of triangles.

8.9 Expressions, equations, and relationships.
The student applies mathematical process standards to use multiple representations to develop foundational concepts of

simultaneous linear equations. The student is expected to identify and verify the values of x and y that simultaneously satisfy two linear equations in the form $y = mx + b$ from the intersections of the graphed equations.

8.10 Two-dimensional shapes. The student applies mathematical process standards to develop transformational geometry concepts. The student is expected to:

8.10.A generalize the properties of orientation and congruence of rotations, reflections, translations, and dilations of two-dimensional shapes on a coordinate plane;

8.10.B differentiate between transformations that preserve congruence and those that do not;

8.10.C explain the effect of translations, reflections over the x- or y-axis, and rotations limited to 90°, 180°, 270°, and 360° as applied to two-dimensional shapes on a coordinate plane using an algebraic representation; and

8.10.D model the effect on linear and area measurements of dilated two-dimensional shapes.

8.11 Measurement and data. The student applies mathematical process standards to use statistical procedures to describe data. The student is expected to:

8.11.A construct a scatterplot and describe the observed data to address questions of association such as linear, non-linear, and no association between bivariate data;

8.11.B determine the mean absolute deviation and use this quantity as a measure of the average distance data are from the mean using a data set of no more than 10 data points; and

8.11.C simulate generating random samples of the same size from a population with known characteristics to develop the notion of a random sample being representative of the population from which it was selected.

8.12 Personal financial literacy. The student applies mathematical process standards to develop an economic way of thinking and problem solving useful in one's life as a knowledgeable consumer and investor. The student is expected to:

8.12.A solve real-world problems comparing how interest rate and loan length affect the cost of credit;

8.12.B calculate the total cost of repaying a loan, including credit cards and easy access loans, under various rates of interest and over different periods using an online calculator;

8.12.C explain how small amounts of money invested regularly, including money saved for college and retirement, grow over time;

8.12.D calculate and compare simple interest and compound interest earnings;

8.12.E identify and explain the advantages and disadvantages of different payment methods;

8.12.F analyze situations to determine if they represent financially responsible decisions and identify the benefits of financial responsibility and the costs of financial irresponsibility; and

8.12.G estimate the cost of a two-year and four-year college education, including family contribution, and devise a periodic savings plan for accumulating the money needed to contribute to the total cost of attendance for at least the first year of college.

Numerical Relationships

Unit Overview

In this unit, you will extend your knowledge of numbers as you investigate patterns, study powers and roots, and exponents and scientific notation. You will apply your knowledge of numbers to practical situations and real-world problems.

Key Terms

As you study this unit, add these and other terms to your math notebook. Include in your notes your prior knowledge of each word, as well as your experiences in using the word in different mathematical examples. If needed, ask for help in pronouncing new words and add information on pronunciation to your math notebook. It is important that you learn new terms and use them correctly in your class discussions and in your problem solutions.

Academic Vocabulary

- refute

Math Terms

- sequence
- conjecture
- absolute value
- reciprocal
- power
- base
- exponent
- exponential form
- square root
- perfect square
- cubing a number
- index
- cube root
- rational number
- terminating decimal
- repeating decimal
- irrational number
- scientific notation
- standard form

ESSENTIAL QUESTIONS

? Why is it important to understand procedures for working with different kinds of numbers?

? How are exponents and scientific notation useful in solving problems?

EMBEDDED ASSESSMENTS

These assessments, following activities 2, 5, and 8 will give you an opportunity to demonstrate your understanding of numbers and numerical relationships.

Embedded Assessment 1:

Patterns and Quantitative Reasoning p. 31

Embedded Assessment 2:

Representing Rational and Irrational Numbers p. 69

Embedded Assessment 3:

Exponents and Scientific Notation p. 101

**Write your answers on notebook paper.
Show your work.**

1. Find the product and quotient of each pair of numbers.
   a. 24.6 and 1.2
   b. 1.95 and .25

2. Arrange the following numbers in increasing order.

   2.3, 45.1, 18.735, 0.9862, 7

3. Give the next term or figure in the following patterns.
   a. 2, 8, 14
   b. $\frac{1}{2}, \frac{2}{3}, \frac{3}{4}$

   c.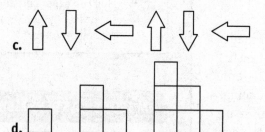

   d.

4. Create a visual representation of each of the following fractions.
   a. $\frac{1}{8}$ **b.** $\frac{1}{4}$ **c.** $\frac{1}{2}$ **d.** 1

5. Simplify each of the following rational numbers.
   a. $\frac{9}{243}$ **b.** $\frac{27}{243}$ **c.** $\frac{81}{243}$

6. For each number, place a check in the box of any set of which the number is a member.

Number	Natural Numbers	Whole Numbers	Rational Numbers	Integers
0				
$\frac{2}{5}$				
3.4				
13				
−27				

7. Copy the number line shown and plot the following numbers on your line.

   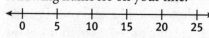

   a. 2.5   **b.** 8   **c.** $21\frac{1}{3}$

8. Explain 2 ways you could find the product of $4 \times 4 \times 4 \times 4$.

Investigating Patterns
Laws and Orders
Lesson 1-1 Analyzing Sequences

Learning Targets:

- Analyze simple sequences.
- Describe patterns in simple sequences and give the next terms in a sequence.

> SUGGESTED LEARNING STRATEGIES: Think-Pair-Share, Look for a Pattern, Visualization, Discussion Groups, Role Play

For much of the late 19th and early 20th centuries, the fictional character Sherlock Holmes was known for his great detective work. In this activity, you will be asked to perform many tasks similar to those Holmes used to solve his cases.

In order to solve mysteries, Holmes used a deductive process that led him to a logical conclusion. First, he would observe a situation and gather as many facts as possible. Next, he would analyze each fact to determine its relevance to the situation. Then he would search for even more clues by considering the smallest of details. Finally, he would use his imagination to link all of the clues together in the most logical manner.

The Case of the Arabic Symbols

At first glance, the following picture would appear to be a representation of the numbers one through nine. However, the way they are drawn gives a clue to how the symbols for each number were originally created.

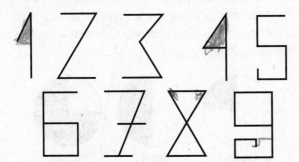

1. **Make sense of problems.** Observe, analyze, and search for clues in the diagram to come up with a guess about why the numbers were first written this way.

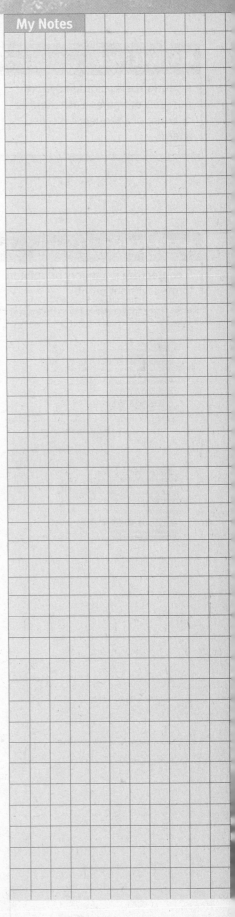

My Notes

My Notes

MATH TERMS

A **sequence** is an ordered list of numbers or figures. Each number or figure of a sequence is called a term.

MATH TERMS

A **conjecture** is a theory or opinion formed without proof.

2. Discuss your observations with your group.

   a. Describe the pattern you and your group noticed in the *sequence*. As you share your ideas with your group, make sure that you are presenting those ideas clearly and that you can support your ideas with evidence. Listen to group members' ideas and determine if they are presenting their ideas clearly and can support their ideas with evidence.

   b. As a group, write a *conjecture* about the pattern of the sequence based on your shared observations.

3. Based on your group's conclusions, explain how this pattern could also be used to describe zero with the symbol 0.

The Case of the Multiple Viewpoints
The next case involves investigating the sequence shown below. In order to reconstruct the pattern and solve the mystery, several witnesses have been asked to describe the sequence.

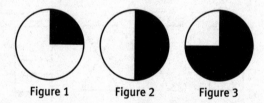

Figure 1   Figure 2   Figure 3

4. The description provided by the first witness, Bob, is given in terms of percents. Bob has determined that Figure 1 represents 25%, Figure 2 represents 50% and Figure 3 represents 75%. Is he right? Explain.

My Notes

5. The second witness uses fractions to describe the sequence. Provide an example of what this description might be.

6. Construct viable arguments. Witnesses #3, Julie, and #4, Greg, provide different accounts of the pattern. They have the following conversation.

> Julie: "Analyzing the sequence I noticed that it was increasing."
> Greg: "I disagree; I believe the sequence is decreasing."

Explain how both of their descriptions could be considered correct.

7. Analyze the descriptions of all four witnesses and draw Figure 4 if the sequence continued.

Check Your Understanding

Analyze the sequence below to answer Items 8–9.

  Figure 1   Figure 2   Figure 3

8. Draw the figure you think is next in the sequence.

9. Write a conjecture for the pattern of the sequence.

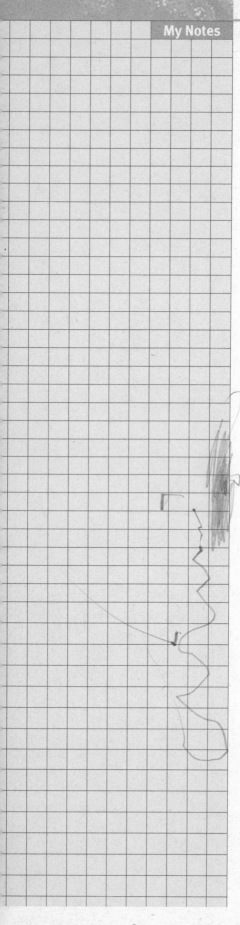

My Notes

LESSON 1-1 PRACTICE

Analyze the sequence below to answer Items 10–12.

10. Draw and name the figure you think is next in the sequence.

11. Write a description for the figure that you drew in Item 10.

12. Write a conjecture for the pattern of the sequence.

Analyze the sequence below to answer Items 13–14.

13. Draw the figure you think is next in the sequence.

14. **Express regularity in repeated reasoning.** Draw the eighth figure in the sequence.

Learning Targets:

- Analyze more complex sequences.
- Describe patterns in sequences and develop methods for predicting any term in a sequence.

> **SUGGESTED LEARNING STRATEGIES:** Quickwrite, Self/Peer Revision, Create Representations, Discussion Groups, Graphic Organizer

Continue to investigate patterns as Sherlock Holmes would with the following case.

The Case of the Revolving Figure

This next case involves the sequence of figures shown below.

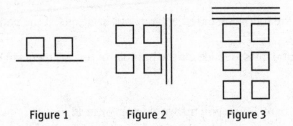

Figure 1   Figure 2   Figure 3

1. **Attend to precision.** Observe and analyze the patterns in the sequence. Describe the sequence in as much detail as possible.

2. Explain your descriptions with your group members. List any details you may not have considered before. Make sure that you are presenting your details clearly and that you can support them with evidence. Listen to group members' details and determine if they are presenting them clearly and can support their details with evidence.

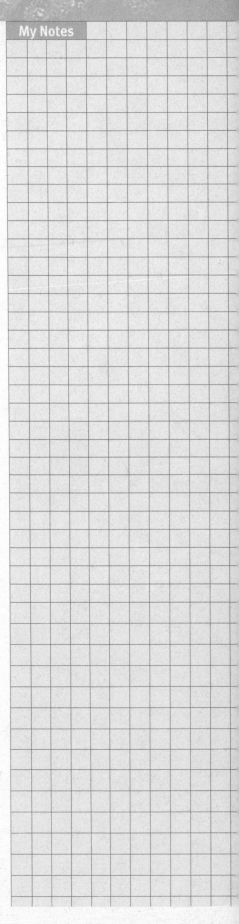

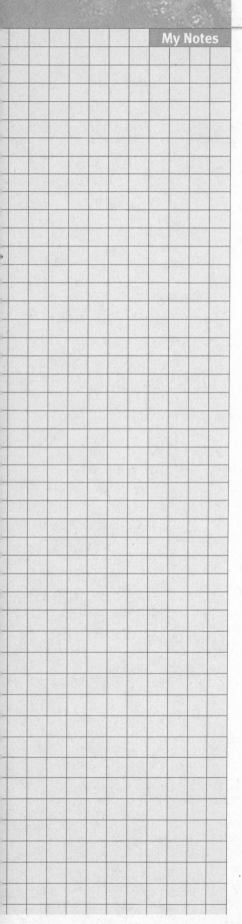

My Notes

3. Use the evidence gathered in Items 1 and 2 to draw representations of the fourth and fifth figures in the sequence.

4. Answer the following based on your observations of the patterns in the sequence.
   a. Describe the sequence for the number of line segments in each figure.

   b. How many line segments would appear in Figure 16?

   c. How many line segments would appear in Figure 49?

   d. Explain how you could determine the number of line segments in any figure in the sequence.

5. Organize the evidence you gathered about line segments and continue to explore the pattern in the table below.

Figure	Number of Line Segments	Number of Squares	Sum of Line Segments and Squares
1			
2			
3			
4			
5			
16			
49			

6. Reason quantitatively. Write a conjecture on how you could determine the number of squares and the sum of line segments and squares in any figure in the sequence.

Check Your Understanding

Analyze the sequence below to answer Items 7–9.

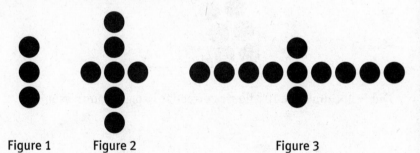

Figure 1   Figure 2   Figure 3

7. Draw the figure you think is next in the sequence.

8. Write a conjecture for the pattern of the sequence.

9. Otis describes the pattern using the number of dots in each figure: 3, 7, 11, ... How many dots would appear in the ninth figure?

WRITING MATH

One way to describe a number pattern in a sequence is to list several terms in order, followed by ellipses (…) to indicate that the pattern continues. For example, writing

1, 3, 5, 7, …

implies that the pattern of adding two to each digit continues indefinitely.

My Notes

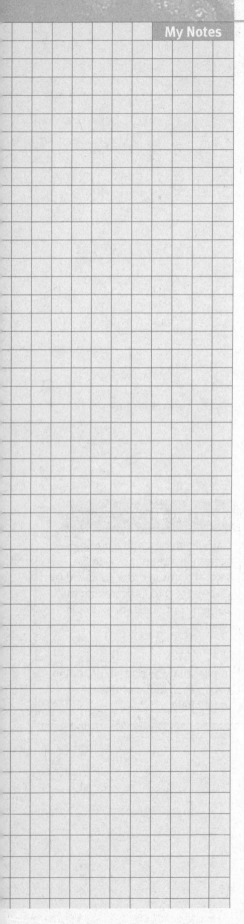

My Notes

LESSON 1-2 PRACTICE

Analyze the sequence below to answer Items 10–11.

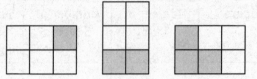

10. Draw what you think are the next two figures in the sequence.

11. Write two different descriptions that could describe the pattern of the sequence.

Analyze the sequence below to answer Items 12–14.

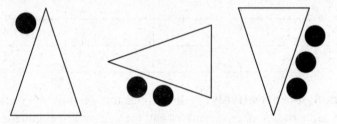

12. Draw what you think are the next two figures in the sequence.

13. Write a conjecture of the pattern of the sequence.

14. **Critique the reasoning of others.** Felipe predicts that the 10th figure in the sequence will look like this:

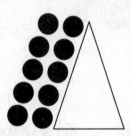

Did Felipe draw the 10ᵗʰ figure correctly? Explain your reasoning.

Learning Targets:

- Understand increasing and decreasing sequences.
- Analyze sequences containing mathematical operations and those based on other patterns.

SUGGESTED LEARNING STRATEGIES: Marking the Text, Think-Pair-Share, Sharing and Responding, Look for a Pattern, Group Presentation

An increasing sequence is a sequence of numbers where the value of the numbers is increasing, and a decreasing sequence is one where the value of the numbers is decreasing.

1. **Express regularity in repeated reasoning.** Examine the following sequences and state whether they are increasing or decreasing. Support your answer by describing the pattern.

    a. 3, 6, 12, 24, . . .

    b. 17, 14, 11, 8, . . .

2. Provide an example of an increasing and a decreasing sequence. Describe the pattern in the sequence.

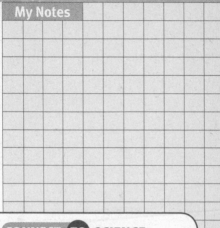

CONNECT TO SCIENCE

One well-known increasing sequence is the Fibonacci numbers. The sequence is represented as:

0, 1, 1, 2, 3, 5, 8, ...

Each number in the sequence is the sum of the two previous numbers. Applications of this sequence occur in the patterns of certain plants as well as in nautilus shells, art, and architecture.

My Notes

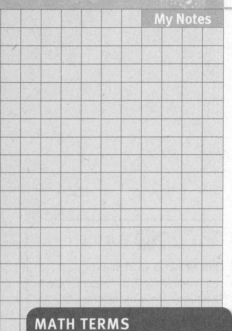

My Notes

3. Complete the table below by investigating each sequence.

Sequence	Increasing or Decreasing?	Next Term in the Sequence	Description of Pattern
0, 5, 10, 15 …			
−8, −4, −2, −1, …			
1.5, 2.75, 4, …			
$\frac{1}{8}, \frac{1}{4}, \frac{1}{2}, \ldots$			
$2, \frac{5}{4}, \frac{1}{2}, \ldots$			

MATH TERMS

The **absolute value** of a number is its distance in units from 0 on a number line. Absolute value is always nonnegative. For instance, $|-3|$ and $|3|$ are both 3 since −3 and 3 are the same distance from zero—three units.

4. Consider this sequence that uses **absolute values** of numerical expressions.

$$|5-2|, |5-3|, |5-4|, |5-5|, |5-6|, |5-7|$$

   a. Express the next term in the sequence.

   b. Describe the pattern of the sequence.

5. Arrange the numbers below so they form an increasing sequence. Describe the pattern of the sequence.

$$|-16| \times |5|$$

$$|-18-2|$$

$$|3-13|$$

$$|38| + |-2|$$

$$\left| -\frac{10}{2} \right|$$

6. **Reason abstractly.** Sequences do not always have to include mathematical operations. Look at the sequences below. Give verbal descriptions of what the pattern of the sequence is and give the next three terms.

   a. 3.12, 3.1212, 3.121212, . . .

   b. $\frac{1}{2}, \frac{1}{22}, \frac{1}{222}, \ldots$

   c. 1, 12, 123, . . .

   d. Z, Y, X, W, . . .

   e. J, F, M, A, . . .

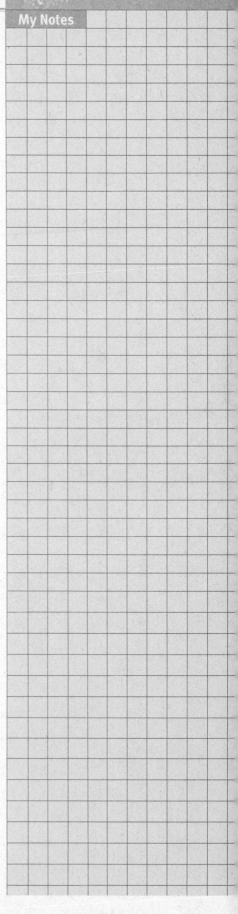

My Notes

My Notes

Check Your Understanding

Describe the following sequences using a mathematical operation and state the next three terms.

7. 0, 8, 16, 24, . . .

8. 27, 9, 3, 1, . . .

9. Arrange the numbers below so they form a decreasing sequence. Describe the pattern of the sequence.

$-2|-4|$

$\dfrac{|-24|}{6}$

$|-2|\times|-5|$

$40|2 \div 5|$

$|7|-|-9|$

LESSON 1-3 PRACTICE

Describe the following sequences using either a mathematical operation or a verbal description, indicate if the sequence is increasing or decreasing (if it involves numbers in some way), and state the next three terms.

10. 2, −4, −10, −16, . . .

11. 4.5, 3.25, 2, 0.75, . . .

12. $\dfrac{1}{64}, \dfrac{1}{16}, \dfrac{1}{4}, 1, \ldots$

13. A, C, E, G, . . .

14. Make sense of problems. Darlene wrote a sequence and gave it the following description: "The sequence is increasing by adding 6 to each previous term, and all of the terms are odd." Write five terms from a sequence that could be the one Darlene described.

ACTIVITY 1 PRACTICE
Write your answers on notebook paper.
Show your work.

Lesson 1-1

For Items 1–2, describe the pattern of the sequence and draw what you think are the next two terms.

1.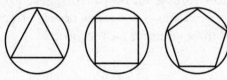

2.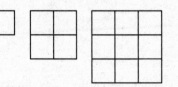

3. Which is the next term in this sequence?

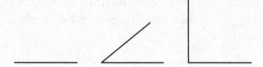

A.
B.
C.
D.

4. Write a conjecture for the pattern of the sequence in Item 3.

5. Draw what you think is the 6th figure in the following sequence:

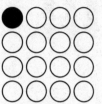

Figure 1   Figure 2

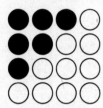

Figure 3

6. Write a conjecture for the pattern of the sequence in Item 5.

Lesson 1-2

For Items 7–9, determine two different ways to represent the fourth term in each pattern.

7.

8. $\frac{1}{1}, \frac{1}{4}, \frac{1}{9}, \ldots$

9.

10. Which is the next term in this sequence?

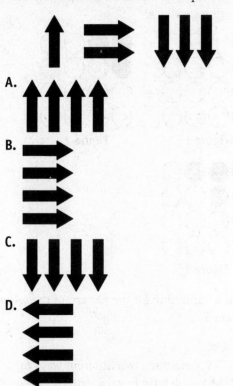

A.

B.

C.

D.

11. Copy and complete the table for the following sequence:

Figure 1   Figure 2   Figure 3   Figure 4

Figure	Number of squares	Number of line segments	Sum
1	1	0	1
2			
3			
4			
5			
10			
25			

Lesson 1-3

12. The numbers below are known as Fibonacci numbers. What is the pattern? Give the next three numbers in the sequence.

1, 1, 2, 3, 5, 8, . . .

For Items 13 – 16, describe the pattern, indicate if the sequence is increasing or decreasing or neither, and list the next three terms for each sequence.

13. 5, 2, −1, . . .

14. 0.25, 0.5, 1, . . .

15. 64, −16, 4, . . .

16. $-\frac{1}{2}$, 0, $\frac{1}{2}$, . . .

For Items 17–20, describe the following sequences using either a mathematical operation or a verbal description, indicate if the sequence is increasing or decreasing or neither, and list the next two terms.

17. 1, 3, 2, 6, 4, 9, . . .

18. 0.2, 0.04, 0.008, . . .

19. $\frac{1}{2}$, $\frac{3}{4}$, $\frac{5}{6}$, . . .

20. $|-3 + (-2)|, |-3 + 0|, |-3 + 2|, |-3 + 4|, \ldots$

MATHEMATICAL PRACTICES
Look For and Make Use of Structure

21. Describe the different ways that sequences can be represented. Create a sequence that can be represented in more than one way and describe what the pattern of the sequence is.

Operations with Fractions

And The Beat Goes On
Lesson 2-1 Adding and Subtracting Fractions

Learning Targets:

- Represent a real-world context with fractions.
- Simplify expressions involving fractions by adding and subtracting.

> **SUGGESTED LEARNING STRATEGIES:** Create Representations, Visualization, Graphic Organizer, Think-Pair-Share, Create a Plan

Math can be found in many places in our daily lives. One place you might not realize where math is used is in music.

1. Take a few moments to think about the following questions and discuss them with your group.

What is your favorite song?
Why do you like it?
Why do you prefer one type of music over another?

Believe it or not, the answers you came up with may have more to do with mathematics than you may realize. Consider the following diagrams:

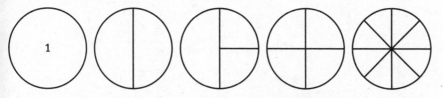

2. The first circle has no division and is represented by the number 1.
   a. Write the fractional equivalents in the sections of the other circles.

   b. For each of the circles, justify that the sum of each combination of fractions is 1.

   c. Which circle was not like the others? Explain what made it different and the process you used to determine your answer.

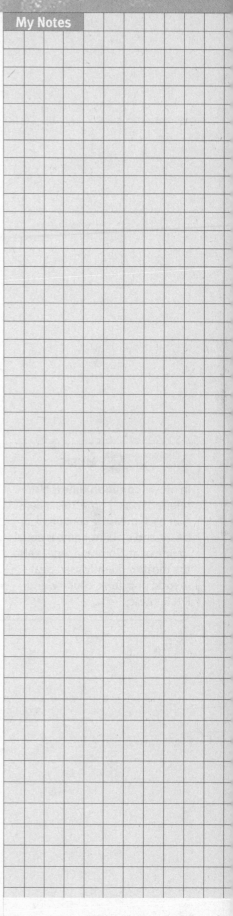

My Notes

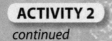
My Notes

3. **Model with mathematics.** Determine two additional ways to divide the circle using combinations of the same fractions that you used in Item 2a. Label each portion with the appropriate fractions, and justify that the sum of each combination of fractions is 1.

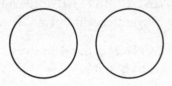

So what does all this have to do with music? As shown in the chart below, certain musical notes correspond to different fractional portions of a measure. In order to write sheet music, a composer must have a working knowledge of fractions.

Note	Relative Length in Common Time	Beats in Common Time	Fraction of Measure
O	Whole note	4 beats	1
♩	Half note	2 beats	$\frac{1}{2}$
♩	Quarter note	1 beat	$\frac{1}{4}$
♪	Eighth note	$\frac{1}{2}$ beat	$\frac{1}{8}$
♫	Sixteenth note	$\frac{1}{4}$ beat	$\frac{1}{16}$

4. Based on the note chart, how many of each note would it take to fill one measure in common time? Explain your reasoning.

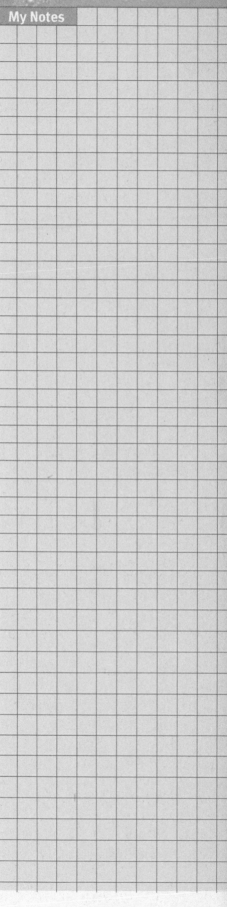

5. For each measure shown above, express each note as the fraction of its respective measure.

   a. Measure 1:

   b. Measure 2:

   c. Measure 3:

   d. Measure 4:

6. **Attend to precision.** Show that the sum of the fractions in each measure is equal to 1.

7. Based on your observations in Item 4, explain why you think the note in the fourth measure is called a "whole note."

My Notes

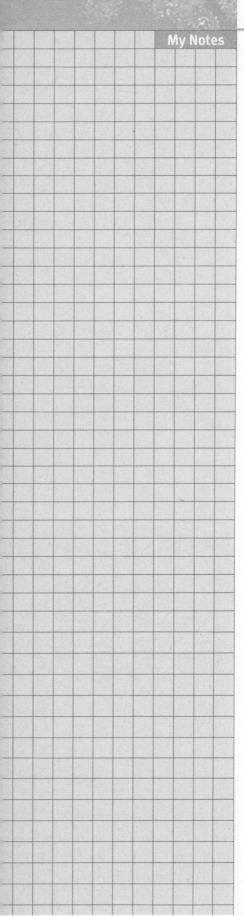

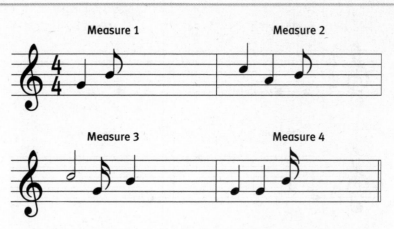

Measure 1   Measure 2

Measure 3   Measure 4

8. The measures shown above do not contain the required number of beats. Fill out the table below to explore various ways to complete each measure.

Measure	Fraction of Measure Shown	Fraction of Measure Remaining	Notes to Complete Measure (Example 1)	Notes to Complete Measure (Example 2)
1				
2				
3				
4				

9. Explain the processes you used to determine the fraction of the measures shown and the fraction of the measures remaining.

10. What can you conclude about each of the following expressions? Justify your reasoning.

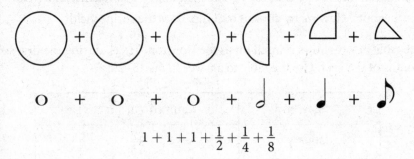

$$1 + 1 + 1 + \frac{1}{2} + \frac{1}{4} + \frac{1}{8}$$

11. Write the sum of the expressions in Item 10 as:

a. a mixed number

b. an improper fraction

c. a decimal
d. a percent

Check Your Understanding

In Items 12–16, simplify the expression.

12. $\frac{1}{3} + \frac{1}{6}$

13. $\frac{2}{5} + \frac{3}{8}$

14. $\frac{5}{12} - \frac{5}{6}$

15. $4\frac{1}{4} + 2\frac{1}{2}$

16. $6\frac{3}{5} - 2\frac{2}{3}$

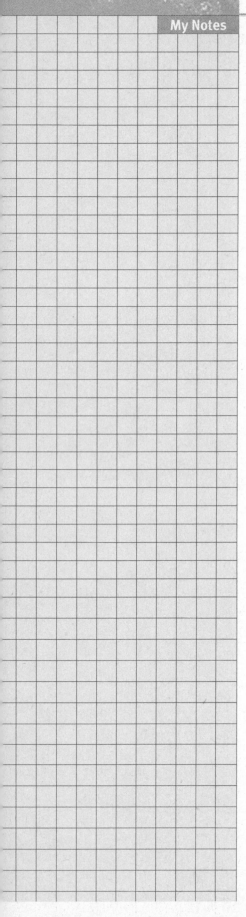

LESSON 2-1 PRACTICE

17. A trail mix recipe calls for $1\frac{1}{2}$ cups granola, $\frac{3}{4}$ cup raisins, and $\frac{2}{3}$ cup peanuts. How many cups of trail mix does the recipe yield?

The table below shows rainfall totals for Houston, Texas, during the first six months of the year. Use the table to answer Items 18–20.

Month	Rainfall (in inches)
January	$3\frac{2}{3}$
February	$2\frac{11}{12}$
March	$3\frac{1}{3}$
April	$3\frac{1}{2}$
May	$5\frac{1}{4}$
June	$5\frac{1}{2}$

18. How much rain fell during the two rainiest months?

19. What is the difference in rainfall between the wettest month and the driest month?

20. During which period did more rain fall: January to February or March to April? Explain your reasoning.

21. **Reason quantitatively.** Write a scenario for the following problem:

$$5\frac{1}{8} + 2\frac{4}{5} = 7\frac{37}{40}.$$

Learning Targets:

● Represent a real-world context with fractions.

● Simplify expressions involving fractions by multiplying and dividing.

● Write the reciprocal of a number.

SUGGESTED LEARNING STRATEGIES: Predict and Confirm, Create Representations, Visualization, Vocabulary Organizer, Paraphrasing

When multiplying fractions such as $\frac{3}{4} \cdot \frac{1}{2}$, it is helpful to think of the multiplication symbol • as the word "of." So you read, "Find $\frac{3}{4}$ of $\frac{1}{2}$."

1. **Reason abstractly.** Without completing the problem, do you think the answer will be greater than or less than $\frac{1}{2}$? Explain your reasoning.

2. Consider the model below.

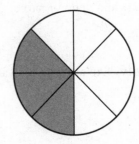

a. Explain how this model could be used to represent $\frac{3}{4}$ of $\frac{1}{2}$.

b. Express the shaded portion of the circle as a single fraction.

When discussing ideas in groups, use precise language to present your ideas. Speak using complete sentences and transition words such as *for example, because,* and *therefore.* Listen to others as they speak and ask for clarification of terms and phrases they use.

My Notes

WRITING MATH

Sometimes a dot is used as a symbol for multiplication. $3 \times 2 = 6$ and $3 \cdot 2 = 6$ are both ways to show 3 times 2 equals 6.

MATH TIP

After writing explanations to mathematical prompts, share your writing with a peer or your teacher. Have them confirm that your writing demonstrates clear understanding of mathematical concepts.

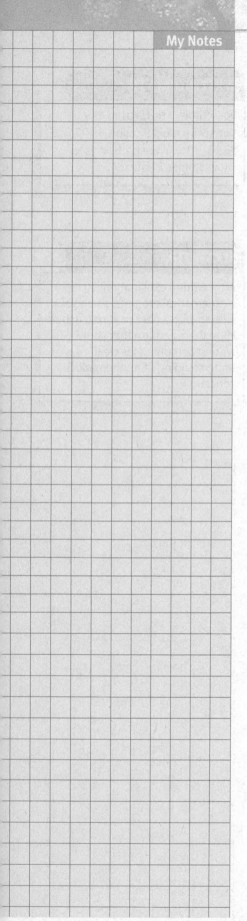

The problem $\frac{2}{3} \cdot \frac{3}{4}$ could be modeled in the same way. This problem is asking you to find $\frac{2}{3}$ of $\frac{3}{4}$.

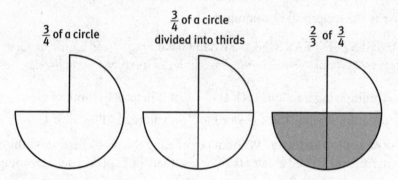

$\frac{3}{4}$ of a circle

$\frac{3}{4}$ of a circle divided into thirds

$\frac{2}{3}$ of $\frac{3}{4}$

Depending on how the problem is completed, several different answers could be given. Using the diagrams above, the answer could be expressed as $\frac{2}{4}$ or $\frac{1}{2}$.

By multiplying the numerators and denominators, the answer could be shown as $\frac{2}{3} \cdot \frac{3}{4} = \frac{2 \cdot 3}{3 \cdot 4} = \frac{6}{12}$.

3. **Reason quantitatively.** Explain why $\frac{1}{2}$, $\frac{2}{4}$ and $\frac{6}{12}$ are the same number.

Example A

Find the product of $\frac{1}{8} \cdot \frac{2}{3}$.

Step 1: Multiply the numerators and multiply the denominators.

$$\frac{1}{8} \cdot \frac{2}{3} = \frac{1 \cdot 2}{8 \cdot 3} = \frac{2}{24}$$

Step 2: Simplify to write the product in lowest terms.

$$\frac{2}{24} \div \frac{2}{2} = \frac{1}{12}$$

Solution: The product of $\frac{1}{8}$ $\frac{2}{3}$ is $\frac{1}{12}$.

Try These A

Multiply. Express each product in lowest terms.

a. $\frac{9}{10} \cdot \frac{2}{5}$

b. $\frac{3}{7} \cdot \frac{3}{4}$

c. $\frac{1}{4} \cdot \frac{1}{8}$

Check Your Understanding

Multiply. Express each product in lowest terms.

4. $\dfrac{4}{5} \cdot \dfrac{1}{3}$

5. $\dfrac{6}{7} \cdot \dfrac{3}{10}$

6. $\dfrac{8}{3} \cdot \dfrac{13}{15}$

7. $1\dfrac{2}{3} \cdot \dfrac{1}{2}$

8. $2\dfrac{1}{2} \cdot 3\dfrac{2}{3}$

A common strategy used to divide fractions uses the directions "invert and multiply." The problem, however, is that the phrase can often raise more questions than answers. For example:

What does invert mean?
What do I invert?
Why do I invert?
Why do I multiply?

These are all valid questions that deserve equally valid answers. The first two questions are easy to answer. To invert something is to turn it upside down. In mathematics, this is referred to as finding the *reciprocal* of a number. In other words, inverting the fraction $\dfrac{2}{3}$ would give the reciprocal $\dfrac{3}{2}$. When dividing fractions such as in the problem $\dfrac{2}{5} \div \dfrac{2}{3}$, the second fraction is inverted to produce $\dfrac{2}{5} \cdot \dfrac{3}{2}$.

MATH TIP

You can gain a greater understanding of a concept by learning about "why" something works as opposed to memorizing "how" something works.

MATH TERMS

The **reciprocal** of a number is its multiplicative inverse. The product of a number and its multiplicative inverse is 1.

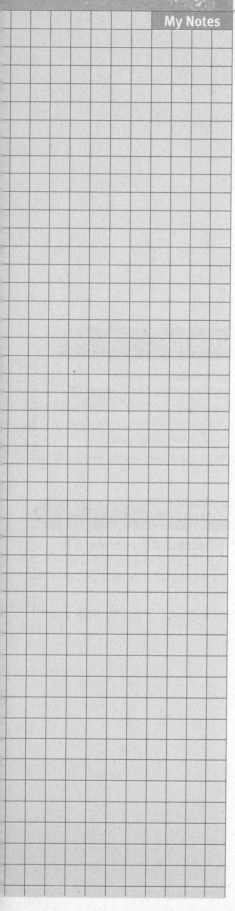

My Notes

9. Make use of structure. Determine the reciprocal of the following:

a. $\frac{4}{3}$

b. $\frac{5}{18}$

c. 15

d. $5\frac{3}{5}$

As for the last two questions concerning *why* this works, it's important to understand the concept of inverse operations.

10. Consider the expression $10 \div 2$.

a. Without using the words "divided by," explain what this problem is asking you to do.

b. What number could be multiplied by 10 to reach the same solution?

c. What do you notice about the number 2 and your answers to part b?

d. Use your answer to part b to rewrite the expression using multiplication.

e. Based on your observation, explain what is meant by describing multiplication and division as inverse operations of one another.

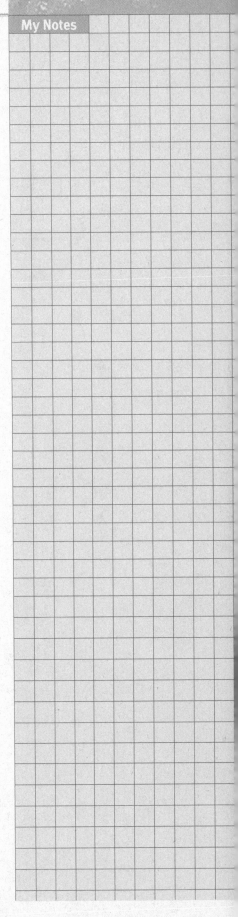

Example B

Divide $\frac{1}{2} \div \frac{2}{3}$.

Step 1: Find the reciprocal of $\frac{2}{3}$ by inverting the numerator and denominator.

$$\frac{2}{3} \rightarrow \frac{3}{2}$$

Step 2: Multiply $\frac{1}{2}$ by the reciprocal of $\frac{2}{3}$, which is $\frac{3}{2}$.

$$\frac{1}{2} \times \frac{3}{2} = \frac{1 \times 3}{2 \times 2} = \frac{3}{4}$$

Step 3: Simplify so that the quotient is in lowest terms.
$\frac{3}{4}$ is already in lowest terms, the numerator and denominator cannot be further reduced.

Solution: $\frac{1}{2} \div \frac{2}{3} = \frac{3}{4}$.

Try These B

Divide. Simplify so the quotient is in lowest terms.

a. $\frac{5}{6} \div \frac{1}{3}$

b. $\frac{1}{2} \div 4$

c. $1\frac{3}{4} \div \frac{1}{8}$

Background music in movies and television is not chosen at random. In fact, the music is often chosen so that it directly relates to the emotions being portrayed on the screen.

11. The following table lists the average beats per minute of music meant to express various emotions.

Emotion	Beats per Minute
Joy and Triumph	120
Mystery and Suspense	115
Comfort and Peace	100
Loneliness and Regret	120

a. Describe a scene from a movie or television show that would match each of the four categories in the table.

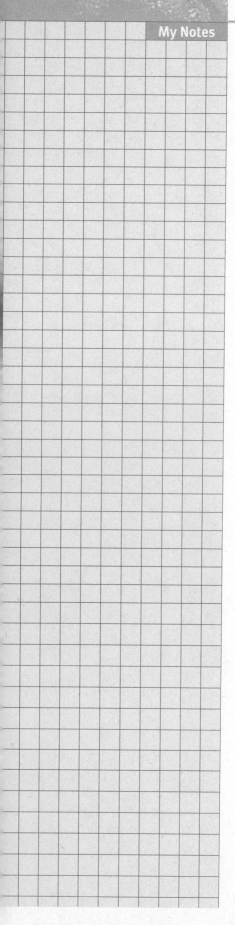

b. Explain how you could use multiplication or division to determine the number of beats in a three-minute song.

Check Your Understanding

In Items 12–14, divide and simplify to lowest terms.

12. $\frac{4}{5} \div \frac{3}{7}$

13. $\frac{6}{15} \div \frac{2}{9}$

14. $4\frac{2}{3} \div 4$

LESSON 2-2 PRACTICE

15. Write a scenario for this problem: $8\frac{2}{3} \times 4 = 34\frac{2}{3}$.

16. Miranda made some cupcakes for the school bake sale. Of the cupcakes, $\frac{1}{2}$ are chocolate and $\frac{1}{2}$ are strawberry. Of the strawberry cupcakes, $\frac{1}{3}$ are frosted with vanilla frosting, and the rest are frosted with chocolate frosting. What portion of the cupcakes are strawberry with chocolate frosting?

17. Ennis has a length of rope that measures $3\frac{3}{4}$ yards. He cuts all of the rope into smaller pieces that measure $\frac{3}{4}$ yard each. How many cuts did Ennis make?

18. Draw a picture that proves $\frac{3}{4} \div \frac{1}{8} = 6$.

19. **Critique the reasoning of others.** Brody and Lola each found the product of $4\frac{2}{3} \times 1\frac{1}{2}$ in a different way shown below. Who multiplied correctly? Explain your reasoning.

Brody	Lola
$4 \times 1 = 4$ $\frac{2}{3} \times \frac{1}{2} = \frac{2}{6} = \frac{1}{3}$ $= 4\frac{1}{3}$	$\frac{14}{3} \times \frac{3}{2} = \frac{42}{6} = 7$

ACTIVITY 2 PRACTICE

Write your answers on notebook paper.
Show your work.

Lesson 2-1

In Items 1–6, simplify the expression.

1. $\frac{3}{5} + \frac{4}{6}$

2. $\frac{5}{8} - \frac{1}{3}$

3. $2\frac{3}{4} + 7\frac{3}{5}$

4. $7\frac{1}{6} - 4\frac{1}{2}$

5. $12\frac{3}{8} + 6\frac{5}{6}$

6. $8\frac{9}{10} - 3\frac{1}{4}$

7. Judy has $4\frac{2}{3}$ yards of fabric and Marie has $5\frac{1}{2}$ yards. How much fabric do they have altogether?

8. Describe the process you would use to find the solution to the problem $3\frac{1}{4} - 1\frac{1}{3}$. Express your answer numerically and with a graphical representation.

9. Angelo weighed $5\frac{1}{4}$ pounds when he was born. His sister, Carmen, weighed $7\frac{1}{2}$ pounds when she was born. How much heavier was Carmen than Angelo at birth?

10. Copy and complete:

$$\frac{1}{2} + \frac{1}{3} = \frac{\square}{6} + \frac{2}{6}$$

11. Gwen went walking three days one week. The first day, she walked $3\frac{1}{2}$ miles. Each day after that, she walked $\frac{1}{4}$ mile more than the day before. How many miles did Gwen walk this week?

    A. $10\frac{1}{2}$ **B.** $10\frac{3}{4}$

    C. $11\frac{1}{4}$ **D.** $11\frac{1}{2}$

12. The following week, Gwen walked a total of $15\frac{7}{8}$ miles. How many more miles did she walk the second week than the first week?

13. Yuri measured the snowfall over a four-day period and calculated a total of $15\frac{1}{3}$ inches of snowfall. If it snowed $4\frac{3}{4}$ inches on the first day and $2\frac{1}{2}$ inches on the second day, how much snow fell on the third and fourth days?

Lesson 2-2

In Items 14–19, simplify the expression.

14. $\frac{2}{5} \cdot \frac{7}{12}$

15. $3\frac{1}{2} \cdot 4\frac{1}{4}$

16. $24 \div 2\frac{2}{3}$

17. $\frac{2}{3} \cdot \frac{2}{9}$

18. $8 \div 1\frac{1}{5}$

19. $6\frac{1}{6} \div 2\frac{1}{2}$

20. Without performing any calculations, determine which of the following problems will produce the greatest result. Explain your reasoning.

    a. $\frac{3}{5} \cdot \frac{4}{7}$ b. $\frac{3}{5} \div \frac{4}{7}$

21. Tony has 36 pages left in the book he is reading. He plans to read $\frac{1}{4}$ of the pages tonight before going to bed. Which of the following expressions would not produce the number of pages Tony is going to read before he goes to bed?

    A. $36 \cdot \frac{1}{4}$

    B. $36 \div \frac{1}{4}$

    C. $36 \div 4$

    D. $36 \cdot 0.25$

22. The gas tank in Mr. Yang's car is $\frac{2}{3}$ full. The tank holds a total of 15 gallons of gasoline. How many gallons of gas are in Mr. Yang's car?

    A. 10

    B. $10\frac{1}{3}$

    C. $10\frac{2}{3}$

    D. 11

23. One-third of the students in Mr. Rose's class have corrected vision. Of those students, $\frac{3}{8}$ wear glasses. What fraction of the class wears glasses?

24. Bananas cost 30¢ per pound. How much will $2\frac{5}{6}$ pounds of bananas cost?

25. A recipe for fried rice yields $4\frac{1}{2}$ cups, or 6 servings. How big is each serving of fried rice?

26. Owen is having a dinner party and plans to serve the fried rice recipe from Item 25. He needs to make 10 servings. How many cups of fried rice will Owen need to make?

MATHEMATICAL PRACTICES
Look For and Make Use of Structure

27. Copy and complete this table to examine the similarities and differences between adding, subtracting, multiplying, and dividing fractions.

Operation	Steps to Evaluate	Example
Add fractions		
Subtract fractions		
Multiply fractions		
Divide fractions		

    a. How are addition and subtraction of fractions similar?

    b. How are multiplication and division of fractions similar?

    c. How are the operations different?

Patterns and Quantitative Reasoning

GAME ON

Piper and Lily are in the school math club and they are going to participate in an "Are You Smarter Than An Eighth Grader?" competition. Help Piper and Lily answer the following questions to ensure that they gain the most points possible in this competition.

The first category is finding patterns in sequences.

1. Write what you think are the next two terms of the pattern.
    a. 45, 34, 23, . . .
    b. 27, 18, 12, . . .
    c. 13, 103, 1003, . . .
    d. $\frac{1}{2}, \frac{2}{3}, \frac{3}{4}, \ldots$

    e.

2. For parts a and b in Item 1, state if the sequences were increasing or decreasing sequences. Describe the patterns using a mathematical operation.

The second category is story problems. Show your work on how to solve the problems.

3. Luke needs to tie his dog Duke to the deck while they are working on the fence. He finds two short leashes with lengths of $6\frac{1}{2}$ feet and $5\frac{7}{8}$ feet. If Luke connects the two leashes, how far can Duke travel from the deck?

4. Fletch is making shelves. He has $14\frac{1}{2}$ feet of wood. He wants each shelf to be $2\frac{1}{3}$ feet long. How many shelves can Fletch make with the wood he has? How much wood would be left over?

5. Greg is planning a new city park. He has a rectangular piece of land that is $50\frac{1}{2}$ feet by $25\frac{2}{3}$ feet. What is the area of Greg's park?

Scoring Guide	Exemplary	Proficient	Emerging	Incomplete
	The solution demonstrates these characteristics:			
Mathematics Knowledge and Thinking (Items 1a-e, 2, 3, 4, 5)	• Clear and accurate understanding of operations with fractions and mixed numbers. • Effective understanding of finding the pattern and missing terms in a sequence.	• Operations with fractions and mixed numbers that are usually correct. • Finding the pattern in a sequence and extending it.	• Partially correct operations with fractions and mixed numbers. • Errors in extending sequences and finding the pattern.	• Incorrect or incomplete computation in operations with fractions and mixed numbers. • Little or no understanding of sequences.
Problem Solving (Items 1a-e, 2, 3, 4, 5)	• An appropriate and efficient strategy that results in a correct answer.	• A strategy that may include unnecessary steps but results in a correct answer.	• A strategy that results in some incorrect answers.	• No clear strategy when solving problems.
Mathematical Modeling / Representations (Items 1a-e, 2, 3, 4, 5)	• Writing accurate expressions for operations with fractions and mixed numbers. • Accurately writing an expression to represent a sequence.	• Writing an expression for operations with fractions and mixed numbers. • Writing an expression to represent a sequence.	• Errors in writing expressions for a given problem situation. • Errors in writing an expression to represent a sequence.	• Inaccurately written expressions. • Little or no understanding of writing an expression to represent a sequence.
Reasoning and Communication (Item 2)	• Precise and accurate description of a sequence.	• An adequate description of a sequence.	• A misleading or confusing description of a sequence.	• An incomplete or inaccurate description of a sequence.

Powers and Roots
Squares and Cubes
Lesson 3-1 Area, Squares, and Square Roots

Learning Targets:

- Interpret and simplify the square of a number.
- Determine the square root of a perfect square.

> **SUGGESTED LEARNING STRATEGIES:** Interactive Word Wall, Paraphrasing, Create Representations, Look for a Pattern, Note Taking, Critique Reasoning

Dominique Wilkins Middle School is holding its annual school carnival. Each year, classes and clubs build game booths in the school gym. This year, the student council has asked Jonelle's math class for help in deciding what size the booths should be and how they should be arranged on the gym floor. The class will begin this work by reviewing some ideas about area.

Example A

Find the area of this rectangle. The rectangle has been divided into squares. Assume that the length of each side of a small square is 1 cm.

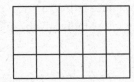

Step 1: Find the length and the width of the rectangle.
The rectangle is 5 cm long and 3 cm wide.

Step 2: To find the area, multiply the length times the width.
Area = length × width
Area = 5 cm × 3 cm = 15 cm^2

Solution: The area of the rectangle is 15 cm^2. Note that the units are centimeters squared and this represents the amount of surface the rectangle covers.

Try These A

Before deciding on how to arrange the booths, the student council needs to know the area of the gym floor. Several class members went to the gym to measure the floor. They found that the length of the floor is 84 feet and the width of the floor is 50 feet.

a. Find the area of the gym floor. Explain how you found the area and include units in your answer.

b. Explain what the area of the gym floor means.

My Notes

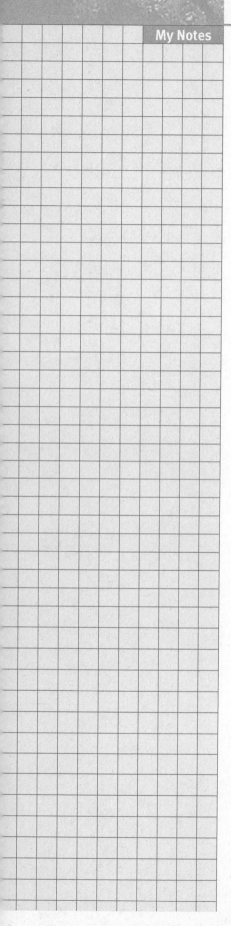

The class is now going to focus on the area of squares, because this is the shape of the base of many of the game booths.

Example B

Find the area of the square below. Do you need to know both the length and width of a square to be able to determine its area?

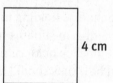

4 cm

Step 1: The length of one side is given and as this is a square, we know that all four sides have equal lengths.

Step 2: To find the area of the square, multiply the length of a side by itself. In this case, the length is 4 cm.
$4 \text{ cm} \times 4 \text{ cm} = 16 \text{ cm}^2$

Solution: The area of the square is 16 cm^2. You can find the area of a square with only one length given, since all four sides are equal lengths.

Try These B

This drawing shows the floor space of one of the carnival booths. It is a square with the length of one side labeled with the letter *s*. The *s* can be given any number value since the booths are going to be different sizes.

s

a. **Express regularity in repeated reasoning.** Complete this table by finding the areas of some different sized booths. The length of a side in feet is represented by *s*, as in the drawing above. Include units for area in the last column.

Length of Side (in feet)	Calculation	Area of the Square
$s = 3$	3×3	9 ft^2
$s = 6$		
$s = 8$		
$s = 11$		
$s = 4.2$		
$s = 10\frac{1}{2}$		

For each calculation in Try These B, you found the product of a number times itself. The product of a number times itself can be written as a *power* with a *base* and an *exponent*.

Example C

Write $5 \cdot 5$ as a power with a base and an exponent.

Step 1: Identify the base, which is the number being multiplied. The base is 5.

Step 2: Identify the exponent, which is the number of times the base is multiplied by itself.
In $5 \cdot 5$, the base 5 is multiplied by itself two times, so the exponent is 2.

Step 3: The base is written normally and the exponent is written as a superscript: 5^2

Solution: $5 \cdot 5 = 5^2$. Numbers expressed as powers with a base and an exponent are written in *exponential form*.

Try These C

Write the following in exponential form.

a. $12 \cdot 12$ **b.** $\frac{1}{3} \cdot \frac{1}{3}$ **c.** $3.25 \cdot 3.25$

MATH TERMS

A **power** is a number multiplied by itself. A number or expression written with an exponent is in **exponential form**.

Check Your Understanding

1. The table below gives some booth sizes in exponential form. Copy and complete the table.

Exponential Form	Product Using the Base as a Factor Twice	Standard Form
5^2	$5 \cdot 5$	25
2^2		
1^2		
7^2		
15^2		

READING MATH

Read the expression 5^2 as "5 squared" or the "square of 5." 5^2 means 5 times 5, or 5×5.

1. Find the value of the expression 9^2.

2. The number 49 is the square of what number?

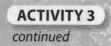

My Notes

Example D

The area of the floor of a square booth is 36 ft^2. What is the length of the side s of this booth?

36 ft^2 $\quad s$

Step 1: The area is the square of the length of a side. Here, 36 ft^2 is the square of s. To find s, find the **square root** of 36 ft^2. The symbol for square roots is $\sqrt{}$.

$$\sqrt{36} = s$$

Step 2: To solve $\sqrt{36} = s$, think about which number times itself equals 36.

$$\sqrt{36} = 6$$

Solution: The length of a side of the booth is 6 ft.

Try These D

Find each square root.

a. $\sqrt{16}$ **b.** $\sqrt{81}$ **c.** $\sqrt{100}$

d. The carnival booth sizes are assigned according to the number of members in the club or class. Copy and complete the table.

Club or Class Size	Area of Square Booth's Floor	Side Length of Booth's Floor
1–30 members	36 ft^2	
31–60 members		8 ft
61–90 members		9 ft
91–120 members	121 ft^2	
121–150 members	144 ft^2	

You can use equations to model problems involving sides and areas of squares. The situation in Example D can be modeled with the equation $s^2 = 36$, where s represents the side of the square and 36 is the area in square feet.

Example E

Solve the equation $s^2 = 36$.

Step 1: To find s, you need to find the square root of s^2.

Step 2: If you take the square root of one side of an equation, you must take the square root of the other side.

$$s^2 = 36$$
$$\sqrt{s^2} = \sqrt{36}$$
$$\sqrt{s^2} = s \text{ and } \sqrt{36} = 6$$

Solution: The solution of the equation $s^2 = 36$ is $s = 6$.

Try These E
Solve each equation.
a. $x^2 = 64$
b. $x^2 = 121$
c. $x^2 = 1.44$

Check Your Understanding

For Items 2–6, simplify each expression.

2. 11^2 **3.** 5.5^2 **4.** $\left(\frac{2}{3}\right)^2$ **5.** $\sqrt{144}$ **6.** $\sqrt{64}$

7. What would the area of a square booth be if the side length is 9 feet?

8. Solve for x: $x^2 = 16$

LESSON 3-1 PRACTICE

9. Find the area of this square:

8 cm

10. Write a rule, in words, for finding the area of a square.

11. Label the diagram using the terms base and exponent.

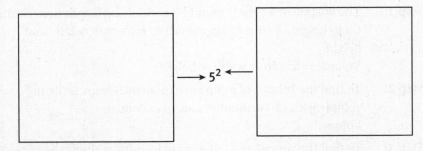

5^2

12. Why do you think the number 25 is called the square of 5? Draw a model in the My Notes space as part of your explanation.

13. Reason abstractly. Think about what you have discovered about the area of a square and finding the side length of a square. Write a sentence to explain what the square root of a number means.

14. Solve each equation for x.
a. $x^2 = 49$
b. $x^2 = 0.49$
c. $x^2 = \frac{1}{4}$

My Notes

My Notes

Learning Targets:

● Interpret and simplify the cube of a number.
● Determine the cube root of a perfect cube.

> **SUGGESTED LEARNING STRATEGIES:** Interactive Word Wall, Paraphrasing, Create Representations, Look for a Pattern, Note Taking, Critique Reasoning

The student council is very happy with the work that the class has done on the carnival so far. The class has found the areas of the floors and the side lengths of the booths. One concept remains for the class to review before completing all the needed work. The booths do not just take up floor space; they also have height.

The diagram below represents a cubic foot. Its dimensions are 1 ft · 1 ft · 1 ft.

Build a solid with the cubes given to you by your teacher with dimensions of 2 units by 2 units by 2 units. This solid is a cube with equal edge lengths of 2 units.

Example A

Find the volume of the cube you built with edge lengths of 2 units each. Find the volume in exponential form and in cubic units.

Step 1: The volume of a cube is found by multiplying length times width times height. A cube has equal values for length, width, and height.
Volume = length × width × height

Step 2: To find the volume of a cube in exponential form, write the volume with a base number and an exponent.
Volume = $2 \times 2 \times 2 = 2^3$

Step 3: To find the volume of a cube in cubic units, multiply the edge lengths and include the cubic units label.
Volume = 2 units × 2 units × 2 units = 8 cubic units

Solution: The volume of the cube is 2^3 or 8 cubic units.

My Notes

Try These A

a. **Make use of structure.** Complete this table to show the volume of each cube in exponential form and in cubic feet.

Length of an Edge of a Cube (in feet)	Calculation for Finding Volume of Cube	Volume of Cube (in exponential form)	Volume of the Cube (in cubic feet)
2	$2 \times 2 \times 2$	2^3	8 ft^3
4			
5			
6			
8			
9			

The exponent used in each exponential expression of volume in Try These A is the same. This exponent can be used for the volume of a cube. Using this exponent is known as *cubing a number*.

Example B

Find the cube of 10 or 10^3.
Cubing a number means to multiply it by itself three times.

$$10 \cdot 10 \cdot 10 = 1,000$$

Solution: The cube of 10 is 1,000 or $10^3 = 1,000$.

Try These B

Simplify each expression.

a. 3^3
b. $7 \cdot 7 \cdot 7$
c. 11^3
d. $1.5 \cdot 1.5 \cdot 1.5$

If you know the volume of a cube you can determine the length of the edge of the cube. The operation you use to find the edge length when you know the volume is called finding the ***cube root***. The symbol used for cube roots is $\sqrt[3]{}$.

Example C

The volumes of four cubes are given in this table. Find the length of the edge of each cube by finding the cube root of the volume.

Volume of the Cube (in cubic units)	Length of the Edge (in units)
1	
8	
27	
64	

WRITING MATH

The **index** 3 in the radical sign $\sqrt[3]{}$ shows a **cube root**. $\sqrt[3]{8}$ is read "the cube root of 8."

My Notes

Step 1: When the volume of a cube is 1 cubic unit, simplify $\sqrt[3]{1}$ to find the length of the edge. $\sqrt[3]{1} = 1$ unit

Step 2: When the volume of a cube is 8 cubic units, simplify $\sqrt[3]{8}$ to find the length of the edge. $\sqrt[3]{8} = 2$ units

Step 3: When the volume of a cube is 27 cubic units, simplify $\sqrt[3]{27}$ to find the length of the edge. $\sqrt[3]{27} = 3$ units

Step 4: When the volume of a cube is 64 cubic units, simplify $\sqrt[3]{64}$ to find the length of the edge. $\sqrt[3]{64} = 4$ units

Solution: Complete the table with the values found in the steps above.

Try These C

Complete the table to the left. All numbers are in standard form.

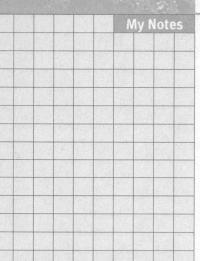

Side Length	Volume of Booth
2	
	27
	64
	125
9	
	1000
n	

Check Your Understanding

In Items 1–4, simplify each expression.

1. 5.1^3 **2.** $\sqrt[3]{1,728}$ **3.** $\left(\dfrac{1}{4}\right)^3$ **4.** 20^3

5. Copy and complete the table for the booths listed.

Volume of the Cubical Booth	Length of each Edge of the Booth
216 ft³	
343 ft³	
729 ft³	
1000 ft³	

MATH TIP

You can solve equations such as $x^3 = 8$ by taking the cube root of both sides.

LESSON 3-2 PRACTICE

6. What is the exponent used in cubing a number?

7. Find the volume of the cube shown.

7 cm

8. Think about what you have discovered about the volume of a cube and finding the edge length of a cube. Write a sentence to explain what the cube root of a number means.

9. A cube has a volume of 216 cubic feet. What is the length of an edge of this cube?

10. Critique the reasoning of others. Aaron says that to find the volume of a cube he uses the formula $l \cdot w \cdot h$. Jonelle says that the formula she uses is l^3. Whose formula is correct? Justify your answer.

11. Solve each equation for x.
   a. $x^3 = 64$
   b. $x^3 = 216$
   c. $x^3 = 1$

My Notes

Learning Targets:

- Simplify expressions with powers and roots.
- Follow the order of operations to simplify expressions.

SUGGESTED LEARNING STRATEGIES: Interactive Word Wall, Paraphrasing, Create Representations, Look for a Pattern, Note Taking, Critique Reasoning

Exponents other than 2 and 3 can be used. The exponent tells you the number of times the base is used as a factor.

Example A

Simplify 2.4^5.

Step 1: 2.4^5 means 2.4 raised to the power of 5, which means 2.4 appears 5 times as a factor.

$2.4 \cdot 2.4 \cdot 2.4 \cdot 2.4 \cdot 2.4$

Step 2: Simplify by multiplying. Use a calculator.

$2.4 \cdot 2.4 \cdot 2.4 \cdot 2.4 \cdot 2.4 = 79.62624$

Solution: 2.4^5 equals 79.62624.

Try These A

a. Copy and complete this table.

Number (in exponential form)	Product Using the Base as a Factor	Number (in standard form)
4.5^3		
2.1^4		
$\left(\dfrac{4}{5}\right)^3$		
$\left(1\dfrac{1}{2}\right)^4$		
$\left(\dfrac{2}{3}\right)^5$		

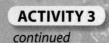
My Notes

ORDER OF OPERATIONS

1. Parentheses
2. Exponents/Roots (from left to right)
3. Multiplication/Division (from left to right)
4. Addition/Subtraction (from left to right)

When terms with exponents and roots appear in an expression, use the correct order of operations to simplify: (1) parentheses, (2) exponents and roots (in order from left to right), (3) multiplication and division (in order from left to right), and (4) addition and subtraction (in order from left to right).

Example B

Use order of operations to evaluate the expression: $250 - (3 \cdot 5)^2$.

Step 1: Simplify the expression in parentheses first.
$(3 \cdot 5) = 15$
The expression is now: $250 - (15)^2$

Step 2: Simplify the exponent next.
$15^2 = 225$
The expression is now: $250 - 225$

Step 3: Subtract.
$250 - 225 = 25$

Solution: $250 - (3 \cdot 5)^2 = 25$

Try These B

Attend to precision. Use the order of operations to evaluate each expression.

a. $4(3+2)^2 - 7$ **b.** $6 - 2 + \sqrt{4}$ **c.** $19 + 36 \div 3^2$

Check Your Understanding

Evaluate the following expressions.

1. 2^6 **2.** 1.7^4 **3.** $1^2 - 6 + (-2)^4$

LESSON 3-3 PRACTICE

Evaluate the following expressions.

4. $5^2 \cdot 2^4$ **5.** 9^5 **6.** $6 \times (5+3) \div 3 - 2^3$

7. Construct viable arguments. Jose and Juan were given the expression $3 + 24 \div 2 \times 3$; however, they solved it differently. Who solved it correctly and why?

Jose: $3 + 24 \div 2 \times 3$
$3 + 24 \div 6$
$3 + 4$
7

Juan: $3 + 24 \div 2 \times 3$
$3 + 12 \times 3$
$3 + 36$
39

ACTIVITY 3 PRACTICE
Write your answers on notebook paper.
Show your work.

Lesson 3-1

1. Evaluate each expression.
   a. $\sqrt{81}$
   b. 3.3^2
   c. $\left(\dfrac{1}{5}\right)^2$

2. If the side length of a square is 7.2 inches, what is the area of the square?

3. This figure has an area of 196 in.^{2} and is made up of four small squares. What is the side length of a small square?

4. Which is NOT a way to express 8^2?
   A. eight multiplied by two
   B. eight to the second power
   C. eight squared
   D. eight times eight

5. Complete the table for a booth with a floor in the shape of a square.

Side Length (in cm)	Perimeter of Booth (in cm)	Area of Booth (in cm)
2		
3		
	16	
	20	
		49
		100
n		

6. What patterns do you notice in the table you made in Item 5?

7. Which of the following numbers is a perfect square?
   A. 32   **B.** 36
   C. 40   **D.** 44

8. Solve each equation for x.
   a. $x^2 = 81$
   b. $x^2 = 0.16$
   c. $x^2 = \dfrac{1}{100}$

9. Daisy cut a square out of a sheet of graph paper. The square had an area of 16 square cm. She then trimmed 1 cm from each side of the square. What is the area of the smaller square?

Lesson 3-2

10. Evaluate each expression.
    a. 0.4^3
    b. $\sqrt[3]{27}$
    c. $\sqrt[3]{0.001}$

11. Write "four cubed" in exponential form.

12. What is the volume of a cube with an edge length of $\dfrac{2}{3}$ foot?

13. What is the edge length of a cube with a volume of 216 cubic feet?

14. A picture frame cube has a volume of 64 cubic cm. Each of the six faces holds a picture of the same size as the face. What size picture does each face hold?

   A. 3×3
   B. 4×6
   C. 4×4
   D. 6×6

15. The dimensions of a cube are 5 cm × 5 cm × 5 cm. What is the volume of this cube?

16. The edge length for a cube is c. Which of the following does NOT represent how to find the volume of this cube?
A. c^3
B. $c \cdot c \cdot c$
C. $3 \times c$
D. c cubed

17. Solve each equation for x.
a. $x^3 = 125$
b. $x^3 = 0.008$
c. $x^3 = \dfrac{1}{27}$

Lesson 3-3

18. Write $3 \cdot 3 \cdot 3 \cdot 3$ in exponential form.

19. In science we find that some cells divide to form two cells every hour. If you start with one cell, how many cells will there be after 7 hours?

20. Use $=$, $>$, or $<$ to complete the following:
a. 1^9 _____ 1^4
b. 3^4 _____ 4^3
c. 2^6 _____ $\sqrt{144}$

21. If you know that $9^3 = 729$, describe how to find 9^4 without having to multiply four 9s.

22. Which of the following expressions results in the largest amount?
A. 2^9
B. 4.5^3
C. 9^2
D. 8.3^3

23. Evaluate the following expressions.
a. $(16 - 10)^2 \div 4$
b. $7^2 + (5 - 3)^3$
c. $\sqrt[3]{125} \times 2^3$
d. $\left(\dfrac{1}{2}\right)^4$
e. 1.8^5
f. $\sqrt{(50 + 50)}$

24. Write 9 raised to the power of 6 in exponential form.

25. What is the first step in simplifying the expression $(8 + 2)^3 \div \sqrt{(20 - 4)} - 50$?
A. add $8 + 2$
B. cube 2
C. subtract 50
D. cube 8

26. Complete the table.

3^1	
	9
3^3	27
3^4	
	243
3^6	
	2,187

MATHEMATICAL PRACTICES
Reason Abstractly and Quantitatively

27. Write a letter to the student council that describes the relationship between the side of a booth and its area and volume. Use examples to illustrate your relationship.

Rational Numbers

Know When to Fold 'Em

Lesson 4-1 Modeling Fractions

Learning Targets:

- Model fractions graphically.
- Convert between fractions, decimals, and percents.

> **SUGGESTED LEARNING STRATEGIES:** Manipulatives, Discussion Group, Graphic Organizer, Sharing and Responding

A popular urban myth is that it is impossible to fold a piece of paper in half more than seven times.

1. Remove a sheet of paper from your notebook and try it for yourself. You may fold the paper in any direction you wish as long as you fold the paper in half each time. When you're done experimenting, share your results with your group members.

2. Complete the following table based on the first six folds you made in your paper.

Folds	Number of Regions on Paper	Each Region's Fraction of the Original Paper	Sketch of Unfolded Paper Showing Folds
0			
1			
2			
3			
4			
5			
6			

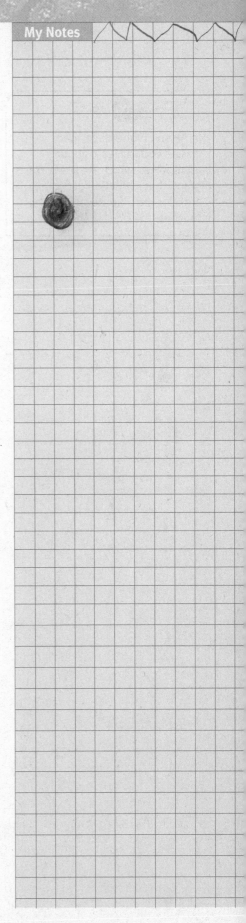

My Notes

CONNECT TO AP

In AP and higher-level math classes you will learn about asymptotes, which are lines on a graph that a function gets closer and closer to, but never actually touches.

3. Consider the dimensions of the paper each time it is folded.
   a. What is happening to the size of the regions?

   b. What size is the paper approaching?

   c. Is it possible for the paper to actually reach this size? Explain your answer.

4. Fold your paper into thirds as shown below:

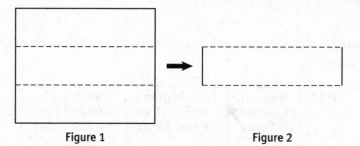

Figure 1   Figure 2

   a. Beginning with the paper folded as shown in Figure 2 above, fold the paper in half repeatedly and complete the table below.

	Figure 2	Figure 3	Figure 4	Figure 5	Figure 6	Figure 7
Each Region's Fraction of Original Paper						

b. The region's fractions are different than the previous fractions. Why?

5. Use another piece of paper to show how you could find other fractional values between 0 and 1. Discuss your results with your group.

The fractions you created in the previous tables can also be represented in different forms, including decimals, percents and graphical representations.

6. When given a fraction, decimal, or percent, it can be converted into either of the other two. Use the graphic organizer below to discuss the process of converting between the different representations. Describe how to interpret the graphic organizer.

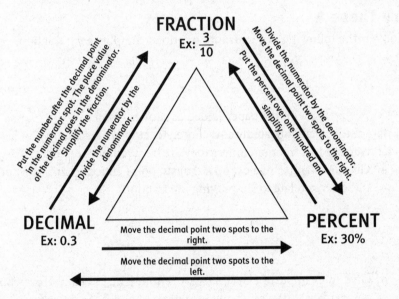

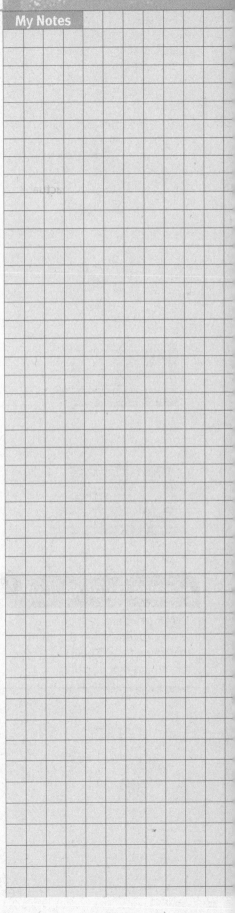

Example A

Convert 0.75 to a fraction.

Step 1: Determine the power of 10 for the fraction's denominator. Count the number of digits to the right of the decimal.

For the number 0.75, there are 2 digits to the right of the decimal so the exponent is 2.

Step 2: Write the whole number 75 for the numerator, and 10 with an exponent of 2 for the denominator.

$$\frac{75}{10^2} = \frac{75}{100}$$

Step 3: Simplify the fraction: $\frac{75}{100} = \frac{3}{4}$

Solution: $0.75 = \frac{3}{4}$

Try These A

Convert the following decimals into fractions. Simplify each fraction.

a. 0.59   **b.** 0.4   **c.** 0.235

7. Janice says that you can remove any zeros after the decimal point before converting to a fraction, unless they are between nonzero digits.
   a. Give an example of a decimal that supports Janice's claim. How do these zeros relate to simplifying the fraction?

   b. Give an example of a decimal that *refutes* Janice's claim. How would you explain to Janice when her statement doesn't make sense?

ACADEMIC VOCABULARY

To *refute* a claim is to prove it wrong. To remember this, think that you refuse to believe something that is wrong.

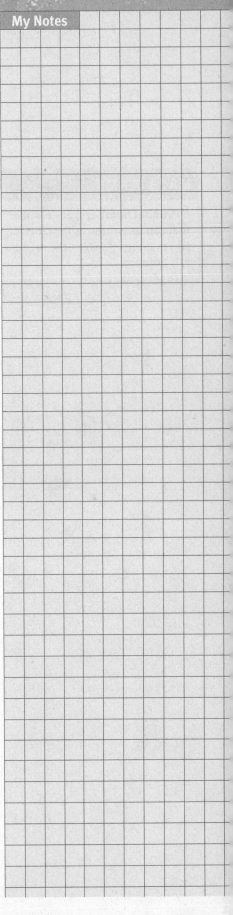

Check Your Understanding

8. Copy and complete the table. Round decimals to the nearest hundredth.

Fraction	Decimal Form	Percent
$\frac{1}{10}$		
	0.2	
		25%
$\frac{1}{3}$		$33\frac{1}{3}\%$
$\frac{1}{2}$		
	0.6	
$\frac{2}{3}$		$66\frac{2}{3}\%$
	0.75	
		80%
$\frac{9}{10}$		

LESSON 4-1 PRACTICE

9. Write the fraction and decimal equivalents for each percent.
   a. 60%   b. 80%

10. Show the graphical representation of $\frac{2}{3}$ using a pie chart.

11. Convert 0.14 to a fraction and percent.

12. **Model with mathematics.** Describe how you could use paper folding to illustrate the fraction $\frac{1}{9}$.

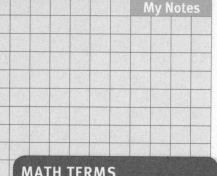

My Notes

Learning Targets:
- Define and recognize rational numbers.
- Represent repeating decimals using bar notation.
- Convert a repeating decimal to a fraction.

SUGGESTED LEARNING STRATEGIES: Activating Prior Knowledge, Group Presentations, Think-Pair-Share, Debriefing

Rational numbers may be represented as fractions or as decimals.

1. If rational numbers need to be able to be expressed as fractions, how can decimals also be rational numbers?

2. Convert the following fractions into decimals.

   a. $\dfrac{7}{20} =$

   b. $\dfrac{6}{25} =$

Some decimals are *terminating decimals*. Terminating decimals have a finite or limited number of digits following the decimal point. It is possible to express these numbers as the ratio of two integers, or as a fraction.

3. Write the decimals below as a ratio of two integers. Express each answer as a fraction.

   a. 0.65

   b. 0.004

4. Describe how any terminating decimal can be written as a fraction.

MATH TERMS

A **rational number** is any number that can be written as the ratio of two integers, $\dfrac{a}{b}$, where the divisor, b, is not zero.

Some decimals are ***repeating decimals***. Repeating decimals have one or more digits following the decimal point that repeat endlessly. For instance, 0.777 . . . is a repeating decimal as well as 2.5111 . . . . Repeating decimals are also rational numbers.

5. Rewrite each of the following rational numbers as a decimal.

    a. $\frac{1}{3} =$ **b.** $\frac{4}{9} =$ **c.** $\frac{5}{6} =$

Repeating decimals can also be converted into fractions.

> **My Notes**

> **READING MATH**
>
> Bar notation can be used to represent the repeating digits of a repeating decimal.
>
> $0.777\ldots = 0.\overline{7}$
> $2.5111\ldots = 2.5\overline{1}$

Example A

Convert 0.51111 . . . to a fraction.

Step 1: Let $x =$ the repeating decimal.

$$x = 0.51111\ldots$$

Step 2: Determine the repeating digit or digits.

The repeating digit is 1.

Step 3: Multiply both sides of the original equation by the least power of 10 so that the digits that repeat align after the decimal point.

$$x = 0.5111\ldots$$
$$10x = 5.1111\ldots$$

Step 4: Subtract one equation from the other. The repeating digits will not be in the difference.

$$10x = 5.1111\ldots$$
$$\underline{- x = 0.5111\ldots}$$
$$9x = 4.6$$

Step 5: Solve the resulting equation.

$$\frac{9x}{9} = \frac{4.6}{9}$$
$$x = \frac{46}{90} = \frac{23}{45}$$

Try These A

Convert the following repeating decimals into fractions.

    a. 0.444444 . . .   **b.** 0.121212 . . .   **c.** 2.505050 . . .

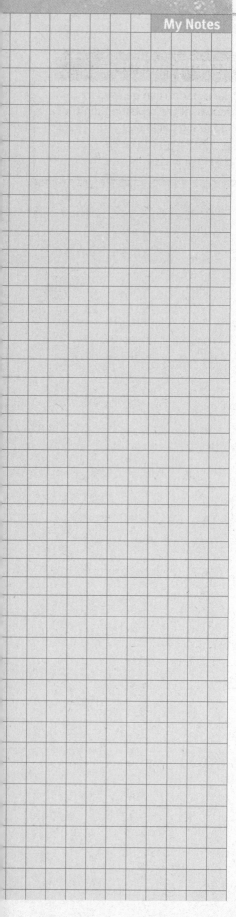

My Notes

Check Your Understanding

6. Convert the following to decimals.

  a. $\frac{6}{15}$

  b. $\frac{7}{9}$

  c. $\frac{23}{99}$

  d. $\frac{5}{9}$

7. Is the decimal 0.12345... a repeating decimal? Explain.

LESSON 4-2 PRACTICE

8. How are terminating decimals different than repeating decimals?

9. Write $\frac{7}{8}$ as a decimal. What type of decimal is it?

10. Convert the decimals to fractions.

  a. 0.50   **b.** 0.60   **c.** 0.25

11. Write 0.2222222 . . . as a fraction.

12. Attend to precision. Write 1.024242424 . . . as a fraction.

13. Hannah knows that the repeating decimal 0.0545454 . . . is equal to $\frac{3}{55}$.

  a. What decimal can be added to 0.0545454 . . . to get 0.1545454 . . . ?

  b. Write your answer from part a as a fraction.

  c. Add two fractions to determine the fraction equal to 0.1545454 . . . .

Learning Targets:
- Compare rational numbers in different forms.
- Represent repeating decimals using bar notation.
- Utilize various forms of rational numbers.

> **SUGGESTED LEARNING STRATEGIES:** Activating Prior Knowledge, Group Presentations, Think / Pair / Share, Sharing and Responding

1. What is the difference between the decimals $0.\overline{7}$ and $0.00\overline{7}$?

To convert a repeating decimal to a fraction, it is often necessary to multiply by a greater power of 10.

Example A

Convert $1.0525252\ldots$ to its fractional form.

Step 1: Let $x =$ the repeating decimal.

$$x = 1.0525252\ldots$$

Step 2: Determine the repeating digit or digits.

The repeating digits are 52.

Step 3: Multiply both sides of the original equation by the least power of 10 so that the digits that repeat align after the decimal point.

$$x = 1.052525252\ldots$$
$$100x = 105.252525252\ldots$$

Step 4: Subtract one equation from the other. The repeating digits will not be in the difference.

$$100x = 105.252525252\ldots$$
$$\underline{-\ x = \quad 1.052525252\ldots}$$
$$99x = 104.2$$

Step 5: Solve the resulting equation.

$$\frac{99x}{99} = \frac{104.2}{99}$$
$$x = \frac{1{,}042}{990} = \frac{521}{495}$$

Solution: $1.0525252\ldots = \dfrac{521}{495}$

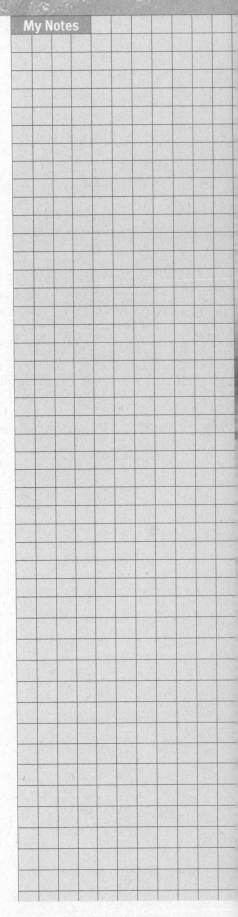

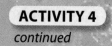
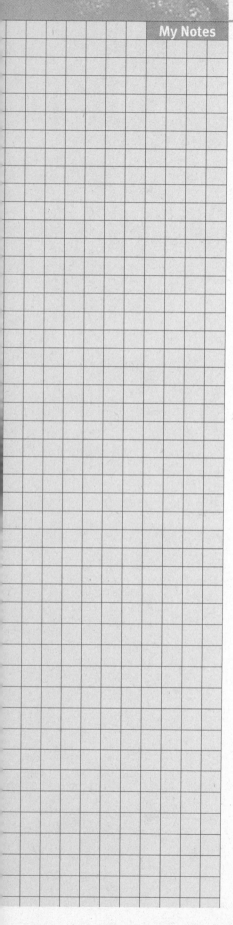

My Notes

Try These A
Convert each repeating decimal to a fraction.
a. 0.0555555 . . .

b. 3.00121212 . . .

c. 0.023333 . . .

2. Rational numbers can be written as fractions, decimals, or percents. How does the ability to convert between these forms help to compare the values of rational numbers?

3. For each type of rational number, explain how to compare two numbers.
   a. fractions

   b. decimals

   c. percents

Check Your Understanding

4. Convert $1.\overline{30}$ to a fraction.

5. Compare the number from Item 4 to the following rational numbers. Explain your reasoning.

   a. $\frac{4}{3}$ **b.** 1.30

Example B

List the rational numbers $2.\overline{4}$, $\frac{49}{20}$, and 240% in increasing order.

Step 1: Convert the fraction and percent to a decimal.
$$\frac{49}{20} = 2\frac{9}{20} = 2.45$$
$$240\% = 2.4$$

Step 2: Align the values on the decimal point and compare the digits from the right.
$$2.\overline{4} = 2.444\ldots$$
$$\frac{49}{20} = 2.450$$
$$240\% = 2.400$$

Step 3: List the rational numbers in increasing order.
$$240\%, 2.\overline{4}, \frac{49}{20}$$

Try These B

List the rational numbers in increasing order.

a. 25%, $\frac{1}{5}$, $0.\overline{2}$

b. $\frac{1}{3}$, 0.33, 33.5%

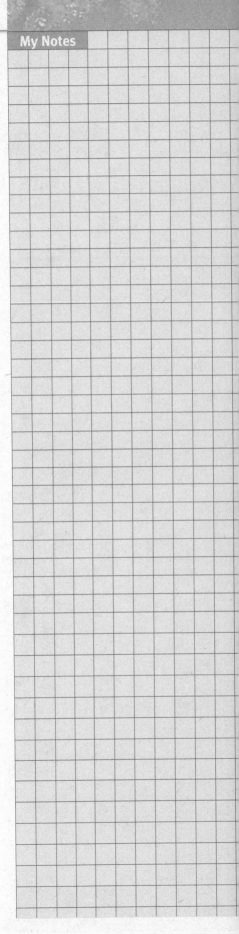

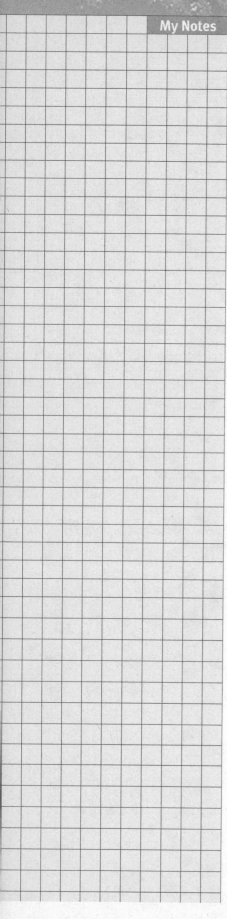

My Notes

6. Fill the blank in with a >, < or = sign.

   a. 40% _____ $\frac{4}{10}$

   b. $0.\overline{3}$ _____ $0.0\overline{3}$

   c. $\frac{2}{9}$ _____ 29%

7. **Critique the reasoning of others.** Samuel enters the fraction $\frac{5}{17}$ on his calculator. The display shows .2941176471, which are the most digits that can be displayed. He concludes that the fraction is a terminating decimal. Is Samuel correct?

8. Write the rational numbers from Example B on the previous page as fractions. Use the fractions to list the numbers in increasing order.

LESSON 4-3 PRACTICE

9. Which number is $\frac{3}{10}$ greater than?

   a. $\frac{4}{10}$ b. 28%   c. $\frac{3}{5}$

10. What is a rational number? Give three examples in different forms.

11. Convert 1.063636363… to a fraction.

12. Convert $8.6\overline{3}$ to a fraction.

13. How can you compare fractions with the same denominators? How can you compare fractions with the same numerators?

14. **Reason quantitatively.** List the rational numbers in increasing order. 0.555, $\frac{5}{9}$, 50.9%

ACTIVITY 4 PRACTICE

Write your answers on notebook paper.
Show your work.

Lesson 4-1

1. George ate the portion of pizza represented by the letter A in the pizza pie shown below. What fraction is this portion equivalent to?

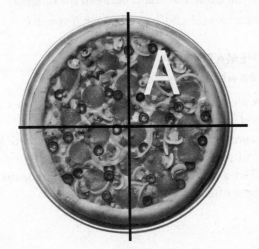

   A. $\frac{1}{4}$ B. $\frac{1}{2}$
   C. $\frac{3}{4}$ D. 4

2. How much pizza would be left after George eats his portion? Write as a fraction.

3. Convert the fractions to decimals and percents.
   a. $\frac{3}{5}$
   b. $\frac{2}{25}$

4. Convert the decimals to fractions and percents.
   a. 0.8
   b. 0.32

5. Convert the percents to decimals and fractions.
   a. 20%
   b. 72%

6. Convert the following to decimals.
   a. $\frac{3}{9}$
   b. $\frac{123}{999}$
   c. $\frac{45}{99}$

7. Which of the following is NOT equivalent to $\frac{60}{80}$?
   A. $\frac{3}{4}$ B. 0.6
   C. $\frac{6}{8}$ D. 0.75

Lesson 4-2

8. Which of the following does NOT describe a rational number?
   A. a decimal that terminates
   B. a decimal that does not terminate and does not repeat
   C. a decimal that repeats
   D. a fraction

9. Convert each of the following repeating decimals to a fraction.
   a. $0.\overline{6}$
   b. $0.\overline{12}$

10. Write three examples of each type of rational number.
    a. fractions that are repeating decimals
    b. fractions that are terminating decimals

11. Is 0.232323 a repeating decimal? Why or why not?

12. Are all whole numbers also rational numbers? Justify your answer.

13. Consider the two repeating decimals shown below.

    0.31313131…
    0.02020202…

    a. By simply looking at the decimal representations, what is the sum of these two rational numbers? Write as a decimal and as a fraction.
    b. Verify your answer by finding fractions that represent each decimal. Add the fractions.
    c. Write the difference of the two numbers as a repeating decimal.

14. Which number represents a repeating decimal?
    $\frac{1}{6}$, 25%, 0.5020202

15. Which repeating decimal is equivalent to the fraction $\frac{1}{9}$?

Lesson 4-3

16. Arrange the following rational numbers from least to greatest.

    a. $\frac{1}{6}$, 16%, $0.\overline{16}$

    b. $\frac{6}{11}$, $0.\overline{5}$, 5.9

17. Fill the blank in with a >, < or = sign.

    a. 45% _____ $\frac{4}{10}$

    b. $0.\overline{38}$ _____ $0.03\overline{2}$

    c. $\frac{21}{9}$ _____ $2.\overline{33}$

18. Which number is the largest of the group? 70%, $\frac{1}{2}$, 15%

19. Convert 1.0353535 . . . to a fraction.

20. Convert 0.022222 . . . to a fraction.

21. List the fractions below in increasing order. Describe the method you used. $\frac{1}{2}$, $\frac{5}{6}$, $\frac{7}{10}$, $\frac{2}{3}$

22. Write a convincing argument that the repeating decimal 0.999… is equal to 1.

23. Tanya says that 1 out of every 3 students at her school plays a sport. William says the actual number is 33% of the students. Who thinks a greater number of students plays a sport than the other does?

24. Write a fraction that is between the rational numbers 0.3 and $\frac{1}{3}$. Explain what you did.

MATHEMATICAL PRACTICES
Reason Abstractly and Quantitatively

25. Rational numbers are used every day. Write three instances in which you use each of the representations of a rational number—fraction, decimal, and percent—in your daily activities. Does a certain representation appear to be used most often?

Rational and Irrational Numbers

Where Am I?

Lesson 5-1 Estimating Irrational Numbers

Learning Targets:

- Differentiate between rational and irrational numbers.
- Approximate an irrational number in terms of a rational number.

SUGGESTED LEARNING STRATEGIES: Vocabulary Organizer, Create Representations, Look for a Pattern, Critique Reasoning, Simplify the Problem

Many early mathematicians believed that all numbers were *rational*; that is, they could be written as a quotient of two integers. However, as early as the seventh century BCE, mathematicians from India became aware of numbers that could not be expressed as the quotient of two integers. Eventually, it became accepted that the square roots of most real numbers could not be expressed rationally. These numbers were considered *irrational.*

1. Some examples of irrational numbers are $\sqrt{2}$ or π. Look at the screen shots in the My Notes sections of $\sqrt{2}$ and π.

   a. Based on what you know about π, is the screen shot the entire value of π?

   b. Based on your answer to part a, is the screen shot the entire value of $\sqrt{2}$?

   c. What is the difference between the decimal forms of rational numbers and the decimal forms of irrational numbers?

   d. The set of rational numbers and the set of irrational numbers together form the set of real numbers. Are there any numbers that are both rational and irrational? Explain. Use a Venn diagram to illustrate your explanation.

Even though irrational numbers cannot be expressed as a quotient of two numbers, it is possible to determine reasonable estimates for these numbers. To do so, it's helpful to become familiar with the relative size of some common irrational numbers.

My Notes

TECHNOLOGY TIP

While some decimals continue on forever, calculator screens will round the decimal when there is no space left on the screen.

| $\sqrt{2}$ | 1.414213562 |
| π | 3.141592654 |

MATH TERMS

Irrational numbers are real numbers that cannot be written as a ratio or fraction.

Rational numbers are real numbers that can be written as a ratio or fraction.

My Notes

2. Use this number line and the method described in parts a–f below to determine the approximate square root of 18.

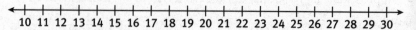

10 11 12 13 14 15 16 17 18 19 20 21 22 23 24 25 26 27 28 29 30

a. Which perfect square is less than 18 but closest to 18? Mark this integer on the number line.

b. Which perfect square is greater than 18 but closest to 18? Mark this integer on the number line.

c. What is the square root of the first integer you marked? Write the square root above the integer on the number line.

d. What is the square root of the second integer you marked? Write the square root above the integer on the number line.

e. Put an X on 18. The X should be between the two perfect squares. Is the X closer to the smaller or the larger perfect square?

f. **Attend to precision.** Above the X you put on 18, write a decimal number to the nearest tenth that you think is the square root of 18.

g. Check your estimate by squaring your approximation to see how close you are.

h. Using the number line below, fill in the two perfect squares that you determined were below and above 18 on the top of the number line. Write the whole numbers that represent those perfect squares on the bottom of the number line. Put your estimation of √18 on the number line.

My Notes

3. Using the method you used in Item 2, estimate the value of the number.

   a. $\sqrt{42}$

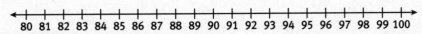

   b. $\sqrt{98}$

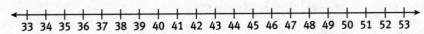

4. **Use appropriate tools strategically.** Use a calculator to determine the values of the square roots you estimated using a number line in Items 2 and 3. Round the answer to the nearest tenth. How close were your estimates?

   a. $\sqrt{18}$

   b. $\sqrt{42}$

   c. $\sqrt{98}$

5. Using the method you used in Items 2 and 3, estimate the value of the cube root.
   $\sqrt[3]{20}$

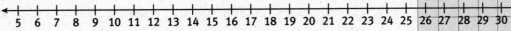

6. Explain why $\sqrt[3]{64}$ is rational and $\sqrt[3]{12}$ is not.

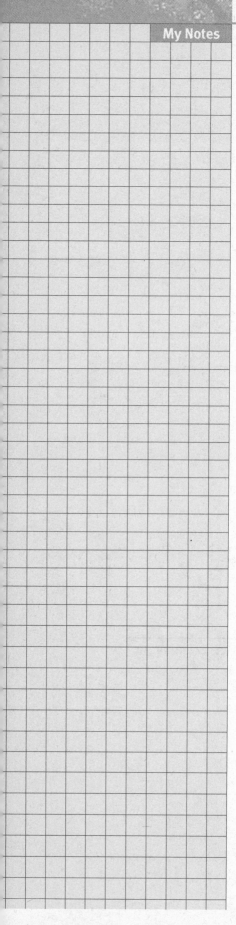

Check Your Understanding

Name the irrational number in each set.

7. $\left\{ \frac{17}{2}, \sqrt{8}, \sqrt[3]{8} \right\}$ **8.** $\left\{ -0.578\overline{9}, 6^3, \sqrt{65} \right\}$

9. Estimate the following square roots to the tenths place without using a calculator.

a. $\sqrt{10}$ **b.** $\sqrt{28}$ **c.** $\sqrt{73}$

d. Place the above square roots on their approximate location on the number line.

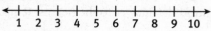

LESSON 5-1 PRACTICE

10. Name the irrational number in each set:

a. $\left\{ 12.89, \sqrt{12}, \frac{12}{144} \right\}$ **b.** $\left\{ \sqrt[3]{16}, \quad \sqrt{16}, \quad 2.5\overline{6} \right\}$

11. Estimate the following square and cube roots to the tenths place without using a calculator.

a. $\sqrt{92}$ **b.** $\sqrt{139}$ **c.** $\sqrt{68}$

d. $\sqrt{19}$ **e.** $\sqrt[3]{24}$ **f.** $\sqrt[3]{56}$

12. Place the approximate value of $\sqrt{26}$ on the number line below.

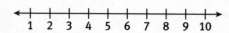

13. Place the approximate value of $\sqrt{74}$ on the number line below.

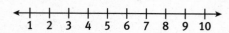

14. In previous math courses, you have studied the sets of whole numbers and integers.

a. Create a Venn diagram showing the relationship of the set of whole numbers and the set of integers.

b. How would you add the set of rational numbers to the Venn diagram you made in part a?

c. Would the set of irrational numbers have any overlapping regions with the Venn diagram you made in part a?

15. Critique the reasoning of others. Dale says that every number can be represented as a decimal. Is Dale correct? Explain.

Learning Targets:

- Approximate an irrational number in terms of a rational number.
- Compare and order irrational and rational numbers.

SUGGESTED LEARNING STRATEGIES: Predict and Confirm, Think Aloud, Construct an Argument, Simplify the Problem

Approximate an irrational number in terms of a rational number to understand its value.

1. Using a calculator, $\sqrt{3}$ is shown to be 1.7320508 . . .

    a. Explain where $\sqrt{3}$ would be in relation to the estimates of 1.7 and 1.8.

    b. Explain the connection between these estimates and the actual value with rational and irrational numbers.

Example A

Find examples of a rational number and an irrational number between 4.8 and 4.9.

Step 1: A rational number can be expressed as a ratio of integers or a decimal that terminates or repeats.
4.859 is between 4.8 and 4.9
4.859 terminates and can be expressed as the ratio: $\dfrac{4,859}{1,000}$.

Step 2: An irrational number cannot be expressed as a ratio of integers and, when expressed as a decimal, does not terminate or repeat.
4.8598979486 . . . is between 4.8 and 4.9
4.8598979486 . . . does not terminate and does not repeat.

Solution: A rational number between 4.8 and 4.9 is 4.859. An irrational number between 4.8 and 4.9 is 4.8598979486 . . .

MATH TIP

There are infinitely many examples of rational and irrational numbers between any two numbers.

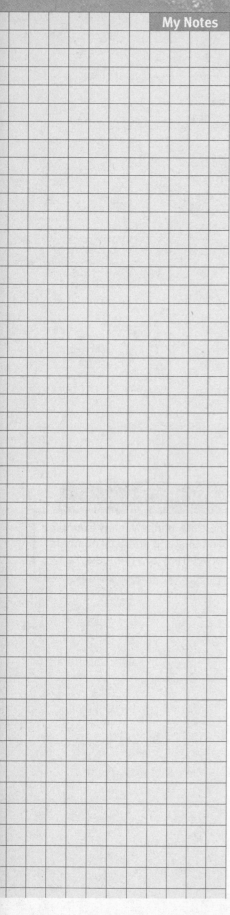

My Notes

Try These A

Give an example of a rational and an irrational number that is between the following numbers.
  a. 2 and 2.1
  b. 5.3 and 5.4
  c. 10.6 and 10.7

2. Explain why it is always possible to find another number (rational or irrational) between any two numbers.

Example B

Order the following numbers from least to greatest.

$$\sqrt{71}, \quad 9.3, \quad \sqrt{84}, \quad 8.1$$

Step 1: Approximate values for the irrational numbers in terms of rational numbers.

$\sqrt{71}$ is between $\sqrt{64} = 8$ and $\sqrt{81} = 9$.

$\sqrt{71} \approx 8.4$

$\sqrt{84}$ is between $\sqrt{81} = 9$ and $\sqrt{100} = 10$.

$\sqrt{84} \approx 9.2$

Step 2: Using the approximated values for the irrational numbers, order the numbers from least to greatest.

8.1, 8.4, 9.2, 9.3

Solution: The numbers in order from least to greatest are

$$8.1, \quad \sqrt{71}, \quad \sqrt{84}, \quad 9.3.$$

Try These B

Order the following numbers from least to greatest.
  a. $\sqrt{16}, \sqrt{14}, 4.1, 3.6$
  b. $\sqrt{150}, 12, 11.8, \sqrt{135}$
  c. $\pi, \sqrt{6}, 3.4, \sqrt{14}$

My Notes

3. Complete the comparisons using $>$ or $<$. Explain your reasoning.

   a. $\sqrt{10}$ ◯ 2.5

   b. 7 ◯ $\sqrt{50}$

   c. $\sqrt[3]{8}$ ◯ $\sqrt[3]{9}$

   d. $\sqrt{110}$ ◯ $\sqrt{66}$

4. **Reason quantitatively.** In Item 3d above, explain how you could have completed the comparison without using rational number approximations for $\sqrt{110}$ and $\sqrt{66}$.

Check Your Understanding

5. Give an example of a rational and an irrational number that is between the following numbers:

   a. 12 and 12.1

   b. 3.4 and 3.5

6. Complete the comparison with $>$ or $<$:

   $$11.2 \ \bigcirc \ \sqrt{120}$$

7. A right trapezoid has sides that measure 2 units, 6 units, $\sqrt{13}$ units, and 3 units. Order the lengths of the sides from least to greatest.

My Notes

LESSON 5-2 PRACTICE

8. Give an example of a rational and an irrational number between the following numbers:
   a. 8 and 8.1
   b. 9.6 and 9.7
   c. 10.2 and 10.3

Order the numbers from greatest to least.

9. $\sqrt[3]{18}$, 2.4, π, 2.7

10. 5.6, $\sqrt{25}$, $\sqrt[3]{140}$, 6.2

11. $\sqrt[3]{343}$, 7.4, $\sqrt{52}$, 8.2

12. The following numbers were placed in order from greatest to least. Complete the list with irrational numbers.

   6.8, ____ , 6.2, ____ , 5.1

13. **Construct viable arguments.** Describe the vastness of the sets of rational and irrational numbers. Why is it always possible to find a rational or irrational number between any two numbers?

ACTIVITY 5 PRACTICE
Write your answers on notebook paper.
Show your work.

Lesson 5-1
Name the irrational numbers in each set.

1. $\left\{8.4, \sqrt{12}, \pi, \sqrt{64}, \sqrt{65}\right\}$

2. $\left\{\frac{5}{6}, 2.1, \sqrt{45}, \sqrt{78}, \frac{2}{3}\right\}$

3. $\left\{\sqrt{25}, \sqrt{36}, \sqrt{17}, \frac{1}{8}, 3\right\}$

4. $\left\{1.24562\ldots, 5.9, \sqrt{82}, \sqrt{20}, \frac{9}{16}\right\}$

Determine a reasonable estimate to the tenths place.

5. $\sqrt{18}$

6. $\sqrt{130}$

7. $\sqrt{2}$

8. $\sqrt{86}$

9. $\sqrt[3]{117}$

10. $\sqrt[3]{24}$

11. $\sqrt[3]{41}$

12. $\sqrt[3]{56}$

13. Which of the following square roots would not be between 5 and 6?

    A. $\sqrt{27}$

    B. $\sqrt{32}$

    C. $\sqrt{37}$

    D. $\sqrt{29}$

14. Which of the following square roots would not be between 8 and 9?

    A. $\sqrt{74}$

    B. $\sqrt{62}$

    C. $\sqrt{80}$

    D. $\sqrt{77}$

15. Describe the relationship between irrational numbers and rational numbers.

16. Cody is asked to find a cube root that is found between 4.2 and 4.3. He provides the number, $\sqrt[3]{75}$. Is he correct? Explain.

17. Ling marked the approximate value of $\sqrt{32}$ on the number line as shown. Did Ling mark the value correctly? Explain your reasoning.

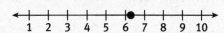

18. Which is not an irrational number?

    A. $\sqrt{15}$

    B. $\sqrt{16}$

    C. $\sqrt{17}$

    D. $\sqrt{18}$

Lesson 5-2
Determine a rational and an irrational number between each of the following pairs of numbers.

19. 12.1 and 12.2

20. 4.5 and 4.6

21. 9 and 9.1

22. 14.2 and 14.3

23. 15 and 15.1

Order the following from least to greatest.

24. $\sqrt{27}, 5.5, \sqrt{24}, 5$

25. $\sqrt[3]{19}, \pi, 2.65, \sqrt{4}$

26. $6.8, \sqrt{49}, 7.1, 6.8556546\ldots$

27. $\sqrt[3]{67}, \sqrt{16}, 4.2, 4.15$

28. $12\frac{1}{3}, \sqrt{144}, 12.99, 3^2$

29. $\sqrt[3]{88}, \sqrt[3]{8}, \sqrt[3]{108}, \sqrt[3]{18}$

Compare using $>$, $<$, or $=$.

30. $\sqrt[3]{729} \bigcirc \sqrt[3]{729}$

31. $13.225 \bigcirc \sqrt{170}$

32. $\sqrt[3]{5} \bigcirc \sqrt{5}$

33. $\sqrt{72} \bigcirc 8$

34. Roxie thinks that the irrational number 6.00289467… is less than the rational number 6. Do you agree with Roxie? Explain your reasoning.

35. Which of the following irrational numbers is the greatest?

A. $\frac{\pi}{2}$

B. 2π

C. π^2

D. $\frac{3\pi}{2}$

36. Which of the following is an irrational number between 8.8 and 8.9?

A. 8.089703487 …

B. 8.888888888 …

C. 8.912984065 …

D. 8.871985703 …

MATHEMATICAL PRACTICES
Look for and Make Use of Structure

37. Consider the following numbers:

$$\sqrt[3]{8}, \sqrt[3]{9}, \sqrt[3]{27}, \sqrt[3]{42}, \sqrt[3]{110}, \sqrt[3]{125}$$

a. Which of these are rational?

b. Which of these are irrational?

c. Write a conjecture explaining why some of these cube roots are rational and why some are irrational.

d. Support your conjecture with a different example of a rational cube root and an irrational cube root.

Natural disasters can happen anywhere in the world. Examples of natural disasters include tornados, earthquakes, hurricanes, and tsunamis. Two of the most well-known natural disasters are Hurricane Katrina (2005), which hit New Orleans, Louisiana, and Japan's tsunami (2011).

1. After Hurricane Katrina, $\frac{8}{10}$ of the city of New Orleans was flooded. Represent this number in the following ways:
   a. decimal
   b. visual representation
   c. percent

2. Only 58% of the people in the coastal areas of Japan took the warning system seriously that a tsunami was coming and evacuated the area. Represent this number in the following ways:
   a. decimal   b. fraction

The area of land that is affected by a natural disaster can vary greatly. While the destruction areas of these disasters were not perfect squares, thinking about the areas as squares can give you a good visualization of how much area was affected.

3. The total square miles affected by the natural disasters are given below. Find the side length of the area affected if it was a square.
   a. Hurricane Katrina: 90,000 square miles
   b. Japan tsunami: 216 square miles

4. Given that a storm has a destruction area in the shape of a square, give the total area affected if the side lengths of the square were:
   a. 315.2 miles   b. $30\frac{1}{2}$ kilometers

When natural disasters occur, organizations such as the Red Cross help by sending in crates of supplies to those who are affected. The crates contain first aid, food, drinks, and other supplies.

5. Explain how, given an edge length of a cubical crate, the volume of the crate could be determined. Provide an example with your explanation.

6. Given the following volumes of the cubical crates, determine the edge length. Explain how you found the edges.
   a. 8 ft^3 b. 27 ft^3

Scoring Guide	Exemplary	Proficient	Emerging	Incomplete
	The solution demonstrates these characteristics:			
Mathematics Knowledge and Thinking (Items 1a-c, 2a-b, 3a-b, 4a-b, 5, 6a-b)	• Clear and accurate understanding of converting between fractions, decimals, and percent. • Effective understanding of squares and square roots; cubes and cube roots.	• Converting between fractions, decimals, and percent. • Understanding of squares and square roots; cubes and cube roots.	• Errors in converting between fractions, decimals, and percent. • Some errors in working with squares and square roots; cubes and cube roots.	• Incorrect or incomplete converting between fractions, decimals, and percent. • Little or no understanding of squares and square roots; cubes and cube roots.
Problem Solving (Items 3a-b, 4a-b, 6a-b)	• An appropriate and efficient strategy that results in a correct answer.	• A strategy that may include unnecessary steps but results in a correct answer.	• A strategy that results in some incorrect answers.	• No clear strategy when solving problems.
Mathematical Modeling / Representations (Items 1a-c, 2a-b, 3a-b, 4a-b, 5, 6a-b)	• Clear and accurate understanding of representing a rational number as a fraction, decimal, or percent. • Clearly and accurately relating a volume to a cube, an area to a square, and the root to a side length.	• Representing a rational number as a fraction, decimal, or percent. • Relating a volume to a cube, an area to a square, and the root to a side length.	• Errors in representing a rational number as a fraction, decimal, or percent. • Errors in relating volume to a cube, area to a square, and the root to a side length.	• Inaccurately representing a rational number as a fraction, decimal, or percent. • Little or no understanding of relating volume to a cube, area to a square, and the root to a side length.
Reasoning and Communication (Items 5, 6a-b)	• Precise explanation of the difference between rational and irrational numbers. • Clear and precise explanation of the relationship between volume and edge length of a cube.	• Adequate explanation of the difference between rational and irrational numbers. • Adequate explanation of the relationship between volume and edge length of a cube.	• A misleading or confusing explanation of the difference between rational and irrational numbers. • A confusing explanation of the relationship between volume and edge length of a cube.	• An incomplete or inaccurate explanation of the difference between rational and irrational numbers. • An incomplete or inaccurate explanation of the relationship between volume and edge length of a cube.

Properties of Exponents

That's a Lot of Cats

Lesson 6-1 Multiplying and Dividing with Exponents

Learning Targets:

- Understand and apply properties of integer exponents.
- Simplify multiplication expressions with integer exponents.
- Simplify division expressions with integer exponents.

> **SUGGESTED LEARNING STRATEGIES:** Marking the Text, Paraphrasing, Look for a Pattern, Critique Reasoning, Work Backward

As I was going to St. Ives,
I met a man with seven wives.
Every wife had seven sacks,
And every sack had seven cats.
Every cat had seven kittens.
Kittens, cats, sacks, wives,
How many were going to St. Ives?

In addition to being an 18th century translation of what the *Guinness Book of World Records* claims is the oldest mathematical riddle in history, this riddle can be used to explain how exponents work.

Use this table to determine the number of kittens in the riddle—in expanded form, exponential form, and standard form. Expanded form is expressing the number in terms of multiplication, exponential form is expressing the number with a base and exponent, and standard form is the product.

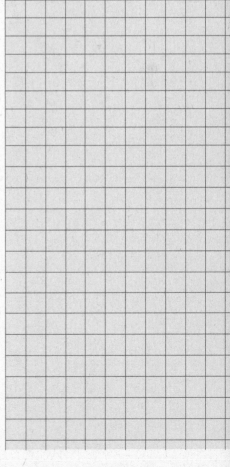

CONNECT TO HISTORY

Problem 79 on the *Rhind Mathematical Papyrus* (c. 1650 BCE) contains the algorithm that is said to be the basis for the mathematics in this riddle.

	Number Written in...			
	Expanded Form	**Exponential Form**	**Standard Form**	**Base**
Wives	7	7^1	7	7
Sacks	7•7	7^2	49	7
Cats	7•7•7	7^3	343	7
Kittens				

1. Describe any patterns you observe in the table.

2. Use the patterns you observe to complete the last row of the table.

3. **Make sense of problems.** Suppose each kitten had seven stripes. Write an expression to determine the total number of stripes. Write your expression in the following forms.
   a. Expanded form:

   b. Exponential form:

   c. Standard form:

When you multiply two exponential expressions with the same base, add the exponents.

Example A

Simplify $7 \cdot 7 \cdot 7 \cdot 7 \cdot 7 \cdot 7 \cdot 7$ in various ways. Then compare your results

Step 1: Use the associative property of multiplication to rewrite the expanded form $7 \cdot 7 \cdot 7 \cdot 7 \cdot 7 \cdot 7 \cdot 7$ as

$(7 \cdot 7 \cdot 7)(7 \cdot 7 \cdot 7 \cdot 7)$ or $(7 \cdot 7)(7 \cdot 7 \cdot 7 \cdot 7 \cdot 7)$

Step 2: Rewrite each expression in exponential form.

$$(7 \cdot 7 \cdot 7)(7 \cdot 7 \cdot 7 \cdot 7) = 7^3 \cdot 7^4$$
$$(7 \cdot 7)(7 \cdot 7 \cdot 7 \cdot 7 \cdot 7) = 7^2 \cdot 7^5$$

Step 3: Simplify each power. Notice that the exponents are being added as the bases are multiplied.

$$7^3 \cdot 7^4 = 7^{3+4} = 7^7 = 823{,}543$$
$$7^2 \cdot 7^5 = 7^{2+5} = 7^7 = 823{,}543$$

Solution: Each of these expanded forms simplifies to the same product, 823,543, and same exponential form, 7^7.

Try These A

Consider the product $(x \cdot x)(x \cdot x \cdot x)$.
a. Rewrite the product using exponents.
b. Simplify the expression, and write the answer in exponential form.

Check Your Understanding

Simplify the expressions.

4. $3^9 \cdot 3^3$

5. $a^7 \cdot a^4$

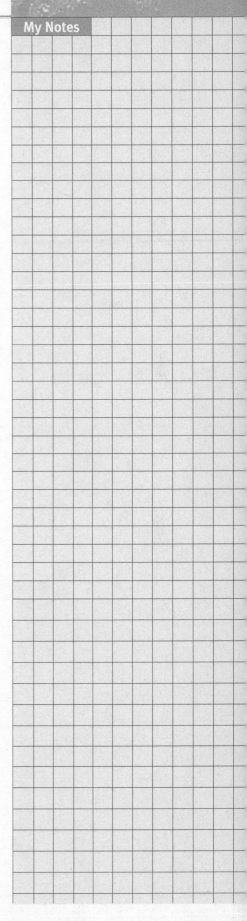

My Notes

Example B

Simplify $\dfrac{7^4}{7^3}$.

Step 1: Write $\dfrac{7^4}{7^3}$ in expanded form.

$$\frac{7 \cdot 7 \cdot 7 \cdot 7}{7 \cdot 7 \cdot 7}$$

Step 2: Simplify by dividing common factors.

$$\frac{\cancel{7} \cdot \cancel{7} \cdot \cancel{7} \cdot 7}{\cancel{7} \cdot \cancel{7} \cdot \cancel{7}} = 7$$

Solution: $\dfrac{7^4}{7^3} = 7$

Try These B

Consider the expression $\dfrac{x^8}{x^5}$.

a. Rewrite the expression with the numerator and denominator in expanded form.

b. Simplify the expression you wrote in part a.

c. Describe how you could simplify the original expression without writing it in expanded form.

6. What is the exponent of the solution to Example B?

7. How does the exponent of the solution to Example B relate to the exponents of the original expression?

8. **Reason quantitatively.** What pattern do you notice about the exponents when dividing two powers with the same base?

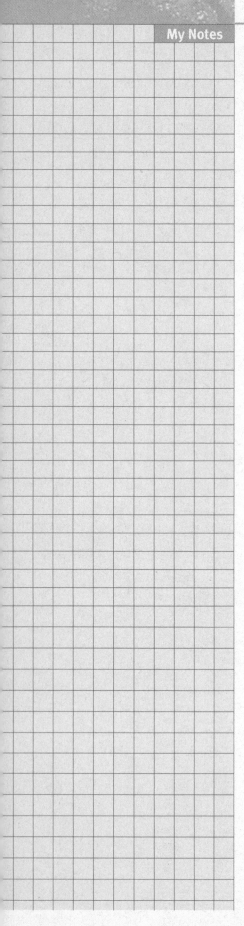

My Notes

> **Check Your Understanding**
>
> Simplify the expressions.
>
> **9.** $\dfrac{12^{15}}{12^{10}}$
>
> **10.** $\dfrac{r^9}{r}$

LESSON 6-1 PRACTICE

11. Re-read the riddle at the beginning of the lesson. This riddle has been the subject of great debate over the years as the riddle is said to have multiple answers. Determine which of the following could be considered a reasonable answer to the riddle. Justify your reasoning.
   A. 1   **B.** 30   **C.** 2,403   **D.** 2,802

12. Simplify each expression:
   a. $t^2 \cdot t^5$ **b.** $\dfrac{8^8}{8^6}$

13. Write a rule for multiplying terms with exponents that have the same base in your own words.

14. Write a rule for dividing terms with exponents that have the same base in your own words.

15. **Critique the reasoning of others.** Sebastian and Georgia are examining the expression $\dfrac{4^7}{4^5}$. Sebastian says the answer is 1^2. Georgia knows the answer is 4^2. Help Georgia explain to Sebastian what he did incorrectly.

Learning Targets:
- Understand and apply properties of integer exponents.
- Simplify expressions with negative exponents.

> **SUGGESTED LEARNING STRATEGIES:** Predict and Confirm, Paraphrasing, Look for a Pattern, Visualization

Example A

Consider the expression $\dfrac{4^3}{4^8}$. Simplify the expression by dividing and by writing the numerator and denominator in expanded form. Compare the results.

Step 1: Divide by subtracting the exponents.

$$\frac{4^3}{4^8} = 4^{3-8} = 4^{-5}$$

Step 2: Write the numerator and denominator in expanded form and simplify.

$$\frac{4^3}{4^8} = \frac{\cancel{4} \cdot \cancel{4} \cdot \cancel{4}}{\cancel{4} \cdot \cancel{4} \cdot \cancel{4} \cdot 4 \cdot 4 \cdot 4 \cdot 4 \cdot 4} = \frac{1}{4^5}$$

Step 3: Compare the two results.

$$4^{-5} = \frac{1}{4^5}$$

Solution: The two strategies used to divide 4^3 by 4^8 yielded the same answer in two different forms, 4^{-5} and $\dfrac{1}{4^5}$.

Try These A

Consider the expression $\dfrac{x^3}{x^5}$.

a. Rewrite the numerator and denominator in expanded form and simplify.

b. Simplify the expression by dividing (subtract the exponents).

c. Compare your results for parts a and b.

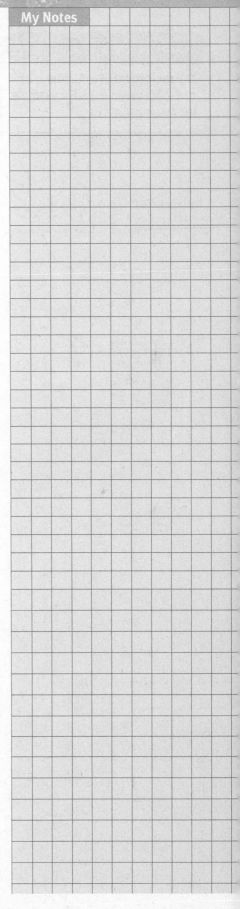

My Notes

MATH TERMS

The **reciprocal** of a number is its multiplicative inverse. For example, the reciprocal of 6 is $\frac{1}{6}$.

When an exponent has a negative value, it actually means to divide 1 by the base that number of times. An expression with a negative exponent can be written as an equivalent expression with a positive exponent by writing the **reciprocal**.

1. Simplify $\frac{x^4}{x^2}$.

2. Simplify $\frac{x^2}{x^4}$.

3. **Reason quantitatively.** Compare and contrast your answers to Items 1 and 2.

Check Your Understanding

Simplify the following expressions. Compare the answers.

4. $\frac{2^9}{2^5}$ and $\frac{2^5}{2^9}$

5. $\frac{a^6}{a^3}$ and $\frac{a^3}{a^6}$

Example B

Write 6^{-2} as an equivalent expression without a negative exponent.

Write the reciprocal of 6^2 to make an equivalent expression with a positive exponent.

Solution: $6^{-2} = \frac{1}{6^2}$.

Try These B

Rewrite these expressions without a negative exponent.

a. a^{-4}

b. 8^{-3}

c. $\frac{1}{3^{-2}}$

Example C

Simplify the expression $\dfrac{r^8}{r^{15}}$. Your final answer should not contain a negative exponent.

Step 1: Divide r^8 by r^{15} by subtracting the exponents.

$$r^{8-15} = r^{-7}$$

Step 2: Rewrite r^{-7} without a negative exponent by writing the reciprocal.

$$r^{-7} = \dfrac{1}{r^7}$$

Solution: $\dfrac{r^8}{r^{15}}$ equals $\dfrac{1}{r^7}$.

Try These C

Attend to precision. Simplify these expressions. Your final answer should not contain a negative exponent.

a. $\dfrac{y^4}{y^8}$

b. $\dfrac{10^{12}}{10^{15}}$

c. $\dfrac{4^{-2}5^7}{4^3 5^{-2}}$

Check Your Understanding

Simplify the follow expressions.

6. x^{-7}

7. $\dfrac{5^6}{5^9}$

8. $\dfrac{x^5 y^{-2}}{x^{-4} y^4}$

LESSON 6-2 PRACTICE

Simplify the expressions in Items 9–12. Write final answers in exponential form without negative exponents.

9. 9^{-10}

10. $\dfrac{k^{-5}}{k^2}$

11. $3^3 \cdot 3^{-6}$

12. $\dfrac{2^4 \cdot 10^{-6}}{2^2 \cdot 10^{-2}}$

13. **Reason abstractly.** Write in your own words how to write an expression with a negative exponent as an equivalent expression with a positive exponent.

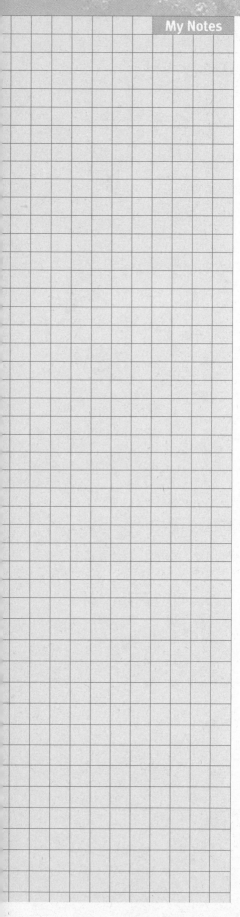

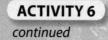

Learning Targets:
- Understand and apply properties of integer exponents.
- Simplify expressions with zero as the exponent.
- Simplify expressions with exponents raised to a power.

SUGGESTED LEARNING STRATEGIES: Paraphrasing, Look for a Pattern, Graphic Organizer, Construct an Argument

Although the riddle *As I was going to St. Ives* has only one narrator, the number 1 can also be written as a base of 7. To see how this works, you can examine several ways to express the number 1.

Example A
Simplify $\frac{7}{7}$ using exponents and explain the result.

Step 1: Rewrite the fraction by expressing the numerator and denominator in exponential form.
$$\frac{7}{7} = \frac{7^1}{7^1}$$

Step 2: Simplify the expression by dividing (by subtracting the exponents).
$$\frac{7^1}{7^1} = 7^{1-1} = 7^0$$

Solution: Since $\frac{7}{7}$ is equal to 1 and also equal to 7^0, it follows that 7 (or any number) raised to the power of 0 is equal to 1.

Try These A
Express regularity in repeated reasoning. Simplify these expressions.
a. y^0
b. 9^0
c. 125^0

Check Your Understanding

1. $83,567^0$

2. $\dfrac{b^4}{b^4}$

Recall from the riddle that the man had 7 wives, each wife had 7 sacks, each sack had 7 cats, and each cat had 7 kittens. Suppose that each kitten had 7 stripes. Now assume each stripe on each kitten contains seven spots. The situation is becoming more complicated, and the need for using exponents has grown . . . exponentially. The number of spots can be written as a power raised to another power.

When an exponential expression is raised to a power, multiply the exponents to simplify.

Example B
Show that $(7^3)^2 = 7^{3 \times 2}$

Step 1: $(7^3)^2 = (7^3) \cdot (7^3)$

Step 2: $7^3 \cdot 7^3 = (7 \cdot 7 \cdot 7) \cdot (7 \cdot 7 \cdot 7) = 7^6 = 7^{3 \times 2}$

Solution: $(7^3)^2 = 7^{3 \times 2}$

Try These B
Simplify these expressions by multiplying the exponents. Write your answer in exponential form.

a. $(6^3)^4$
b. $(n^7)^5$
c. $(12^6)^3$

My Notes

MATH TIP

Create an organized summary of the properties used to simplify and evaluate expressions with exponents.

Check Your Understanding

Simplify these expressions. Write your answer in exponential form.

3. $(n^2)^5$

4. $(7^4)^4$

LESSON 6-3 PRACTICE

5. In your own words, write the outcome of raising any base to the power of zero.

Simplify each expression in Items 6–8. Write your answer in exponential form.

6. $9^0 \cdot (6^{12})^2$

7. $(17^9)^3$

8. $(w^4)^5$

9. Construct viable arguments. Explain how the product $10{,}324^0 \cdot 8{,}576^0$ can be done using mental math.

ACTIVITY 6 PRACTICE

Write your answers on notebook paper.
Show your work.

Lesson 6-1

Simplify. Express your answer in exponential form.

1. $3^5 \cdot 3^4$

2. $5^6 \cdot 5^2$

3. $x^{16} \cdot x^1$

4. $\dfrac{4^3}{4^2}$

5. $\dfrac{10^8}{10^6}$

6. $\dfrac{x^{11}}{x^4}$

7. Which of the following is $12^6 \cdot 12^4$ simplified in exponential form?
   A. 12^2
   B. 12^{10}
   C. 12^{12}
   D. 12^{24}

8. Which of the following is $\dfrac{a^8}{a^3}$ simplified in exponential form?
   A. a^{-5}
   B. a^5
   C. a^{11}
   D. a^{24}

9. Kwon multiplied $5^5 \cdot 5^4$ and found the product to be 5^1. Do you agree with Kwon? Explain your reasoning.

Lesson 6-2

Simplify. Express your answer in exponential form.

10. $\dfrac{2^4}{2^7}$

11. $\dfrac{r^7}{r^{12}}$

12. 3^{-2}

13. z^{-5}

14. $8^{-8} \cdot 8^6$

15. $\dfrac{x^8 y^2}{x^2 y^8}$

16. $\dfrac{5^{-3}}{5^2}$

17. Which of the following is equivalent to 4^{-10}?
    A. $\dfrac{1}{10}$
    B. $\dfrac{4}{10}$
    C. $\dfrac{1}{4^{-10}}$
    D. $\dfrac{1}{4^{10}}$

18. Which of the following is equivalent to $\dfrac{c^{-3} d^5}{c^2 d^{-1}}$?
    A. $c^1 d^4$
    B. $c^5 d^6$
    C. $\dfrac{c^5}{d^6}$
    D. $\dfrac{d^6}{c^5}$

Lesson 6-3

Simplify. Express your answer in exponential form.

19. 5^0

20. $1,734^0$

21. $(b^3)^9$

22. $(4^4)^5$

23. $(6^3)^4$

24. $(99^9)^0$

25. Which of the following is $(4^x)^y$ simplified in exponential form?
  A. 4^{xy}
  B. 4^{x-y}
  C. 4^{x+y}
  D. $4^{\frac{x}{y}}$

26. Victor was asked to simplify this expression in exponential form: $8^0 + 12^0$. He says the answer is 2. Do you agree with Victor? Explain your reasoning.

27. When raising a power to another power, how are the exponents simplified?
  A. The exponents are multiplied.
  B. The exponents are subtracted.
  C. The exponents are divided.
  D. The exponents are added.

MATHEMATICAL PRACTICES
Look For and Make Use of Structure

28. In the table below, summarize the rules for exponents you discovered in this activity.

Situation	Verbal Description	Numeric Example
Multiplying powers with the same base		
Dividing powers with the same base		
Raising a term to an exponent of zero		
Raising a power to another exponent		

Scientific Notation

A Traveler's Tale

Lesson 7-1 Scientific Notation vs. Standard Form

Learning Targets:

- Express numbers in scientific notation.
- Convert numbers in scientific notation to standard form.
- Use scientific notation to write estimates of quantities.

Suggested Learning Strategies: Interactive Word Wall, Graphic Organizer, Marking the Text, Look for a Pattern, Work Backward

The story *Gulliver's Travels* describes the adventures of Lemuel Gulliver, a ship's doctor, who becomes stranded in many strange places. In Lilliput, Gulliver finds that he is a giant compared to the people and the world around him. During another voyage Gulliver is stranded in another land, Brobdingnag, where he is as small to the inhabitants as the Lilliputians were to him.

The story never says how tall Gulliver is, but it does tell how the heights of the Lilliputian people and the people from Brobdingnag compare to Gulliver's height. The many descriptions of size in this tale provide ways to explore the magnitude, or size, of numbers. Powers of 10 will be used to express these very large and very small numbers. For this activity assume that Gulliver is 5 feet tall.

With a partner or in your group, discuss the story of Gulliver. By asking questions and making notes, confirm that you understand who Gulliver and the Lilliputians are, as well as what you know about their heights.

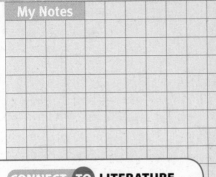

CONNECT TO LITERATURE

Gulliver's Travels was a book written in 1726 by Jonathan Swift. The book has been a popular read since the day it was published and has never been out of print. The book is about Lemuel Gulliver and his voyages.

Example A

A person from Brobdingnag is 10 times as tall as Gulliver. Determine the height of the person.

Step 1: Gulliver is 5 feet tall, and the person from Brobdingnag is 10 times as tall, so multiply to find the height of the person from Brobdingnag:

$$5 \times 10 = 50 \text{ feet tall}$$

Step 2: Write an expression using Gulliver's height and a power of 10 to represent the height of 50 feet:

$$5 \times 10^1 = 50$$

Solution: A person from Brobdingnag is 50 feet tall, or in terms of Gulliver's height, the person from Brobdingnag is 5×10^1 feet tall.

Try These A

a. If Adadahy is 10 times as tall as a person from Brobdingnag, how tall is she?

b. Write an expression using Gulliver's height and a power of 10 to represent the height of the person in part a.

ACTIVITY 7
continued

Lesson 7-1
Scientific Notation vs. Standard Form

Notice the expressions you have written show the product of a factor and a power of 10 with an exponent that is a positive integer.

Example B

Find the value of the expression 6×10^4. This expression is the product of a factor and a power of 10 with an exponent that is a positive integer:

Step 1: Simplify 10^4.

$$10^4 = 10 \cdot 10 \cdot 10 \cdot 10 = 10,000$$

Step 2: Multiply by 6.

$$6 \times 10,000 = 60,000$$

Solution: $6 \times 10^4 = 60,000$

Try These B

Find the value of these expressions.

a. 15×10^3 **b.** 2×10^6 **c.** 43.2×10^3

d. Describe any patterns you noticed in evaluating these expressions.

MATH TERMS

Scientific notation is a way to write a number as a product of the number, a, and 10^n, when $1 \le a < 10$ and n is an integer.

$$7 \times 10^8$$

Standard form is a way to write a number using a digit for each place.

$$700,000,000$$

MATH TIP

Integers consist of all natural numbers, their opposites, and 0: $\{..., -3, -2, -1, 0, 1, 2, 3, ...\}$.

After Gulliver's boat capsizes in a violent storm, he swims ashore to Lilliput and falls asleep. When he wakes, Gulliver finds he has been tied to the ground and can only look up into the bright sun. The sun has a diameter of 1.39×10^9 m and a mass of 2.0×10^{20} kg.

The measurements, 1.39×10^9 m and 2.0×10^{20} kg, are written in *scientific notation*. A number written in scientific notation is the product of a factor, a, and a power of 10 with an exponent that is an integer, n. It is expressed in the form $a \times 10^n$, where $1 \le a < 10$ and n is an integer. A number is written in *standard form* when it is expressed in digits only. Scientific notation is especially helpful when working with numbers with very large and very small magnitudes.

Example C

Rewrite the diameter of the sun, 1.39×10^9 m, in standard form.

Step 1: Simplify 10^9.

$$10^9 = 1,000,000,000$$

Step 2: Multiply by 1.39.

$$1.39 \times 1,000,000,000 = 1,390,000,000$$

Solution: The diameter of the sun, 1.39×10^9 m, in standard form is 1,390,000,000 m.

Lesson 7-1
Scientific Notation vs. Standard Form

ACTIVITY 7
continued

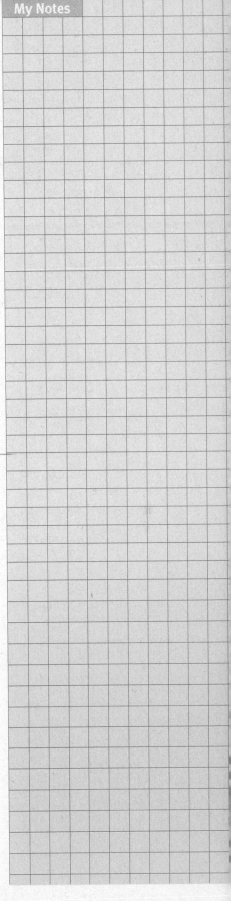

Try These C

a. What is the relationship between the exponent of the power of 10 and the number of places the decimal moves?

b. Rewrite the mass of the sun, 2.0×10^{20} kg, in standard form.

Rewrite these expressions in standard form:

c. 4.3×10^7 **d.** 7×10^{12}

e. 3.2×10^5 **f.** 9×10^{24}

Example D

Convert 25,000,000,000 from standard form to scientific notation.

Step 1: Identify the location of the decimal point in 25,000,000,000.

$$25,000,000,000.$$

↑ decimal point

Step 2: Move the decimal point to the left until you have a number that is greater than or equal to 1 and less than 10. Count the number of places you moved the decimal point.

← move the decimal point 10 places to the left

Step 3: Rewrite the number in scientific notation: 2.5×10^{10}

Solution: $25,000,000,000 = 2.5 \times 10^{10}$

Try These D

Convert each number from standard form to scientific notation. Work backwards from your answer to check your work.

a. 6,000   **b.** 436,000,000   **c.** 16,000

ACTIVITY 7
continued

Lesson 7-1
Scientific Notation vs. Standard Form

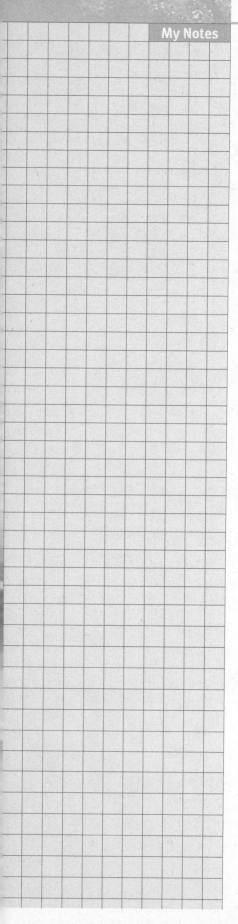

My Notes

Large numbers can also be written using words. For example, you can write 9,000,000,000 or 9 billion or 9×10^9.

This table shows names for some very large numbers.

Standard Form	Power of 10	Name
1,000	10^3	Thousand
1,000,000	10^6	Million
1,000,000,000	10^9	Billion
1,000,000,000,000	10^{12}	Trillion
1,000,000,000,000,000	10^{15}	Quadrillion
1,000,000,000,000,000,000	10^{18}	Quintillion
1,000,000,000,000,000,000,000	10^{21}	Sextillion
1,000,000,000,000,000,000,000,000	10^{24}	Septillion
1,000,000,000,000,000,000,000,000,000	10^{27}	Octillion
1,000,000,000,000,000,000,000,000,000,000	10^{30}	Nonillion
1,000,000,000,000,000,000,000,000,000,000,000	10^{33}	Decillion
There is not enough space to write this number.	10^{100}	Googol

Make use of structure. Complete this table showing standard form, scientific notation, and name of some large numbers.

	Standard Form	Scientific Notation	Name
	7,400,000,000,000,000	7.4×10^{15}	7.4 quadrillion
1.		3×10^3	
2.	1,200,000,000		
3.			5 trillion
4.	9,000,000		

You can use scientific notation to write estimates of large numbers that have many non-zero digits. Estimates consist of a single digit times a power of 10.

Example E

According to the U.S. Census, the population of California in the year 2010 was 37,253,956. Write an estimate of the population using scientific notation.

Step 1:   The greatest place value is ten million, so round the population to the nearest ten million.
$37,253,956 \approx 40,000,000$

Lesson 7-1
Scientific Notation vs. Standard Form

ACTIVITY 7
continued

My Notes

Step 2: Write the population to the nearest ten million in scientific notation.
$$40,000,000 = 4 \times 10^7$$

Solution: An estimate of the population of California in 2010 is 4×10^7.

Try These E

Write an estimate of each number using scientific notation.
a. 284,116   **b.** 5,218,996

Check Your Understanding

Convert each number from scientific notation to standard form.

5. 5.2×10^4 **6.** 4.23×10^6

7. 2×10^3 **8.** 1.03×10^4

Convert each number from standard form to scientific notation.

9. 20,000   **10.** 1,340,000

LESSON 7-1 PRACTICE

11. Gulliver is so much bigger than the Lilliputians that he consumes more food than 1,000 Lilliputians do. Write this number in scientific notation.

For Items 12–16, identify whether the expression is written in scientific notation. For those not written in scientific notation, explain why and rewrite in scientific notation.

12. 6×10^4

13. 15×10^3

14. 2×10^6

15. 3.2×10^5

16. 43.2×10^3

17. The kingdom of Lilliput is said to have an area of 24 million square miles. Write this amount using scientific notation.

18. **Construct viable arguments.** Explain why someone would want to write 52,000,000,000,000,000 in scientific notation instead of standard form.

19. According to the U.S. Census of 2010, the population of persons aged 65 years and older was 40,267,984. Write an estimate of this population using scientific notation.

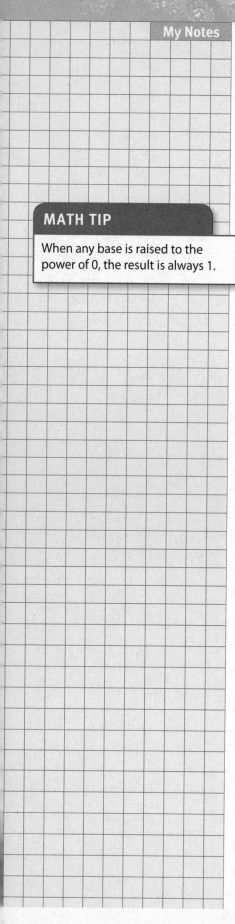

MATH TIP

When any base is raised to the power of 0, the result is always 1.

Learning Targets:
- Express numbers in scientific notation.
- Convert numbers in scientific notation to standard form.
- Compare and order numbers in scientific notation.
- Use scientific notation to write estimates of quantities.

Suggested Learning Strategies: Summarizing, Close Reading, Visualization, Construct an Argument, Work Backward

Suppose that Gulliver is 5 feet tall.

1. **Reason quantitatively.** Describe how to write Gulliver's height in scientific notation.
   a. Is 5 an appropriate factor to use? Why or why not?

   b. What is the exponent for the power of 10? Justify your response.

2. Convert each number from standard form to scientific notation.
   a. 2   b. 8.3

3. Convert each number from scientific notation to standard form.
   a. 9×10^0 b. 6.12×10^0

The Lilliputians are 10 times as short as Gulliver. In other words, they are $\frac{1}{10}$ of Gulliver's height.

4. Express the height of a Lilliputian in scientific notation.
   a. Explain what factor is appropriate for the value of a in the form $a \times 10^n$.

   b. Determine what power of 10 is appropriate for the value of n in the form $a \times 10^n$.

   c. Use the values you found in parts a and b to write the height of a Lilliputian in scientific notation.
   d. What do you notice about a fractional number in standard form when it is written in scientific notation?

5. Convert each number from standard form to scientific notation.
    a. 0.125   **b.** 0.00006

    c. 7   **d.** 0.000000000025

Example A

The heights measured in feet, expressed in scientific notation, of Gulliver, a person from Brobdingnag, and a Lilliputian are shown:

$$5 \times 10^0, 5 \times 10^1, 5 \times 10^{-1}$$

Order these numbers from least to greatest.

Step 1:   Use the values of the exponents to help determine the order.

         5×10^{-1} is the least, then 5×10^0, then 5×10^1

Step 2:   Write the numbers in standard form to check the order.

         $5 \times 10^{-1} = 0.5$ least

         $5 \times 10^0 = 5$ $\downarrow$

         $5 \times 10^1 = 50$ greatest

Solution: From least to greatest, the heights are 5×10^{-1}, 5×10^0, and 5×10^1 feet.

Try These A

Order these numbers from least to greatest.
a. $8 \times 10^0, 9 \times 10^{-2}, 2 \times 10^3$

b. $4.14 \times 10^2, 1.4 \times 10^{-4}, 4.1 \times 10^{-3}$

Order these numbers from greatest to least.
c. $0.007, 5 \times 10^1, 7 \times 10^{-5}$

d. $1 \times 10^0, 0.87, 7.8 \times 10^1$

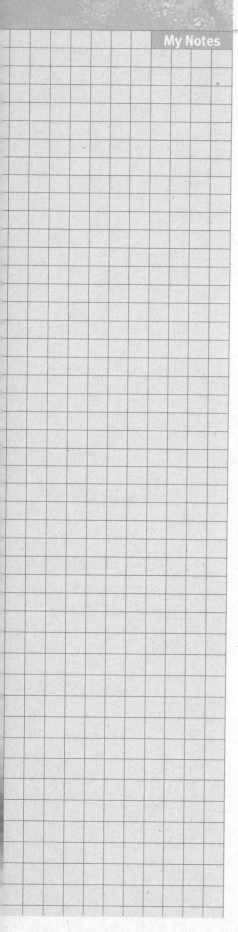

You can use scientific notation to write estimates of small numbers. Estimates consist of a single digit times a power of 10.

Example B

A micrometer is a small metric measure for length. Using her computer, Jenny found that a micrometer equals 0.000039370078740157 inch. Use scientific notation to estimate the inch equivalent of a micrometer.

Step 1: The greatest place value is hundred thousandths, so round to the nearest hundred thousandth.
$0.000039370078740157 \approx 0.00004$

Step 2: Write the measure to the nearest hundred thousandth in scientific notation. $0.00004 = 4 \times 10^{-5}$

Solution: An estimate of the length of a micrometer is 4×10^{-5} inch.

Try These B

Write an estimate for each number using scientific notation.
a. 0.00018
b. 0.00619023

Check Your Understanding

Convert each number from scientific notation to standard form.
6. 5.2×10^{-4} **7.** 4.23×10^{-6} **8.** 2.5×10^{0}
Convert each number from standard form to scientific notation.

9. 0.0002   **10.** 0.000000513   **11.** 6.9

12. Order these numbers from least to greatest.
$0.0051, 8 \times 10^{-4}, 1.89 \times 10^{-3}, 0.00079$

LESSON 7-2 PRACTICE

13. In terms of Gulliver's height, use scientific notation to express the height of an insect if the insect is 10 times shorter than a person from Lilliput.

14. Write a rule for converting a number from scientific notation to standard form that will always work when the scientific notation of a number includes 10^{0}.

15. Lena converted 1.2×10^{-7} to the standard form 12,000,000. Do you agree with Lena? Explain your reasoning.

16. Explain why someone would want to write the number 0.000000000064 in scientific notation instead of standard form.

17. Make sense of problems. The fictional land of Brobdingnag had an area of 1.8×10^{7} square miles. In its army were 32,000 cavalry and 2.07×10^{5} soldiers. Order these numbers from greatest to least.

18. Write an estimate for each number using scientific notation.
a. 0.000079013   **b.** 0.0022978

ACTIVITY 7 PRACTICE
Write your answers on notebook paper.
Show your work.

Lesson 7-1
Write the following in scientific notation.

1. 25,000,000,000

2. 60,000

3. 713,000,000,000,000,000

4. 99

Write the following in standard form.

5. 7×10^2

6. 8.92×10^8

7. 4×10^{20}

8. 6.07×10^6

9. Is 10.2×10^4 written in scientific notation? Explain.

10. Copy and complete.

Standard Form	Scientific Notation	Name
2,300,000,000		
	3.4×10^3	
		9 million

11. Which of the following shows 9,200,000,000,000,000 in scientific notation?
A. 9.2×10^9
B. 9.2×10^{12}
C. 9.2×10^{15}
D. 9.2×10^{18}

12. Which of the following is in correct scientific notation form?
A. 0.8×10^2
B. 8×10^2
C. 80×10^2
D. $8 \times 10^{\frac{1}{2}}$

13. The sun is 93 million miles away from Earth. Write this number in scientific notation.

14. A fast food restaurant claims to have served 245 billion hamburgers. Write this number in standard form.

15. The Milky Way galaxy is estimated to be 13.2 billion years old. Write this number in scientific notation.

16. According to the U.S. Census of 2010, the population of Florida was 18,801,310. Write an estimate of this population using scientific notation.

Lesson 7-2

17. The following table shows the attendance for a year at four major-league baseball stadiums. Order the attendance from greatest to least.

Yankees	Mariners	Red Sox	Dodgers
3.8×10^6	2,000,000	2.5 million	3.2×10^6

18. Copy and complete.

Standard Form	Scientific Notation
0.00009	
	1.7×10^{-3}
	6.99×10^{-7}
0.00086	

19. Wire 1 has a diameter of 9×10^{-2} inches. Wire 2's diameter is 2.4×10^{-3} inches and Wire 3 is 0.0023 inches in diameter. Order the wire diameters from smallest to largest.

20. Describe how scientific notation aids the discussion of very small or very large numbers. Provide an example.

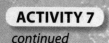
Write the following in standard form.

21. 7.4×10^0

22. 8.6×10^{-5}

23. 2×10^{-4}

24. 5.5×10^0

Write the following in scientific notation.

25. 2.67

26. 0.000000000001

27. 0.825

28. 0.000022

Use the following table for Items 29–32.

Measurement of Length	Power of 10
Meter (m)	10^0
Centimeter (cm)	10^{-2}
Millimeter (mm)	10^{-3}
Micrometer (μm)	10^{-6}
Nanometer (nm)	10^{-9}

29. One of the smallest viruses measured was 17 nanometers. Write this number in scientific notation.

30. Order these from greatest to least:
    0.009 m, 12 cm, 8 nm, 5×10^{-1} m

31. Which of the following is 4 micrometers in standard form?
    A. 0.04
    B. 0.0004
    C. 0.000004
    D. 0.00000004

32. Cooper's best high jump was measured as 1.1 m. Write this number in scientific notation.

33. An insect known as a fairy wasp can be as little as 0.007874 inch long. Write an estimate of this length using scientific notation.

MATHEMATICAL PRACTICES
Reason Abstractly and Quantitatively

34. Think about the value of each expression.

4.3×10^3 3.8×10^{-5} 2.4×10^{12} 3.0×10^0

2.2×10^{-2} 7.8×10^{-4} 7.1×10^0 9.8×10^5

6.4×10^{-3} 3.8×10^{-14} 6.4×10^8 4.8×10^0

a. Copy the table and place each expression in the appropriate column.

Between 0 and 1	From 1 to 10	10 and greater

b. Explain what you notice about the exponents in the scientific notation form of the numbers you sorted.

Numbers between 0 and 1

Numbers from 1 to 10

Numbers 10 and greater

c. Which expression has the greatest value?

d. Which expression has the least value?

Operations with Scientific Notation

How Big is That Planet?
Lesson 8-1 Multiplying and Dividing in Scientific Notation

My Notes

Learning Targets:
- Multiply numbers expressed in scientific notation.
- Divide numbers expressed in scientific notation.

SUGGESTED LEARNING STRATEGIES: Marking the Text, Predict and Confirm, Critique Reasoning, Look for a Pattern, Create a Plan

Our solar system includes eight planets. The one that is closest to the sun is Mercury, followed by Venus, Earth, Mars, Jupiter, Saturn, Uranus and Neptune. In the previous activity, you learned that scientific notation is commonly used to represent very large or very small numbers. Scientific notation can be used to write the numbers representing the distance of the planets from the sun and the mass of the planets.

1. Earth is 93,000,000 miles away from the sun and has an approximate mass of 6,000,000,000,000,000,000,000,000 kilograms.
   a. Write Earth's distance from the sun in scientific notation.

   b. Write Earth's mass in scientific notation.

2. Earth moves at an approximate average speed of 107,000 km/h. It takes Earth approximately 8,800 hours to orbit the sun.
   a. Using the numbers written in standard form, find the total approximate distance Earth travels when orbiting the sun.

   b. Express the average speed of Earth in scientific notation.

   c. Express the total amount of hours it takes Earth to orbit the sun in scientific notation.

   d. Write your answer to part a in scientific notation.

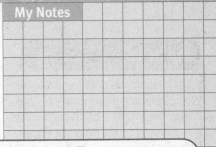

CONNECT TO ASTRONOMY

Astronomers used to consider Pluto a planet, making a total of nine planets in our solar system. In 2006, the International Astronomical Union changed the definition of a planet. The definition excluded Pluto as a planet, in part because it was too small.

MATH TIP

The associative and commutative properties of multiplication state that the product of several factors will be the same, no matter how the factors are grouped or ordered. Discuss with your peers how these properties apply to multiplying and dividing numbers in scientific notation.

Example A

Find the approximate distance Earth travels when orbiting the sun without changing the numbers to standard form.

$$(1.07 \times 10^5) \text{ km/h} \times (8.8 \times 10^3) \text{ h}$$

Step 1: Use the commutative and associative properties of multiplication to reorder and regroup the multiplication problem.

$$(1.07 \times 8.8) \times (10^5 \times 10^3)$$

Step 2: Multiply.

$$(9.416) \times (10^{5+3}) = 9.416 \times 10^8$$

Solution: Earth travels 9.416×10^8 km as it orbits the sun.

Try These A

a. How do you know that the solution is reasonable and correct?

Simplify each expression. Write the answer in scientific notation.
b. $(9 \times 10^5)(3 \times 10^4)$
c. $(1.6 \cdot 10^8)(3 \cdot 10^4)$
d. $(4 \cdot 10^{12})(6 \cdot 10^5)$

3. **Use appropriate tools strategically.** Compare the products of each expression from Try These A using a calculator.
   a. Write each output as shown on your calculator.

   $(9 \times 10^5)(3 \times 10^4)$
   $(1.6 \cdot 10^8)(3 \cdot 10^4)$
   $(4 \cdot 10^{12})(6 \cdot 10^5)$

   b. Explain what the outputs on your calculator mean.

My Notes

4. Jupiter is the largest planet with a mass of about 1,900,800,000,000,000,000,000,000,000 kg and Mercury is the smallest planet with a mass of about 330,000,000,000,000,000,000,000 kg.

   a. Using the numbers that are written in standard form, determine how many times as large Jupiter is than Mercury.

   b. Write Jupiter's mass in scientific notation.

   c. Write Mercury's mass in scientific notation.

   d. Write your answer to part a in scientific notation.

   e. **Reason abstractly.** Using the numbers written in scientific notation, how could you determine how many times as large Jupiter is than Mercury without changing their masses to standard form?

MATH TIP

The law of exponents for dividing powers with the same base states that the exponent of the divisor is subtracted from the exponent of the dividend.

5. Simplify each expression using the process you stated in Item 4e. Write the answer in scientific notation.

   a. $\dfrac{16.4 \times 10^9}{4.1 \times 10^5}$

   b. $\dfrac{2 \times 10^8}{8 \times 10^2}$

   c. $\dfrac{5.5 \times 10^2}{1.1 \times 10^4}$

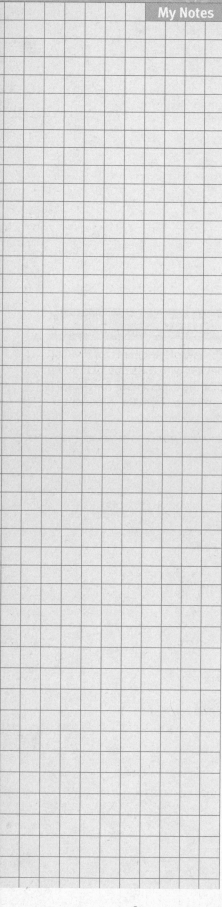

My Notes

Check Your Understanding

Simplify each expression. Write answers in scientific notation.

6. $\dfrac{6 \times 10^5}{3 \times 10^4}$

7. $(2 \times 10^{-5})(3 \times 10^4)$

8. $(4.2 \times 10^8)(3 \times 10^{-5})$

9. $\dfrac{3.2 \times 10^5}{4 \times 10^8}$

LESSON 8-1 PRACTICE

Simplify each expression and write answers in scientific notation for Items 10–13.

10. $(7.5 \times 10^6)(2.3 \times 10^4)$

11. $\dfrac{(1.2 \times 10^4)}{(2.5 \times 10^6)}$

12. $(4 \times 10^{15})(6 \times 10^{-7})$

13. $(2.75 \times 10^{-2})(8 \times 10^{-6})$

The table below shows the approximate mass of some planets. Use this table for Items 14–15.

Planet	Approximate Mass (in kg)
Mercury	3.3×10^{23}
Earth	6×10^{24}
Jupiter	1.9008×10^{27}

14. How many times bigger is Jupiter than Earth?

15. How many times bigger is Earth than Mercury?

16. **Make sense of problems.** The speed of light is 3×10^8 m/s and the distance from Earth to the sun is 1.5×10^{11} m. How many seconds does it take for sunlight to reach Earth? Write your answer in scientific notation.

17. The average distance from Earth to the moon is 3.84×10^{10} cm.
    a. Choose a more appropriate unit of length to use.
    b. Find the approximate distance from Earth to the moon using the unit you chose in part a. Write your answer in scientific notation.

My Notes

Learning Targets:

- Add numbers expressed in scientific notation.
- Subtract numbers expressed in scientific notation.

SUGGESTED LEARNING STRATEGIES: Group Presentation, Critique Reasoning, Look for a Pattern, Graphic Organizer, Summarizing

1. Consider the expression $4.2 \times 10^3 + 2.9 \times 10^3$.
   a. Change the numbers in the expression to standard form and add the numbers together.

   b. Write your answer to part a in scientific notation.

Example A

Add $4.2 \times 10^3 + 2.9 \times 10^3$, keeping the numbers in scientific notation.

Step 1: To add or subtract numbers in scientific notation, the exponents must be the same. If they are not the same, rewrite the terms so that the exponents are the same.

$4.2 \times 10^3 + 2.9 \times 10^3 \rightarrow$ the exponents are the same

Step 2: Add the digits. Write the sum in scientific notation.

$4.2 + 2.9 = 7.1$

7.1×10^3

Solution: $4.2 \times 10^3 + 2.9 \times 10^3 = 7.1 \times 10^3$

Try These A

Add or subtract.
a. $2.3 \times 10^9 + 5.6 \times 10^9$
b. $9.1 \times 10^{-2} - 2.5 \times 10^{-2}$
c. $8.4 \times 10^{-5} + 7.2 \times 10^{-5}$

Mercury is the closest planet to the sun, and Neptune is the farthest planet from the sun. Neptune is 2.8×10^9 miles from the sun and Mercury is 2.6×10^7 miles from the sun.

2. **Critique the reasoning of others.** Colten and Drake wanted to find the distance between the two planets. They each decided to solve the problem different ways. Compare and contrast the two methods they used to find the distance between the two planets.

Colten	Drake
$2.8 \times 10^9 - 2.6 \times 10^7$	$2.8 \times 10^9 - 2.6 \times 10^7$
$2,800,000,000 - 26,000,000$	$280 \times 10^7 - 2.6 \times 10^7$
$2,774,000,000$	277.4×10^7
2.774×10^9	2.774×10^9

3. Earth, the third closest planet to the sun, is 9.3×10^7 miles from the sun. Find the distance from Neptune to Earth using either of the methods shown in Item 2.

Check Your Understanding

4. $(2.5 \times 10^6) + (4 \times 10^6)$

5. $(3.4 \times 10^{-3}) + (8.1 \times 10^{-3})$

6. $(6.23 \times 10^5) - (2.1 \times 10^5)$

7. $(7.2 \times 10^{-2}) - (2.1 \times 10^{-2})$

LESSON 8-2 PRACTICE

8. $(4.08 \times 10^4) - (1.09 \times 10^4)$

9. $(6.7 \times 10^{10}) + (4.1 \times 10^{10})$

10. $(5.5 \times 10^9) + (2.6 \times 10^8)$

11. $(9.9 \times 10^{-4}) - (3.26 \times 10^{-5})$

12. Earth is 9.3×10^7 miles from the sun. Mars is 1.4×10^8 miles from the sun. What is the distance from Earth to Mars?

13. **Reason abstractly.** When adding or subtracting numbers in scientific notation, why do you think the exponents need to be the same?

ACTIVITY 8 PRACTICE

Write your answers on notebook paper.
Show your work.

Lesson 8-1

Simplify each expression. Write the answers in scientific notation.

1. $(2.2 \times 10^5)(4 \times 10^7)$

2. $35,000 \cdot 9,000,000,000$

3. $(8.1 \times 10^{12})(5.3 \times 10)$

4. $(6.5 \times 10^{-13})(2 \times 10^{-4})$

5. $\dfrac{2.7 \times 10^4}{1.2 \times 10^9}$

6. $\dfrac{4.2 \times 10^{10}}{3 \times 10^3}$

7. If Saturn has a mass of about 569,600,000,000,000,000,000,000,000 kg and Mars has a mass of 640,000,000,000,000,000,000,000 kg, how many times as big is Saturn than Mars? Write your answer in scientific notation.

8. When multiplying two numbers in scientific notation, which of the following statements is true?
   A. Add the exponents.
   B. Subtract the exponents.
   C. The exponents must be the same.
   D. The exponents must be different.

9. The diameter of the sun is approximately 1.4×10^9 km and the diameter of Earth is approximately 1.28×10^4 km. About how many times Earth's diameter is the sun's diameter?

10. Brigitte simplified the expression $(7.4 \times 10^6) \div (5 \times 10^{-2})$ as 1.48×10^8. Do you agree with her answer? Explain your reasoning.

11. Neptune is 4.9×10^9 km from the sun and light travels at a speed of 3×10^5 km/s. In seconds, how long does it take for sunlight to reach Neptune? Write your answer in scientific notation.

12. There are 3.6×10^3 seconds in an hour. How many hours does it take for sunlight to reach Neptune?

13. The mass of the moon is approximately 7.3×10^{22} kg, and the mass of Earth is approximately 6×10^{24} kg. How many times the mass of the moon is the mass of Earth?

14. The mass of the sun is 1.9891×10^{30} kg, and the mass of the largest planet, Jupiter, is 1.9008×10^{27} kg. How many times the mass of Jupiter is the mass of the sun? Write your answer in scientific notation.

15. Over the past three years, Gerry has grown at the rate of 6×10^{-2} meter per year. Estimate Gerry's growth using a more appropriate unit.

Lesson 8-2

16. $3.4 \times 10^5 + 9.1 \times 10^5$

17. $7.5 \times 10^{-3} - 2.1 \times 10^{-3}$

18. Which is the answer to $2.3 \times 10^5 + 5.1 \times 10^4$?
    A. 28.1×10^4
    B. 28.1×10^5
    C. 2.81×10^4
    D. 2.81×10^5

19. Which is the answer to $9.1 \times 10^{-2} - 5.4 \times 10^{-4}$?
    A. 9.046×10^{-2}
    B. 9.046×10^{-3}
    C. 9.046×10^{-4}
    D. 9.046×10^{-5}

20. Earth is 9.3×10^7 miles from the sun and Mercury is 2.6×10^7 miles from the sun. Find the distance between Earth and Mercury.

21. When subtracting two numbers in scientific notation, which of the following statements is true?
    A. Add the exponents.
    B. Subtract the exponents.
    C. The exponents must be the same.
    D. The exponents must be different.

The table below shows the distance from the sun traveled by two space probes. Use this table for Items 22–23.

Object	Distance From the Sun (in miles)
Voyager 1	11.3 billion
Voyager 2	9.3 billion

22. The space probes Voyager 1 and Voyager 2 were launched in 1977. How much farther has Voyager 1 traveled than Voyager 2? Express your answer in scientific notation.

23. How many miles total have been traveled by Voyager 1 and Voyager 2? Express your answer in scientific notation.

24. $(2.5 \times 10^8) + (3.8 \times 10^7)$

25. $(6.7 \times 10^4) - (6.1 \times 10^2)$

26. $(3.2 \times 10^3) + (5.4 \times 10^3)$

27. $(1.5 \times 10^{27}) - (1.4 \times 10^{26})$

28. Rupert added 1.72×10^4 to 8×10^6 and got the sum 9.72×10^{10}. Do you agree with his answer? Explain your reasoning.

29. Venus is the second planet from the sun. Earth is the third planet from the sun. The distance from Venus to the sun is 6.72×10^7 miles and the distance from Earth to the sun is 9.3×10^7 miles. What is the distance between Earth and Venus?

MATHEMATICAL PRACTICES
Look For and Make Use of Structure

30. Use a Venn diagram to compare and contrast the processes of adding and subtracting numbers in scientific notation or multiplying and dividing numbers in scientific notation.

While checking her e-mail, Luisa stumbles across a cryptic message from someone named 5up3r H4xx0r. In the message, 5up3r H4xx0r claims to have developed a computer virus and is set to release it on the Internet. Once the virus has infected two computers, the potential exists for it to spread exponentially, because each infected computer has a chance to pass it along to the next computer it connects with.

The only way for the virus to be stopped, says the hacker, is if Luisa correctly answers each of the following questions.

1. The pattern of the spread of the virus will be 1, 2, 4, 8, ... Identify the next three numbers in this pattern.

2. Express the first seven numbers in the pattern as a power of 2.

3. Describe how the 18th term in the pattern could be determined.

4. Determine which base could be used to write the numbers below in exponential form. Rewrite each product using exponential forms of the base you determined.
   a. $32 \cdot 128$ **b.** $4 \cdot 256$ **c.** $16 \cdot 64$

5. Simplify each of the products in Item 4. Leave your answer in exponential form.

6. Describe how to simplify each of the following expressions. Simplify each expression and leave your answer in exponential form.
   a. $(2^{13})^4$ **b.** $\dfrac{2^{12}}{2^3}$

7. Replace the variables with numbers in the expressions so that the expression would result in the answer of 2^6.
   a. $\dfrac{a^x}{a^y}$ **b.** $a^x \cdot a^y$ **c.** $(a^x)^y$ **d.** $\dfrac{1}{a^x}$

8. Write each number in scientific notation.
   a. 20,000,000   **b.** 2,400

9. Simplify each expression. Leave your answer in scientific notation.
   a. $(2 \cdot 10^5)(2 \cdot 10^3)$ **b.** $\dfrac{8 \cdot 10^4}{4 \cdot 10^2}$

10. Write a reply to 5up3r H4xx0r about your success in foiling the virus plan. Include in your reply a description of the problems that were difficult for you, and the ones that you were able to complete easily. Also include a final statement that summarizes your overall success.

Scoring Guide	Exemplary	Proficient	Emerging	Incomplete
	The solution demonstrates these characteristics:			
Mathematics Knowledge and Thinking (Items 1, 2, 3, 4a–c, 5, 6a–b, 7a–c, 8a–b, 9)	• Clear and accurate understanding of multiplying and dividing with exponents and scientific notation. • Clear and accurate understanding of writing numbers in exponential form and in scientific notation.	• Multiplying and dividing with exponents and scientific notation. • Writing numbers in exponential form and in scientific notation.	• Errors in multiplying and dividing with exponents and scientific notation. • Errors in writing numbers in exponential form and in scientific notation.	• Incorrect or incomplete multiplication and division with exponents and scientific notation. • Little or no understanding of writing numbers in exponential form and in scientific notation.
Problem Solving (Items 2, 3, 4, 7a–b, 8a–b)	• An appropriate and efficient strategy that results in a correct answer.	• A strategy that may include unnecessary steps but results in a correct answer.	• A strategy that results in some incorrect answers.	• No clear strategy when solving problems.
Mathematical Modeling / Representations (Items 1, 2, 4a–c, 8)	• Clear and accurate understanding of representing a number in exponential form and in scientific notation.	• Representing a rational number in exponential form and in scientific notation.	• Errors in representing a number in exponential form or in scientific notation.	• Inaccurately representing a number in exponential form and in scientific notation.
Reasoning and Communication (Items 3, 6, 10)	• Precise and accurate explanation of how to multiply and divide with exponents. • Clear and precise explanation of the level of difficulty experienced with the problems.	• Adequate explanation of how to multiply and divide with exponents. • Adequate explanation of the level of difficulty experienced with the problems.	• A misleading or confusing explanation of how to multiply and divide with exponents. • A confusing description of the level of difficulty experienced with the problems.	• An incomplete or inaccurate explanation of how to multiply and divide with exponents. • An incomplete description of the level of difficulty experienced with the problems.

Equations

Unit Overview
In this unit you will extend your knowledge of equations as you study several ways to solve multistep equations, and you will apply your understanding to application problems. You will model and solve problems involving systems of equations.

Key Terms
As you study this unit, add these and other terms to your math notebook. Include in your notes your prior knowledge of each word, as well as your experiences in using the word in different mathematical examples. If needed, ask for help in pronouncing new words and add information on pronunciation to your math notebook. It is important that you learn new terms and use them correctly in your class discussions and in your problem solutions.

Academic Vocabulary
- legend
- persuasive
- coincide

Math Terms
- evaluate
- consecutive terms
- constant difference
- linear
- slope
- discrete data
- continuous data
- coefficient
- constant term
- slope-intercept form
- direct variation
- system of linear equations
- solution to a system of equations

ESSENTIAL QUESTIONS

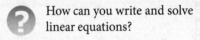

How can you write and solve linear equations?

How can graphs be used to interpret solutions of real-world problems?

EMBEDDED ASSESSMENTS

These assessments, following Activities 10, 13, and 15, will give you an opportunity to demonstrate how you can use your understanding of equations to solve real-world problems.

1. What is the difference between an expression and an equation?

2. Write an expression for the following:
   a. one more than twice a number
   b. a number decreased by six
   c. two-thirds of a number

3. Evaluate the following expressions if $x = 4.1$ and $y = 2.3$.
   a. $2x + 3$
   b. $16 - 5y$
   c. $x + y$

4. Complete the table below so that the data is linear.

Input	Output
1	
2	6
3	10
4	

5. A line contains the points $(2, 5)$ and $(4, 6)$:
   a. Where does it cross the x-axis?
   b. Where does it cross the y-axis?

6. Use the graph below to:
   a. Plot and label the points $R(3, 5)$ and $S(6, 0)$.
   b. Give the coordinates of point T.

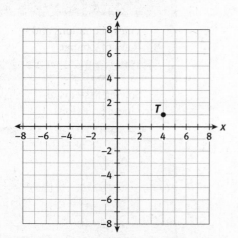

7. Draw a horizontal line that contains the point $(2, 3)$ and a vertical line that contains $(1, 4)$.

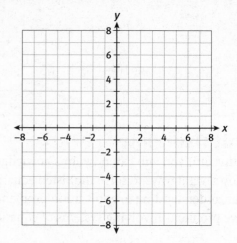

8. Determine if the triangles pictured below are similar, and give a reason for your conclusion.

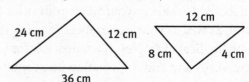

Writing Expressions
Pebbles in the Sand
Lesson 9-1 Representing Patterns

Learning Targets:

- Identify and represent patterns using models, tables, and expressions.
- Write and evaluate algebraic expressions that represent patterns with constant differences.

SUGGESTED LEARNING STRATEGIES: Look for a Pattern, Create Representations, Use Manipulatives, Think-Pair-Share

People have been investigating number patterns for thousands of years. *Legend* has it that Pythagoras and his students arranged pebbles in the sand to represent number patterns. One pattern they studied is shown below.

Figure 1　　　Figure 2　　　Figure 3

1. Draw the fourth, fifth and sixth figures.

2. Organize the number of pebbles in each figure into a table.

Figure Number	Number of Pebbles

3. Extend the pattern to determine how many pebbles are in the 10th figure.

4. Describe the patterns you observe in the pebble drawings and the table in words.

5. How many pebbles are in the 53rd figure? Explain your reasoning.

6. Write a numeric expression using the number 3 for the number of pebbles in the third figure.

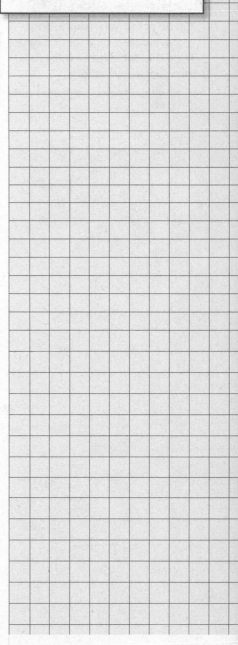

My Notes

ACADEMIC VOCABULARY

A *legend* is a story handed down by tradition that is popularly regarded as historical but unverified.

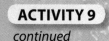

My Notes

> **MATH TIP**
>
> An *expression* is a mathematical phrase using numbers or variables or both. $1 + 1$ and $3x - 5$ are examples of expressions.

> **MATH TERMS**
>
> You do not solve an expression; you **evaluate** it for a specific value. To do this, substitute a value for the variable and simplify.

7. Write a similar numeric expression using the number 7 for the number of pebbles in the seventh figure.

8. Let *n* represent the figure number.
   a. Use *n* to write an expression that could be used to determine the number of pebbles in figure *n*.

   b. What value would you substitute for *n* to determine the number of pebbles in the third figure?

   c. Check to see that your expression from part a is correct by *evaluating* it for the value you chose in part b.

   d. Use your expression to determine the number of pebbles in the 100th figure.

Check Your Understanding

A pattern of small squares is shown. Use the pattern to answer Items 9–13 that follow.

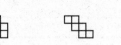

  Figure 1   Figure 2   Figure 3

9. How many small squares are in each figure?

10. Draw the fourth, fifth, and sixth figures and determine the number of small squares in each figure.

11. Create a table to organize the number of squares in each figure into a table.

12. Describe in words the patterns you see in the square pattern and in the table.

13. How many squares would be in the 10th figure? Explain your reasoning.

14. Another pebble arrangement is shown below.

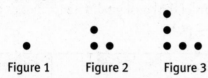

Figure 1   Figure 2   Figure 3

a. Draw the fourth, fifth, and sixth figures.

My Notes

CONNECT TO AP

The ability to identify patterns allows you to understand and describe different types of functions and provides a foundation for understanding rate of change in calculus.

b. Organize the number of pebbles in each figure in the table below.

Figure Number	Pebbles	Difference in Number of Pebbles
1		
2		
3		
4		
5		
6		
7		
8		
9		
10		

c. Describe any patterns you observe in the pebble drawings and in the table above.

15. Subtract *consecutive terms* in the pebbles column and record this information in the last column in the table.

16. Reason quantitatively. How does the *constant difference* in the new column relate to the patterns you observed?

MATH TERMS

Consecutive terms follow each other directly in a sequence. In the table below, 5 and 8 are *consecutive terms*. There is a **constant difference** between the terms in this table that is equal to 3.

n	term	
1	5	3
2	8	3
3	11	3
4	14	

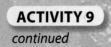

My Notes

17. The number of pebbles in a specific figure can be written using repeated additions of the constant difference. For example, the third figure is $1 + 2 + 2$ or $1 + 2(2)$.

Figure Number	Pebbles	Expression Using Repeated Addition
1	1	$1 + 2(0)$
2	$1 + 2$	$1 + 2(1)$
3	$1 + 2 + 2$	
4		
5		

a. Write the number of pebbles in the fourth and fifth figure using repeated addition of the constant difference.

b. Let n represent the figure number. Use n to write an expression that could be used to determine the number of pebbles in figure n.

c. What value would you substitute for n to determine the number of pebbles in the third figure?

d. Check to see that your expression from part a is correct by evaluating it when $n = 5$.

e. Use your expression to determine the number of pebbles in the 100th figure.

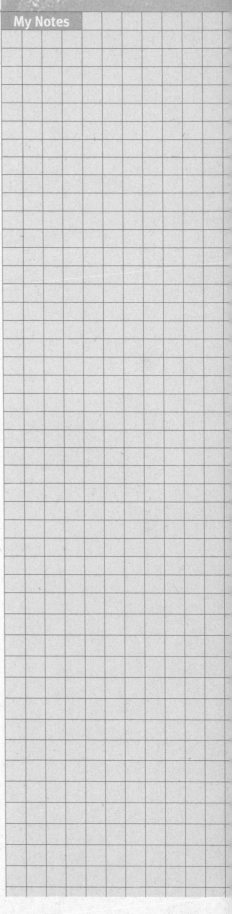

My Notes

Check Your Understanding

18. A pattern of pebbles is shown. Use the pattern to answer parts a–c.

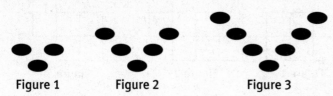

Figure 1   Figure 2   Figure 3

    a. Draw the fourth, fifth, and sixth figures.

    b. Create a table to organize the number of pebbles in each figure for the first six figures.

    c. What is the constant difference?

    d. Write the number of pebbles for each figure using repeated addition of the constant difference.

    e. Let n represent the figure number. Use n to write an expression that could be used to determine the number of pebbles in figure n.

LESSON 9-1 PRACTICE

19. Check to see that your expression from Item 18 part e is correct by evaluating when $n = 6$.

20. Use your expression from Item 18 part e to determine the number of pebbles in the 51st figure.

21. **Critique the reasoning of others.** The expression that represents the number of squares in the nth figure of a pattern is given by $2 + 3(n - 1)$. Mia claims the constant difference is 2. Do you agree? Explain.

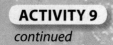

My Notes

22. A pattern of small squares is shown.

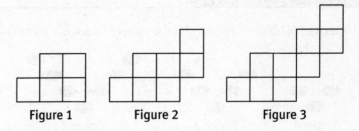

Figure 1   Figure 2   Figure 3

a. Draw the fourth, fifth, and sixth figures.
b. Create a table showing the number of the figure and the number of squares in each figure.
c. Describe the patterns you observe in the square drawings and in your table.
d. What is the constant difference?
e. How many small squares are in the first figure?
f. Let *n* represent the figure number. Use *n* to write an expression that could be used to determine the number of squares in the *n*th figure.

23. Compare the expression you found in Item 22 part f with the expression you found in Item 17 part b. How are they the same? How are they different?

Learning Targets:

- Identify patterns that do not have a constant difference.
- Write and evaluate algebraic expressions that represent patterns that do not have a constant difference.

SUGGESTED LEARNING STRATEGIES: Look for a Pattern, Create Representations, Discussion Group, Group Presentation

1. Four different pebble patterns are shown. Your teacher will assign one to your group. Use your selected pattern to answer parts a–e that follow and then prepare a group presentation of your results.

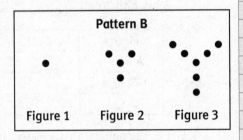

Pattern A

Figure 1   Figure 2   Figure 3

Pattern B

Figure 1   Figure 2   Figure 3

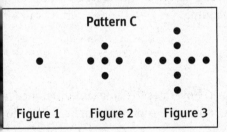

Pattern C

Figure 1   Figure 2   Figure 3

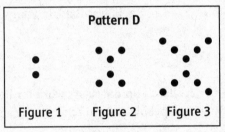

Pattern D

Figure 1   Figure 2   Figure 3

a. Draw a few additional figures and then organize the information in a table. Identify the constant difference.

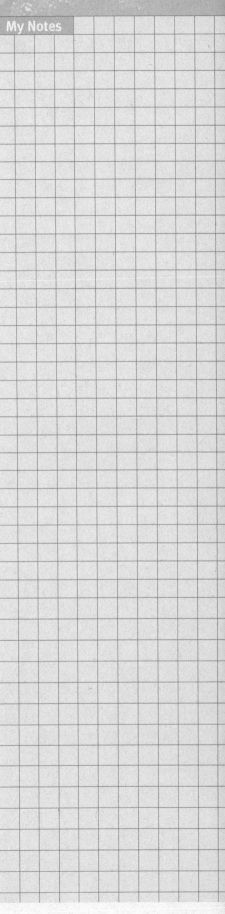

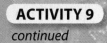

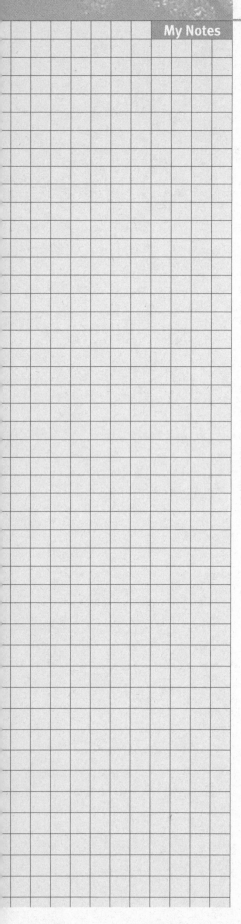

My Notes

b. Describe the pattern in words.

c. **Reason abstractly**. Write an expression using the variable n that could be used to determine the number of pebbles in figure n.

d. Use your expression to determine the number of pebbles in the 10th, 53rd, and 200th figures.

Figure	10th	53rd	200th
A and D			
B			
C			

e. For the pattern you selected, is it possible to have a figure with 100 pebbles? Explain your reasoning.

2. Based on the class's work for Item 1, how does the constant difference in a pebble pattern relate to the algebraic expression that can be written to describe the pattern?

Check Your Understanding

Tables representing two pebble patterns are shown below.

Pebble Pattern A

Figure	1	2	3	4	5
Pebbles	3	7	11	15	19

Pebble Pattern B

Figure	1	2	3	4	5
Pebbles	2	7	12	17	22

3. What is the constant difference for each pebble pattern shown in the tables?

4. For each pebble pattern, use the variable n to write an expression for the nth figure.

5. How many pebbles are in the 50th figure for each pebble pattern?

6. Both pebble patterns have 7 pebbles in Figure 2. If the patterns continue, will they ever have the same number of pebbles as another figure? Explain your reasoning.

7. The Pythagoreans also studied the following pebble pattern.

Figure 1   Figure 2   Figure 3

a. How many pebbles are there in the fourth, fifth, and sixth figures?

b. Does this pattern have a constant difference? Explain your response.

c. Describe the pattern in words.

d. How many pebbles are there in the 10th figure? How did you determine your answer?

e. How many pebbles are there in the 40th figure? In the *n*th figure?

f. The Pythagoreans called the numbers in this pattern the square numbers. Why do you think this is so?

8. The numbers in the pebble pattern shown below are called the rectangular numbers.

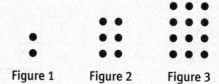

Figure 1   Figure 2   Figure 3

a. How many pebbles are in the fourth, fifth, and sixth figures?

b. Describe the pattern in words. Is there a constant difference? Explain your response.

c. Describe how to find the number of pebbles in the 10th figure.

d. How many pebbles are there in the 30th figure? In the nth figure?

9. The Pythagoreans called the numbers represented by the pebbles in this pebble pattern the triangular numbers.

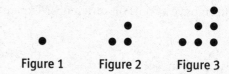

Figure 1   Figure 2   Figure 3

a. Why do you think the Pythagoreans called these numbers triangular?

My Notes

b. How is the triangular number pebble pattern related to the pebble pattern of the rectangular numbers?

c. Use your response to part b to write an algebraic expression for the number of pebbles in the *n*th triangular number.

d. Verify your expression by substituting $n = 4$. Is the result the number of pebbles in the fourth triangular number?

e. Use your expression to predict the number of pebbles in the 30th triangular number.

Check Your Understanding

10. Is the number 72 a square number, rectangular number, or triangular number? Explain your reasoning.

Use the figures below to answer Items 11–15.

 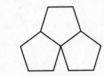

    Figure 1   **Figure 2**   **Figure 3**

11. Assume each side of each pentagon is 1 cm. What is the perimeter of each figure shown?

12. Draw the next three figures and determine the perimeter of each.

13. Organize the results of Items 11 and 12 in a table. What would be the perimeter of the 10th figure? Explain your reasoning.

14. Use *n* to represent the figure number. Write an expression that could be used to determine the perimeter of the *n*th figure.

15. Use your expression to determine the perimeter of the 50th figure.

My Notes

LESSON 9-2 PRACTICE

16. **Critique the reasoning of others.** Nate claims 56 is a rectangular number because a rectangle with base 4 and height 14 can be formed. What is his error?

17. What is the sixth square number? How did you get your answer?

18. Use the expression from Item 9 part c to show that 45 is a triangular number.

19. Use the figures below to answer parts a–d. Assume each figure is a regular octagon with sides of 1 foot.

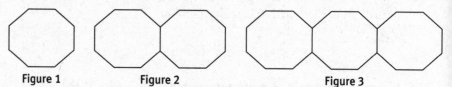

Figure 1   Figure 2   Figure 3

    a. What is the perimeter of each figure?
    b. Draw the next three figures and determine the perimeter of each.
    c. Use n to represent the figure number. Write an expression that could be used to determine the perimeter of the nth figure.
    d. Verify the expression in part c by substituting $n = 6$.

20. **Model with mathematics.** Octagonal blocks are being used to make a walkway along a garden. Use your expression from Item 19 part c to find the perimeter of the walkway if 30 octagonal blocks, each side 1 foot long, are used for the walkway.

ACTIVITY 9 PRACTICE
Write your answers on notebook paper.
Show your work.

Lesson 9-1

1. Use the figures below to answer parts a–c.

  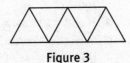

Figure 1   Figure 2   Figure 3

   a. What is the perimeter of each figure shown? Assume each side is 1 unit.
   b. Draw the next three figures.
   c. What would be the perimeter of the 10th figure? Justify your response.

2. Write an expression, using the variable n, that could be used to determine the perimeter of the nth figure in Item 1. Use the expression to determine the perimeter of the 50th figure.

3. A pattern of pebbles is shown.

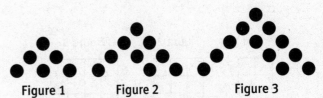

Figure 1   Figure 2   Figure 3

   a. Draw the fourth, fifth, and sixth figures.
   b. Create a table showing the number of the figure and the number of pebbles in each figure.
   c. Describe the patterns you observe in the pebble drawings and the table in words.
   d. What is the constant difference?
   e. Let n represent the figure number. Use n to write an expression that could be used to determine the number of pebbles in the nth figure.
   f. Use the expression in part e to determine the number of pebbles in the 51st figure.

Lesson 9-2

4. Use the pattern of unit squares shown to answer parts a–c.

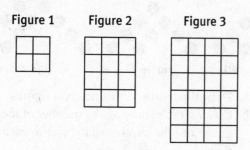

Figure 1   Figure 2   Figure 3

a. What is the area of each figure if each small square has an area of 1 unit?

b. Draw the next three figures in the pattern and determine the area of each.

c. What would be the area of the 10th figure? Justify your response.

5. Write an expression that could be used to determine the area of the *n*th figure in Item 4. Use the expression to determine the area of the 35th figure.

6. Use the figures from Item 4 to answer parts a–c.

a. What is the perimeter of each of the six figures?

b. Is there a constant difference? Explain.

c. Write an expression that could be used to find the perimeter of the *n*th figure.

d. Use the expression in part c to find the perimeter of the 35th figure.

MATHEMATICAL PRACTICES
Model with Mathematics

7. Use the expression $\dfrac{n(n+1)}{2}$.

a. Create a pattern using circles or dots and show the first three figures.

b. Determine the number of circles or dots in the 10th figure. Explain how you determined the number of dots in this figure.

Solving Equations

Bags and Cubes

Lesson 10-1 Solving Linear Equations with Models

Learning Targets:

- Solve linear equations with rational number coefficients.
- Solve linear equations by using the Distributive Property and collecting like terms.

> **SUGGESTED LEARNING STRATEGIES:** Discussion Groups, Visualization, Create Representations, Use Manipulatives, Sharing and Responding

Solving linear equations is a way to solve problems in the real world. Creating a model of a problem can help you break the problem down into parts that you can visualize.

Some small lightweight plastic bags contain an equal number of centimeter cubes. They are placed on a balance scale with some additional cubes.

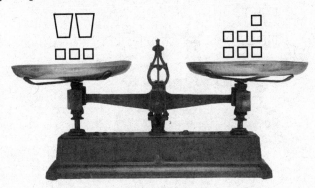

1. If the scale is balanced, how many cubes must be in each bag? Explain how you determined your answer.

2. Write an equation to represent the diagram shown above. Let x represent the number of cubes in a bag.

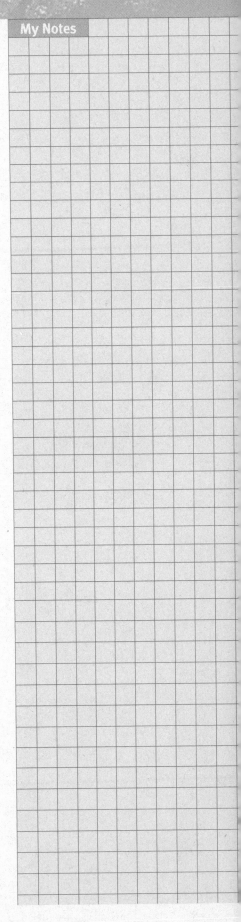

My Notes

My Notes

3. One way to solve the problem involves removing equal amounts from both sides and then regrouping the remaining cubes. The diagrams below illustrate this process. The first diagram is the original diagram. Write an explanation for both the second and third diagrams to the right of each.

Diagram   **Explanation**

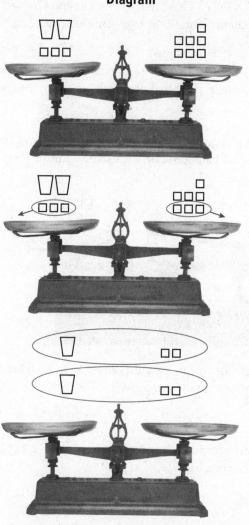

4. From the diagrams shown above, how many cubes are in each bag?

5. Model each of the following problems using bags and cubes, then determine how many cubes are in a bag. Record your work using a diagram like the balance scale. Write an equation for the original problem, an explanation for each step, and the solution. Let *x* be the number of cubes in a bag.

My Notes

a. If 3 bags are on one side of the scale and 12 cubes are on the other side, how many cubes must be in each bag to maintain the balance?

b. If 3 bags and 10 cubes are on one side of the scale and 16 cubes are on the other side, how many cubes must be in each bag to maintain the balance?

The solution to a bags-and-cubes equation can be determined algebraically by using inverse operations to solve the equation.

Example A

Solve $3x + 4 = 7$.

Step 1: Use inverse operations. Subtract 4 from both sides.
$$3x + 4 - 4 = 7 - 4$$
$$3x = 3$$

Step 2: Use inverse operations. Divide both sides by 3.
$$\frac{3x}{3} = \frac{3}{3}$$
$$1x = 1$$

Step 3: Use the Multiplicative Identity Property to isolate the variable.
$$x = 1$$

Solution: In the equation, $3x + 4 = 7$, $x = 1$.
Substitute 1 for x in the equation to verify: $3(1) + 4 = 3 + 4 = 7$.

MATH TIP

Equations can also be solved by working vertically.
$$3x + 4 = 7$$
$$\underline{-4 \quad -4}$$
$$\frac{3x}{3} = \frac{3}{3}$$
$$x \quad = 1$$

My Notes

Try These A

Solve each of the following algebraically, using inverse operations.

a. $2x + 0.4 = 18$

b. $-\frac{1}{3}x - 4 = 12$

c. $1.5 = 5x - 2$

d. $3x + 10 = 16$

e. $14 = 3x - 2$

6. **Construct viable arguments.** How do the steps to solve an equation algebraically represent the bags-and-cubes process from previous items?

7. Use properties of operations or other explanations to describe each step in solving the equation $3(x - 2) = 8$.

$3(x - 2) = 8$	Original equation
$3x - 6 = 8$	a.
$3x - 6 + 6 = 8 + 6$	b.
$3x = 14$	c.
$\dfrac{3x}{3} = \dfrac{14}{3}$	d.
$1x = \dfrac{14}{3}$	e.
$x = \dfrac{14}{3}$	f.

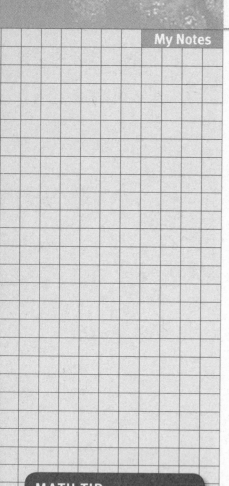

MATH TIP

The *Distributive Property* is used to multiply a factor by both addends in parentheses. For example:

$$a(b + c) = a(b) + a(c)$$

Conversely, the Distributive Property is used to factor and combine addends. For example:

$$ab + ac = a(b + c)$$

Check Your Understanding

8. Kathleen is spending summer vacation hiking in Canada and wants to dress appropriately for the day's hike. The local news reports that the high temperature is expected to be 20° Celsius. Use the formula $F = \frac{9}{5}C + 32$ where C is the degrees Celsius and F is the degrees Fahrenheit to determine the local temperature in degrees Fahrenheit.

9. Solve for the variable in the equation: $-3x + 11 = 26$.

10. Solve $\frac{5}{2}y = 10$ for y.

11. Solve for p in the equation $0.3p + 1.75 = 6.25$.

LESSON 10-1 PRACTICE

12. What is the value of x in the equation $7x - 30 = 180$?

13. Solve $-\frac{3}{4}x = 36$ for x.

14. **Make sense of problems.** Describe each step in solving the equation $3y + 7 - 5y = 13$.

$$3y + 7 - 5y = 13 \quad \text{Original equation}$$
$$-2y + 7 = 13 \quad \text{a.}$$
$$\underline{-7 \quad -7}$$
$$-2y = 6 \quad \text{b.}$$
$$\frac{-2y}{-2} = \frac{6}{-2}$$
$$y = -3 \quad \text{c.}$$

15. Solve for x in the equation $\frac{(x+2)}{7} = 14$.

16. Solve the equation algebraically: $-3x + 6 = -15$.

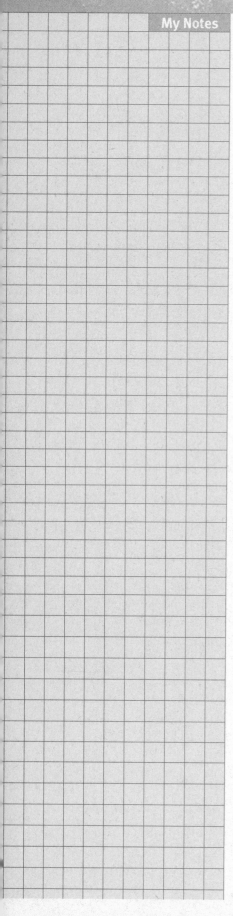

Learning Targets:

- Use linear equations with one variable to model and solve real-world and mathematical problems.
- Solve linear equations with variables on both sides of the equation by using the Distributive Property and collecting like terms.

> **SUGGESTED LEARNING STRATEGIES:** Close Reading, Marking the Text, Think-Pair-Share, Create Representations, Guess and Check

Often, equations have variables on both sides of the equal sign. This type of equation requires multiple steps to solve. Many times these equations are most efficiently solved algebraically. The following is an example of an algebraic solution to a multistep equation.

Example A

Solve $12x + 5 = 6x + 17$.

Step 1: Use inverse operations to combine like variables on one side of the equation. Subtract $6x$ from both sides.

$$\begin{array}{r} 12x + 5 = 6x + 17 \\ \underline{-6x \qquad -6x} \\ 6x + 5 = 17 \end{array}$$

Step 2: Use inverse operations. Subtract 5 from both sides.

$$\begin{array}{r} 6x + 5 = 17 \\ \underline{-5 \quad -5} \\ 6x = 12 \end{array}$$

Step 3: Use inverse operations. Divide both sides by 6.

$$\frac{6x}{6} = \frac{12}{6}$$
$$1x = 2$$

Step 4: Use the Multiplicative Identity Property to isolate the variable.

$$x = 2$$

Solution: In the equation $12x + 5 = 6x + 17$, $x = 2$.
Substitute 2 for x in the equation to verify: $12(2) + 5 = 6(2) + 17$

$$24 + 5 = 12 + 17$$
$$29 = 29$$

Try These A

Solve each equation and provide an explanation for each step.

a. $2 - \frac{3}{2}(x + 1) = 6x - 9$

b. $2(x + 0.7) = 6(x - 0.8)$

c. $2x - 10 = \frac{1}{3}(x - 9)$

d. $8 - x = 3x + 2(x - 4)$

e. $\frac{1}{2}(18x - 8) = 6x - \frac{7}{2}$

Equations can often be written to model mathematical and real-world situations. Solving these equations provides solutions to the problems.

Example B

Kurt is surveying a triangular plot of land. He was told that the longest side of the region is 30 feet longer than $\frac{1}{3}$ the perimeter, and the shortest side is $\frac{1}{4}$ the perimeter. He also knows that the longest side is 60 feet longer than the shortest side of the region. What is the perimeter of the parcel of land?

Step 1: Create a model.

longest side = shortest side + 60 ft

$$\frac{1}{3}p + 30 \text{ ft} = \frac{1}{4}p + 60 \text{ ft}$$

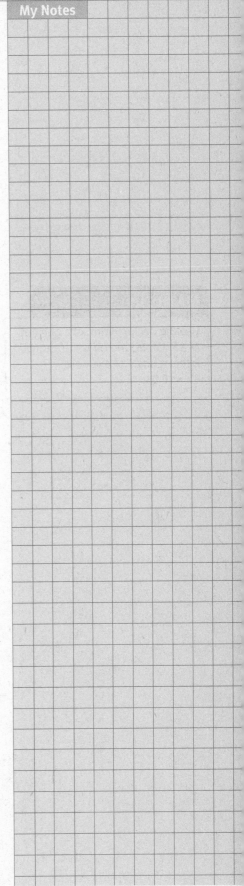

Step 2: Solve the equation.

$$\frac{1}{3}p + 30 = \frac{1}{4}p + 60$$

$$\frac{1}{3}p = \frac{1}{4}p + 30$$

$$\frac{1}{12}p = 30$$

$$p = 360 \text{ feet}$$

Solution: The perimeter of the triangular plot of land is 360 feet.

Example C

Find a number such that one-half the number decreased by two is equal to one-third the number increased by one.

Step 1: Create a model. Let x = the number.

half the number $- 2 = \frac{1}{3}$ the number $+ 1$

$$\frac{1}{2}x - 2 = \frac{1}{3}x + 1$$

Step 2: Solve the equation.

$$\frac{1}{2}x - \frac{1}{3}x - 2 = \frac{1}{3}x + 1 - \frac{1}{3}x$$

$$\frac{1}{6}x - 2 + 2 = 1 + 2$$

$$\frac{1}{6}x = 3$$

$$x = 18$$

Step 3: Check the solution.

$$\frac{1}{2}x - 2 = \frac{1}{3}x + 1$$

$$\frac{1}{2}(18) - 2 = \frac{1}{3}(18) + 1$$

$$9 - 2 = 6 + 1$$

$$7 = 7$$

Solution: The number is 18.

Try These B–C

Create a model and solve.

a. Two-fifths a number increased by six is equal to three-fourths the number decreased by 8.

My Notes

MATH TIP

Use the decimal form of a percent in a formula where *r* is the annual interest rate. For example, 3% = 0.03.

b. Marcus has created a budget for his upcoming trip to the theme park. Admission is 40% of the budget. He plans to spend 32% of his money on food, 23% on souvenirs, and save 5% for emergencies. He knows the admission will be $6 more than he will spend on food and souvenirs. How much money will Marcus need to take to the park?

1. John and Danell know that regular exercise strengthens your heart. They know that a person's heart rate should not exceed a certain limit during exercise. The maximum rate R is represented by the equation $R = 0.8(220 - y)$ where y is the person's age in years. Determine the age of a person whose maximum heart rate during exercise is 164.

2. The formula $A = p + prt$ gives the amount of money A in an account where the initial deposit is p and the money grows at a simple annual interest rate of r for t years. Assume no other deposits or withdrawals are made.
   a. How much money is in the account after 5 years if $20 is deposited and the annual interest rate is 4%?

   b. How much was deposited in the account if the amount in the account after 6 years is $17.70 and the interest rate is 3%?

   c. What would the annual interest rate have to be for $50 to grow to $70 in 10 years?

3. The set of numbers $\{\frac{1}{2}, 3, 6, 0.17, 0, 11\}$ contains possible solutions to the following equations. Determine which of these numbers is a solution to each of the following equations. Show all work to justify your conclusions.
   a. $9x + 5 = 4(x + 2) + 5x$

   b. $7x - 10 = 3x + 14$

   c. $3x - 12 = 3(x + 1) - 15$

An equation has **no solution** if there is no value for the variable that will create a true mathematical statement. An equation has **infinitely many solutions** if there are an unlimited number of values for the variable that will create a true mathematical statement.

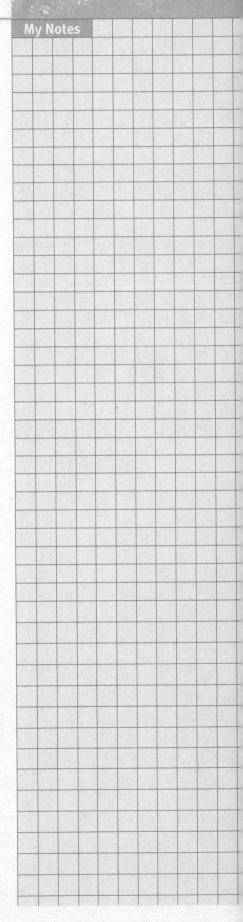

4. **Critique the reasoning of others.** Mikayla, Ryan, and Gabriella solved the following three equations as shown below. Each student has reasoned their equation as having *no solution, one solution,* or *infinitely many solutions,* respectively. Why are the students correct here?

Mikayla	Ryan	Gabriella

Mikayla

$2x + 5 = 5(x - 7) - 3x$
$2x + 5 = 5x - 35 - 3x$
$2x + 5 = 2x - 35$
$\underline{-2x \quad\quad -2x}$
$\quad\quad 5 = -35$

Ryan

$2(x - 3) + 5 = 4(x - 1)$
$2x - 6 + 5 = 4x - 4$
$2x - 1 = 4x - 4$
$\underline{-2x \quad\quad -2x}$
$-1 = 2x - 4$
$\underline{+4 \quad\quad +4}$
$\dfrac{3}{2} = \dfrac{2x}{2}$
$\dfrac{3}{2} = x$

Gabriella

$6(x + 1) - 10 = 6x - 4$
$6x + 6 - 10 = 6x - 4$
$6x - 4 = 6x - 4$
$\underline{-6x \quad\quad -6x}$
$-4 = -4$

5. Write a real-world problem for the equation $7x - 10 = 3x + 14$.

Check Your Understanding

Solve each of the following. Show your work.

6. $\frac{1}{3}(2x - 4) + 5 = -\frac{2}{3}(x + 1)$

7. $2(x + 1) = 3x - x + 2$

8. $6x - 5 = 5(x - 3) + x$

9. $3(2x + 4) = 6(5x + 2)$

10. Write a real-world problem for the equations in Items 6-8.

11. Create a model and solve.
    a. In a recent basketball game between the Storm and the Chargers the number of points scored by the Storm in the first half was equal to the number of points scored by the Chargers in the second half of the game. In the first half the Storm scored one-fourth the total points scored in the game. During the second half the Chargers scored 16 points less than one-third the points scored in the game. How many total points were scored during the game?

    b. Seven-tenths of a number decreased by thirteen is equal to three-tenths the number increased by 13. Find the number.

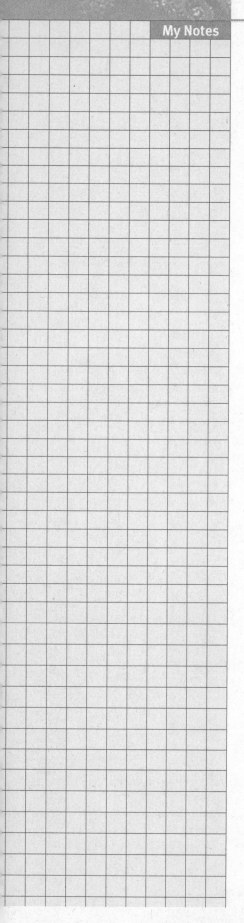

LESSON 10-2 PRACTICE

12. Solve for x: $180 - x = 10 + 2(90 - x)$.

13. The formula for the area of a triangle is $A = \frac{1}{2}bh$, where b is the base of the triangle and h is the height of the triangle. The area of the triangular sail of a sailboat is 126 ft². The base is 12 ft. Find the height of the sail.

14. Solve for x: $8 + 2x - 4 = 6 + 2(x - 1)$.

15. Write a real-world problem for the equation in Item 14.

16. How is an equation different from an expression?

17. Create a model and solve.
   a. Five-sixths a number decreased by three is equal to five-eighths the number increased by 7.

   b. Elleanna is planning to join a DVD club and is investigating the options for membership. Option 1 is a $20 membership fee and $1.25 rental change for each DVD rented. Option 2 has no rental fee and changes $2.50 for each DVD rented. How many DVDs would Elleanna have to rent in order for the total cost of Option 1 to be equal to Option 2?

18. Reason abstractly. What does it mean for an equation to have no solution? How is it possible for one equation to have many solutions?

ACTIVITY 10 PRACTICE
Write your answers on notebook paper.
Show your work.

Lesson 10-1

Solve the equations below.

1. $2x + 8 = 15$

2. $35 = 3x + 14$

3. $2x + 7 + 2x = 19$

4. $5 - 2(x + 5) = 30$

5. $3.5x - 20 = 2.4x + 13$

6. Determine whether the equation $y - y = y$ is *sometimes*, *always*, or *never* true. Justify your response with examples.

7. Which equation is *not* equivalent to $2x + 15 = 35$?

   A. $\frac{4}{5}x = 8$

   B. $2x - 5 = x + 25$

   C. $2x + 7 = 27$

   D. $\frac{4}{3}x = x + \frac{10}{3}$

8. Which of the following could be the first step when solving the equation $4 - 3(x + 6) = 28$?
   A. Add 3 to both sides.
   B. Subtract 4 from both sides.
   C. Divide by -3 on both sides.
   D. Subtract $4 - 3$.

9. Create an equation whose solution is all real numbers.

10. Create an equation that has no solution.

11. The formula for the area of a rectangle is $A = lw$, where l is the length of the rectangle and w is the width of the rectangle. The area of the cell phone screen is 7.5 in². The width is 2.5 in. Find the length of the screen.

Lesson 10-2

Solve for x.

12. $6 + 0.1x = 0.15x + 8$

13. $0.8x - 11 = 0.3x + 41$

14. $8x + 3 - 10x = -2(x - 2) + 3$

15. $2(x - 11) = 6(x + 3)$

16. Which of the following could be the first step when solving the equation $5 + 6(x - 1) = 11 + 5x$?
 A. Multiply $(x - 1)$ by 6.
 B. Subtract 1 from both sides.
 C. Divide by 5 on both sides.
 D. Subtract $5x$ from $6(x - 1)$.

17. Solve $3(x + 1) + 1 + 2x = 2(2x + 2) + x$.

18. What is the next step in solving the equation $\frac{4}{5}x = 36$?

 A. $\frac{4}{5} - \frac{4}{5}x = 36 - \frac{4}{5}$

 B. $\left(\frac{5}{4}\right)\frac{4}{5}x = 36\left(\frac{5}{4}\right)$

 C. $\frac{4}{5}x = 36 - (5 - 4)$

 D. $\frac{4}{5}x = 36 - (4 * 5)$

19. Which equation is *not* equivalent to $6x - 1 = 11 + 5x$?
 A. $x = 12$
 B. $6x = 12 + 5x$
 C. $x - 1 = 11$
 D. $\frac{6}{10}x = 3$

20. Which choice is a solution for the equation $7x + 11 = 10x - 25$?
 A. -10
 B. 5
 C. 12
 D. -6

21. Solve $2x + 1 = x - 3$ for x.

MATHEMATICAL PRACTICES
Look For and Make Use of Structure

22. Why is it important to be able to use properties of numbers and equality when solving an equation?

Muhammad Yunus is the founder of the Grameen Bank and a recipient of the Nobel Peace Prize for his work to find solutions to extreme poverty. The Grameen Bank issues microcredit loans and is the world's original microlending organization. Microcredit loans are one way to help people move out of extreme poverty. The loans involve lending very poor people small amounts of money to start a new business or to expand an existing one.

1. Malik wants to open a bicycle repair shop in India. He will need 800 rupees to buy the tools and equipment necessary to start his business. After that, he will need 1,400 rupees per month to keep his business running.
   a. Copy and complete the table below for Malik's total costs.

Number of Months in Business	Total Costs to Operate (in rupees)
1	
2	
3	
6	
n	

   b. Use the completed table to write an expression to represent Malik's total costs to operate his business in terms of the number of months he has been in business.
   c. Copy and complete the table below for Malik's total profit in terms of the months he is in business. Use the fact that Malik estimates he will make 3,600 rupees in sales each month.

Number of Months in Business	Total Profit (in rupees)
1	
2	
3	
6	
n	

   MATH TIP

   Profit P is defined as Revenue R, or money brought in, minus Costs C, or money paid out.
   $$P = R - C$$

   d. Use the completed table to write an expression to represent Malik's total profits from his business in terms of the number of months he has been in business.
   e. Assume $1.00 is equivalent to 43 rupees. How much profit, in dollars, will Malik make in 1 year?

2. Maria lives in Honduras. She is applying for a microcredit loan to start street food business. The start-up costs for her business include $65 for the cart and $900 for a freezer, plus the cost of bulk foods. She estimate her total start-up cost will be $1,053.

   a. If b represents the cost of the bulk foods, write and solve an equation to find the cost of the bulk foods Maria plans to buy.

   b. Maria has monthly costs of $420 and expects monthly sales of $725. Use the formula $P = n(R - C)$, where P represents profit, R represent monthly revenue or sales, and C represents monthly costs, to find the number of months it will take her to make $2,000 in profit.

3. An organization has raised $5,000 that it would like to use to provide $200 microloans to residents of a particular community. Of the $5,000 they raised, $400 must be used for administrative costs like the salaries of employees who set up the loans and the paperwork required. Write and solve an equation to determine how many microloans the organization can provide.

Scoring Guide	Exemplary	Proficient	Emerging	Incomplete
	The solution demonstrates these characteristics:			
Mathematics Knowledge and Thinking (Items 1a-e, 2a-b, 3)	• Clear and accurate understanding of solving expressions and equations.	• Solving expressions and equations with few if any errors.	• Difficulty solving expressions and equations.	• Incorrect or incomplete solving of expressions and equations.
Problem Solving (Items 1e, 2a-b, 3)	• An appropriate and efficient strategy that results in a correct answer.	• A strategy that may include unnecessary steps but results in a correct answer.	• A strategy that results in some incorrect answers.	• No clear strategy when solving problems.
Mathematical Modeling / Representations (Items 1a-d, 2a-b, 3)	• Writing accurate expressions and equations from a table or a problem situation. • Accurately creating tables to represent a problem situation.	• Writing expressions and equations that usually result in the correct answer. • Creating tables to represent a problem situation.	• Errors in writing expressions and equations to represent a problem situation. • Errors in creating tables to represent a problem situation.	• Writing inaccurate or incomplete expressions or equations. • Creating inaccurate or incomplete tables to represent a problem situation.
Reasoning and Communication (Items 1e, 2b)	• Reasoning to round a numerical answer and clearly communicating the answer in the requested units.	• Giving a correct answer.	• Failing to round an answer to a reasonable number or neglecting the units.	• An incomplete or inaccurate answer.

Exploring Slope
High Ratio Mountain
Lesson 11-1 Linear Equations and Slope

Learning Targets:

- Understand the concept of slope as the ratio $\dfrac{change\ in\ y}{change\ in\ x}$ between any two points on a line.

- Graph proportional relationships; interpret the slope and the y-intercept $(0, 0)$ of the graph.

- Use similar right triangles to develop an understanding of slope.

> **SUGGESTED LEARNING STRATEGIES:** Create Representations, Marking The Text, Discussion Groups, Sharing and Responding, Interactive Word Wall

Misty Flipp worked odd jobs all summer long and saved her money to buy passes to the ski lift at the High Ratio Mountain Ski Resort. In August, Misty researched lift ticket prices and found several options. Since she worked so hard to earn this money, Misty carefully investigated each of her options.

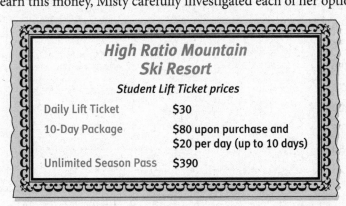

High Ratio Mountain Ski Resort

Student Lift Ticket prices

Daily Lift Ticket	$30
10-Day Package	$80 upon purchase and $20 per day (up to 10 days)
Unlimited Season Pass	$390

1. Suppose Misty purchases a daily lift ticket each time she goes skiing. Complete the table below to determine the total cost for lift tickets.

Number of Days	0	1	2	3	4	5	6
Total Cost of Lift Tickets							

2. According to the table, what is the relationship between the cost of the lift tickets and the number of days?

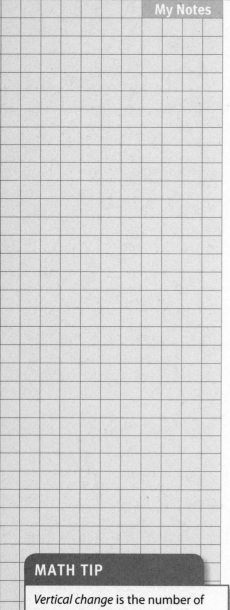

My Notes

3. Let *d* represent the number of days for which Misty bought lift tickets and *C* represent Misty's total cost. Write an equation that can be used to determine the total cost of lift tickets if Misty skis for *d* days.

4. **Model with mathematics.** Plot the data from the table on the graph below. The data points appear to be *linear*. What do you think this means?

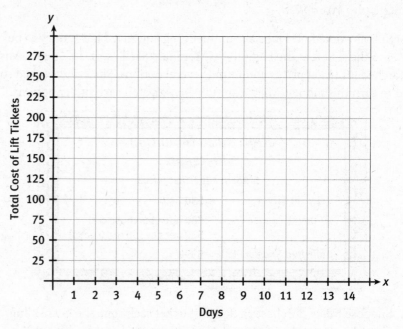

5. Label the leftmost point on the graph point *A*. Label the next 6 points, from left to right, points *B*, *C*, *D*, *E*, *F*, and *G*.

6. **Reason quantitatively.** According to the graph, what happens to the total cost of lift tickets as the number of days increases? Justify your answer.

MATH TIP

Vertical change is the number of spaces moved up or down on a graph. "Up" movement is represented by a positive number. "Down" is a negative number.

Horizontal change is the number of spaces moved right or left on a graph. Movement to the right is indicated by a positive number. Movement to the left is indicated by a negative number.

7. Describe the movement, on the graph, from one point to another.

A to *B*: Vertical Change _____ Horizontal Change _____

B to *C*: Vertical Change _____ Horizontal Change _____

C to *D*: Vertical Change _____ Horizontal Change _____

D to *E*: Vertical Change _____ Horizontal Change _____

E to *F*: Vertical Change _____ Horizontal Change _____

F to *G*: Vertical Change _____ Horizontal Change _____

8. a. The movements you traced in Item 7 can be written as ratios. Write

ratios in the form $\dfrac{vertical\ change}{horizontal\ change}$ to describe the movement from:

A to B: B to C:

C to D: D to E:

b. Vertical change can also be described as the *change in y*. Similarly, the horizontal change is often referred to as the *change in x*.

Therefore, the ratio $\dfrac{vertical\ change}{horizontal\ change}$ can also be written as $\dfrac{change\ in\ y}{change\ in\ x}$. Determine the *change in y* and *change in x* from A to C in Item 4. Write the ratio as $\dfrac{change\ in\ y}{change\ in\ x}$.

Continue to use the data from Item 4. Determine the *change in y* and *change in x* for each movement described below. Then write the ratio $\dfrac{change\ in\ y}{change\ in\ x}$.

c. From B to E: **d.** From A to E:

e. From B to A: **f.** From E to B:

My Notes

READING AND WRITING MATH

When writing a ratio, you can also represent the relationship by separating each quantity with a colon. For example, the ratio 1:4 is read "one to four."

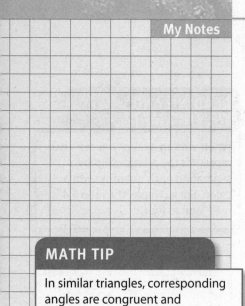

My Notes

MATH TIP

In similar triangles, corresponding angles are congruent and corresponding sides are in proportion.

9. Describe the similarities and differences in the ratios written in Item 8. How are the ratios related?

10. **Make sense of problems.** What are the units of the ratios created in Item 8? Explain how the ratios and units relate to Misty's situation.

11. How do the ratios relate to the equation you wrote in Item 3?

12. The ratio $\dfrac{change\ in\ y}{change\ in\ x}$ between any two points on a line is constant. Use the diagram below and what you know about similar triangles to explain why the $\dfrac{change\ in\ y}{change\ in\ x}$ ratios are equivalent for the movements described.

From W to V:

From W to Z:

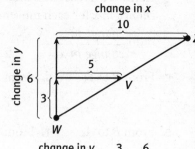

$$\frac{change\ in\ y}{change\ in\ x} = \frac{3}{5} = \frac{6}{10}$$

The *slope* of a line is determined by the ratio $\dfrac{\text{change in } y}{\text{change in } x}$ between any two points that lie on the line.

- The slope is the *constant rate of change* of a line. It is also sometimes called the *average rate of change*.
- All linear relationships have a *constant rate of change*.
- The slope of a line is what determines how steep or flat the line is.
- The *y*-intercept of a line is the point at which the line crosses the *y*-axis, $(0, y)$.

13. Draw a line through the points you graphed in Item 4. Use the graph to determine the slope and *y*-intercept of the line. How do the slope and *y*-intercept of this line relate to the equation you wrote in Item 3?

14. Complete the table to show the data points you graphed in Item 4. Use the table to indicate the ratio $\dfrac{\text{change in } y}{\text{change in } x}$ and to determine the slope of the line.

Number of Days	Total Cost of Lift Tickets
0	
1	
2	
3	
4	
5	
6	

change in y: change in x:

$\dfrac{\text{change in } y}{\text{change in } x}$:   slope:

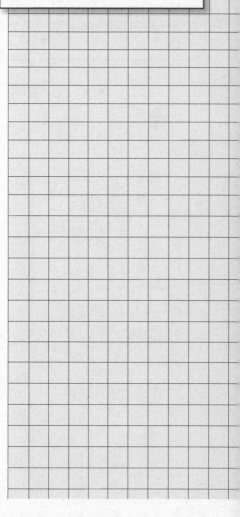

My Notes

MATH TERMS

Slope is the ratio of vertical change to horizontal change, or $\dfrac{\text{change in } y}{\text{change in } x}$

READING MATH

The slope of a line, $\dfrac{\text{change in } y}{\text{change in } x}$, is also expressed symbolically as $\dfrac{\Delta y}{\Delta x}$.

Δ is the Greek letter delta, and in mathematics it means "change in."

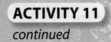

My Notes

Check Your Understanding

15. Find the slope and the y-intercept for each of the following. Remember to use the ratio $\dfrac{change\ in\ y}{change\ in\ x}$.

a.
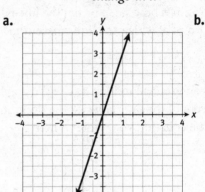

b.
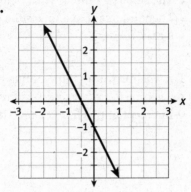

c.

x	y
0	0
1	2.5
2	5
4	10

d.

x	y
−1	4
0	2
1	0
3	−4

e. Look back at the figure for Item 12. Would a point P that is 9 units up from point W and 15 units to the right be on the line that contains points W, V, and Z? Use similar triangles to explain your answer.

16. John is longboarding at a constant rate down the road. If 2 minutes after he leaves his house he is 1,000 feet away and at 5 minutes he is 2,500 feet from his house, what would his average rate of change be?

LESSON 11-1 PRACTICE

The Tran family is driving across the country. They drive 400 miles each day. Use the table below to answer Items 17–20.

Day	Total Miles Driven
1	400
2	800
3	
4	
5	

17. Complete the table.

18. Draw a graph for the data in the table. Be sure to title the graph and label the axes. Draw a line through the points.

19. Write an equation that can be used to determine the total miles, *M*, driven over *d* days.

20. Find the slope and the *y*-intercept of the line you created, using the graph you drew or the equation you wrote. Explain what each represents for the Tran family's situation.

The graph below shows the money a student earns as she tutors. Use the graph to answer Items 21–24.

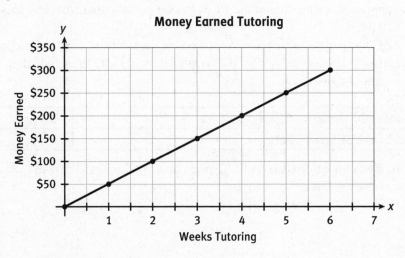

Money Earned Tutoring

21. What is the slope of the line?

22. What is the *y*-intercept of the line?

23. Write an equation that can be used to determine how much money, *D*, the student has earned after *w* weeks.

24. Attend to precision. Calculate how much money the student will have earned after 52 weeks.

My Notes

Learning Targets:

- Understand the connections among proportional relationships, lines, and linear equations.
- Graph proportional relationships; interpret the slope and the y-intercept $(0, y)$ of graphs.
- Examine linear relationships as graphs and as equations to solve real-world problems.

> **SUGGESTED LEARNING STRATEGIES:** Create Representations, Look for a Pattern, Sharing and Responding, Construct an Argument, RAFT

Remember that Misty had saved her money to buy passes to the ski lift at the High Ratio Mountain Ski Resort.

High Ratio Mountain Ski Resort
Student Lift Ticket prices

Daily Lift Ticket	$30
10-Day Package	$80 upon purchase and $20 per day (up to 10 days)
Unlimited Season Pass	$390

1. Suppose Misty purchased the 10-day ticket package that costs $80 plus $20 per day.

   a. Complete the table below to determine the total cost of the lift tickets in the 10-day package for 0 through 6 days. Be sure to include the initial cost of $80.

Number of Days	0	1	2	3	4	5	6
Total Cost of Lift Tickets							

   b. **Reason quantitatively.** Explain how you know the data in the table are linear.

2. Plot the data from the table on the given axes. Then draw a line through the points you plotted.

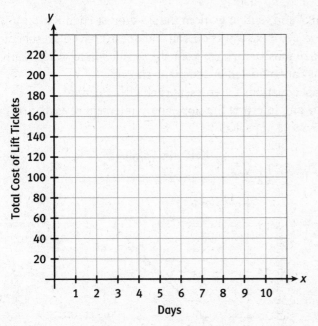

3. Determine the slope and the *y*-intercept of the line graphed in Item 2. Explain how these values relate to Misty's situation.

4. Let *d* represent the number of days Misty plans to ski and let *K* represent Misty's total cost. Write an equation that could be used to determine Misty's total cost if she bought a 10-day package.

5. Compare and contrast the lines associated with the data for the daily lift tickets in Item 4 from Lesson 11-1 and the data for the 10-day package in Item 2. Include the similarities and differences in their equations.

My Notes

Check Your Understanding

6. Veronika and Kaitlyn work in the ski shop at High Ratio Mountain. Because Veronika works on-call and doesn't have a set schedule she earns $10 plus $6 for each hour she is called in to work. Kaitlyn's earnings are modeled by the graph shown.
   a. Write equations to represent each girl's earnings.
   b. State and interpret the slope and *y*-intercept of each girl's equation you wrote in part a.

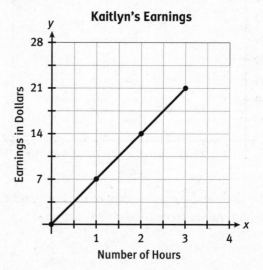

7. A line with a slope of $\frac{-1}{2}$ contains the point (2, 3). Use the My Notes section to graph the point and use the slope to give the coordinates of three other points on the line.

8. Although $390 seemed a little expensive, Misty considered the unlimited season pass.
   a. First, she compared the season pass to the daily lift tickets at $30 each. How many times would Misty have to go skiing before she would save money with the $390 season pass? Explain your reasoning.

   b. Complete the table below for the total cost of the unlimited season pass for 0 through 6 days.

Number of Days	0	1	2	3	4	5	6
Total Cost of Lift Tickets							

   c. Explain how you know the data in the table are linear.

   d. What is the rate of change of the cost of the tickets with the unlimited season pass?

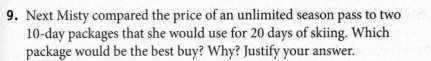
My Notes

9. Next Misty compared the price of an unlimited season pass to two 10-day packages that she would use for 20 days of skiing. Which package would be the best buy? Why? Justify your answer.

10. **Express regularity in repeated reasoning.** If Misty skis the following number of days, which of the three packages should she purchase? Explain your reasoning for each.
    a. 6 days

    b. 8 days

    c. 13 days

    d. 16 days

11. **Construct viable arguments.** Write a *persuasive* letter to Misty based on your analysis that makes a recommendation for which package she should purchase. Include multiple representations (graphs, tables, and/or equations) to support your reasoning. Provide a concluding statement that summarizes your reasoning.

ACADEMIC VOCABULARY

A synonym for ***persuasive*** is convincing.

Check Your Understanding

Emily rides her bike 24 miles in 2 hours.

12. Create a ratio of Emily's miles per hour.

13. Use the ratio you created to determine how far Emily can ride in 5 hours.

14. If Emily rode her bike for 42 miles at the rate you determined, how long did she ride?

15. Raine rides her bike 37 miles in 3 hours. If Raine started at the same time as Emily and also rode her bike at a constant rate for 42 miles, who finished first? Explain your reasoning.

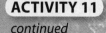

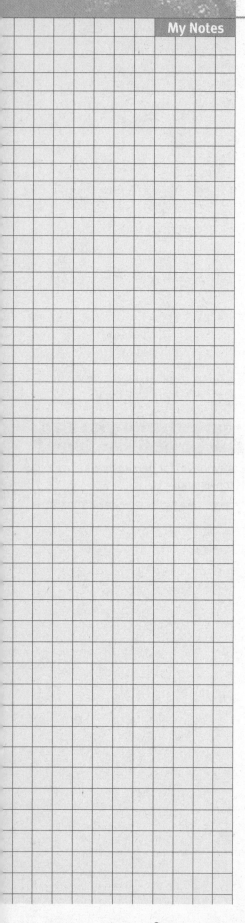

My Notes

LESSON 11-2 PRACTICE

Lucas conducted an experiment on the rate of water evaporation. He placed 500 mL of water in a measuring cup at room temperature and collected data on the amount of water in the cup every day for a week. His results are shown in the data table below:

Day	Water Measurement (mL)
0	500
1	475
2	450
3	425
4	400
5	375
6	350
7	325

16. What is the rate of change in the amount of water in the cup?

17. On a graph of these data, what would be the y-intercept, and what does it represent in Lucas's experiment?

18. Write an equation that can be used to determine the water level, l, after d days.

19. At this same rate of evaporation, how many days will it take for all of the water to evaporate?

Lucas wanted to see how lowering the temperature of the water would change the results of his experiment. He placed 500 mL of water in a measuring cup, but placed the cup in the refrigerator, and collected data as before for a week. His results are shown in the data table below:

Day	Water Measurement (mL)
0	500
1	490
2	480
3	470
4	460
5	450
6	440
7	430

20. What is the rate of change in the amount of water in the cup?

21. Write an equation that can be used to determine the water level, l, after d days.

22. **Make sense of problems.** At this rate of evaporation, how many more days will it take for all of the water to evaporate in the refrigerator experiment than in the room-temperature experiment?

ACTIVITY 11 PRACTICE
Write your answers on notebook paper.
Show your work.

Lesson 11-1

1. Misty determined that she gets 64 miles per
   2 gallons of gas from her car as she drives
   from her house to the ski slope.
   a. Create a ratio of Misty's miles per gallon.
   b. Using the ratio you found in part a, determine
      how far Misty can go on 1 gallon of gas.
   c. How many miles could Misty travel on a full
      tank of 12 gallons of gas?

2. Brynn rides her bike 84 miles in 4 hours.
   a. Create a ratio of Brynn's miles per hour.
   b. Using the ratio you found in part a, determine
      how far Brynn can ride in 7 hours.
   c. If Brynn rides 57 miles at the rate indicated,
      how long will she ride? Justify your response.

3. What is the slope of the line shown?

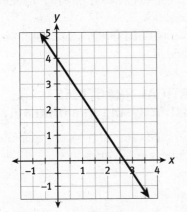

   A. -4
   B. $-\dfrac{3}{2}$
   C. $\dfrac{3}{2}$
   D. 4

4. Find the slope and *y*-intercept of the line
   represented by each of the following.

a.

x	y
0	1
3	7
6	13

b.

x	y
−3	10
0	4
4	−4

c.

x	y
0	−3
2	−1
4	1

d.

x	y
−1	5
0	9
4	25

Lesson 11-2

5. Find the slope and *y*-intercept for each of the
   following graphs.

a.

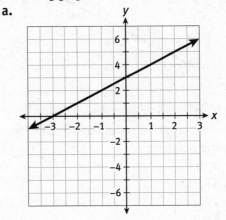

b.

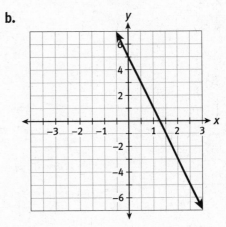

c.

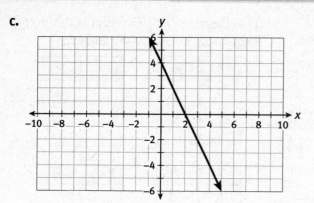

d.

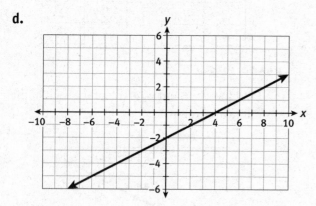

6. If a line has a slope of $-\frac{1}{2}$ and contains the point (2, 3), then it must also contain which of the following points?
   A. (−2, 6)
   B. (0, 5)
   C. (1, 2)
   D. (4, 2)

7. If a line with a slope of $\frac{3}{4}$ contains the point with coordinates (−1, 4), give the coordinates of three other points that must also be on the line.

8. Complete the following tables so that the data are linear.

a.

x	y
0	1
1	3
2	5
3	
4	9

b.

x	y
0	10
1	16
2	22
3	
4	34
5	40

9. Which of the following situations, when graphed, would create a linear graph? Explain your reasoning.
   A. the height of a wedding cake as 5-inch layers are added
   B. the speed of each car passing through an intersection
   C. the weight of a sandbag as shovelfuls of dirt are added

MATHEMATICAL PRACTICES
Reason Abstractly and Quantitatively

10. How does the value of the slope of a line affect the steepness of the line?

Slope-Intercept Form

Leaky Bottle
Lesson 12-1 Identifying Slope Using Tables and Graphs

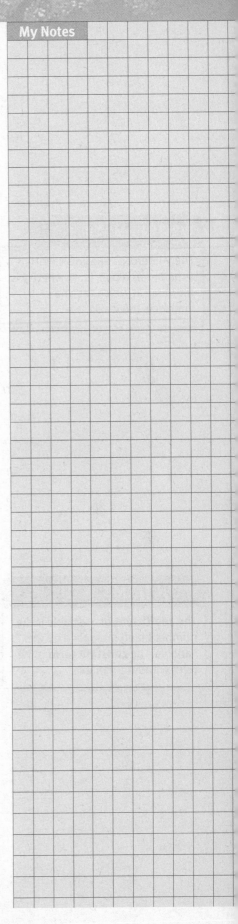

My Notes

Learning Targets:

- Graph linear relationships represented in different forms.
- Write an equation in the form $y = mx + b$ to model a linear relationship between two quantities.
- Interpret the meaning of slope and y-intercept in a problem context.

> **SUGGESTED LEARNING STRATEGIES:** Use Manipulatives, Create Representations, Look for a Pattern, Discussion Group, Sharing and Responding

Owen's water bottle leaked in his book bag. He did the following experiment to find how quickly water drains from a small hole placed in a water bottle.

1. Follow the steps below and fill in the table.
   - Get a water bottle and a container to catch the water.
   - Poke a very small hole in the bottom of the water bottle.
   - Ensure the hole is facing down and open the bottle cap.
   - Draw a line on the bottle every 5 seconds to mark the water level.
   - After the water is drained from the bottle, measure the heights at each of the times you marked.

Time in Seconds	0	5	10	15	20	25	30	35	40
Height of Water (cm)									

2. Graph the data on the grid below.

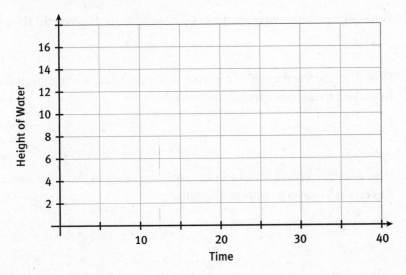

3. Does the relationship between time and the height of the water appear to be linear? Explain your reasoning.

My Notes

Discrete data are data that can only have certain values, such as the number of people in your class. On a graph of discrete data, there will be space between every two possible values. *Continuous data* can take on any value within a certain range, for example, height. On a graph, continuous data have no breaks, holes, or gaps.

4. Are the data you collected continuous or discrete? Justify your response.

5. Draw a line through the points on your graph.
   a. Find the slope of the line.

WRITING MATH

The y-intercept of a line is written as an ordered pair, $(0, y)$, where y is the value at which the line intersects the y-axis.

   b. Determine the y-intercept of the line.

   c. Describe the meaning of the slope of the line in this problem situation.

   d. Describe the meaning of the y-intercept of the line you drew in this problem situation.

6. Write an equation that gives the height of the water H given the time t.

MATH TERMS

The **coefficient** of a variable is the number being multiplied by the variable. The **constant term** is the term without a variable.

7. How does the *coefficient* of t in your equation relate to the experiment? Be certain to include appropriate units.

8. How does the *constant term* in the equation relate to the experiment? Be certain to include appropriate units.

My Notes

9. **Attend to precision.** Find the slope of the line that passes through the points in the table.

x	y
0	11
2	7.5
4	4

Check Your Understanding

Ben's Bells, a community service organization, began hanging ceramic wind chimes randomly in trees, on bike paths, and in parks around the country in 2003. A written message on each bell asked the finder to simply take one home and pass on the kindness. One thousand bells were hung in 2003. The number of bells increased by 2,000 each year after 2003.

10. Complete the table below to indicate the number of bells that were hung each year after 2003.

Years Since 2003	0	1	2	3
Number of Bells Distributed				

11. Graph the data on the grid below.

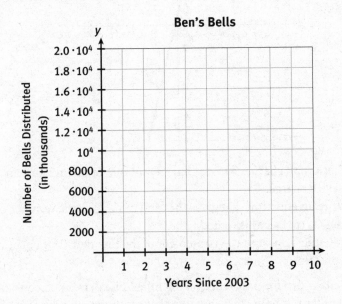

Ben's Bells

12. Is the data continuous or discrete? Justify your response.

13. Use the data in the table or the graph to write an equation that gives the number of bells distributed, N, given the years since 2003, t.

14. Using the graph in Item 11, determine the slope and y-intercept of the line. What do these values represent in this real-life situation?

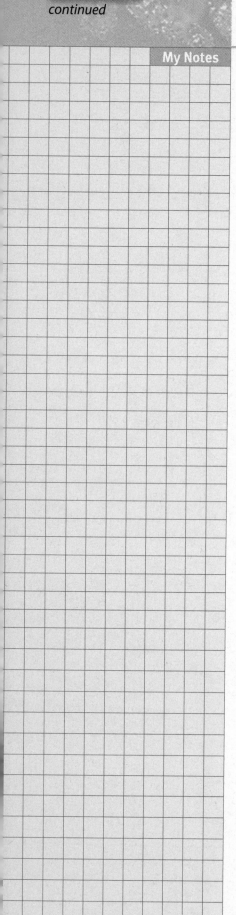

LESSON 12-1 PRACTICE

15. Graph the data in the table. Find the slope of the line created by connecting the data points in the table.

x	y
0	10
3	8.5
6	7

16. Examine the table of values. Write an equation that gives the value of *y* for any given value of *x*. State the slope and *y*-intercept of the line that your equation represents.

x	−3	−2	−1	0	1	2	3
y	15	10	5	0	−5	−10	−15

17. a. Find the slope of the line in the following graph.
   b. Determine the *y*-intercept of the line.

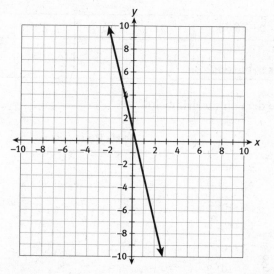

18. MyCar Rental charges $15 per day to rent one of its cars plus an $8 service charge.
   a. Write an equation that gives the total cost, *y*, for the number of days, *x*, that a car is rented.
   b. State the slope and the *y*-intercept of the line that your equation represents.

19. Mariella is driving a distance of 100 miles. She drives at a constant rate of 60 miles per hour. The equation that represents the distance she has left to go is $y = 100 - 60x$, where *x* is the number of hours she has already driven.
   a. Graph the equation.
   b. State the slope and the *y*-intercept of the graph from part a.
   c. **Reason abstractly.** Explain what the slope and *y*-intercept of the line represent in this item.

My Notes

Learning Targets:

- Compare different proportional relationships represented in different ways.
- Graph linear relationships and identify and interpret the meaning of slope in graphs.

> **SUGGESTED LEARNING STRATEGIES:** Create Representations, Think-Pair-Share, Construct an Argument, Discussion Groups, Look for a Pattern

Slope can be seen visually as the slant or the steepness of a line. Using a graph, one can determine the slope of a line (as well as the *y*-intercept). One can also compare the slopes of different lines by considering their graphs or their equations.

1. For each linear equation in the tables below:
   - Complete the table of values.
   - Graph, using a different color for each line.
   - Determine the slope.

a.

x	y = x	y
−3	y = −3	−3
−2		
−1		
0		
1		
2		
3		

b.

x	y = 2x	y
−3	y = 2(−3)	−6
−2		
−1		
0		
1		
2		
3		

c.

x	y = 4x	y
−2	y = 4(−2)	−8
−1.5		
−1		
0		
1		
2		
3		

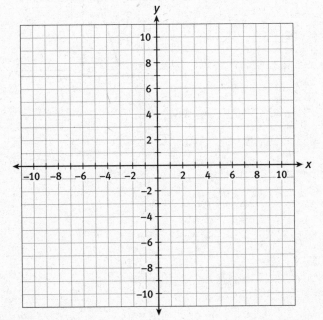

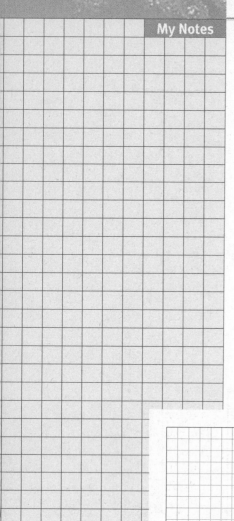

My Notes

2. How does the slope you found for each linear equation relate to the coefficient of x in the equation?

3. How does the slope you found for each linear equation relate to the steepness of each line?

4. Write an equation of a line that is:
   a. steeper (increasing) than $y = 3x$

   b. steeper (decreasing) than $y = -6x + 2$

5. **Critique the reasoning of others.** Jordan and Alex disagree about the following two graphs. Jordan feels that the line in the left graph is steeper, while Alex feels the line in the right graph is steeper. Which line is steeper? Justify your response to Jordan and Alex.

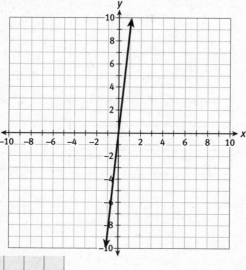
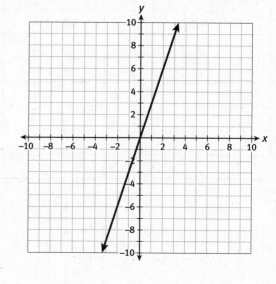

Check Your Understanding

6. Write the equation of a line that has a slope that is greater than 1 but less than 2.

7. Graph the equation $y = 3x$. State the slope of the line.

8. The graph, table, and equation below represent 3 different linear relationships. Which one has the greatest rate of change? Justify your response.

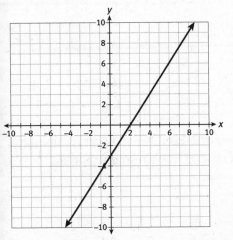

x	y
0	3
1	6
2	9
3	12
4	15

$$y = 0.5x - 4$$

9. For each linear equation in the tables below:
   • Complete the table of values.
   • Graph, on the grid provided, using a different color for each line.
   • Determine the slope.

a. $y = -x$

x	y
−3	
−2	
−1	
0	
1	
2	
3	

slope =

b. $y = -2x$

x	y
−3	
−2	
−1	
0	
1	
2	
3	

slope =

c. $y = -4x$

x	y
−2	
−1.5	
−1	
0	
1	
2	
3	

slope =

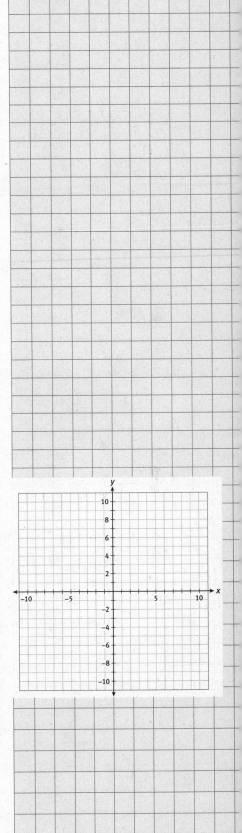

10. How do the slopes you found relate to the coefficients of x in the three equations?

My Notes

LESSON 12-2 PRACTICE

11. Complete the table of values and graph the equation $y = -5x$. State the slope of the line.

x	$y = -5x$	y
−3	$y = -5(-3)$	15
−2		
−1		
0		
1		
2		
3		

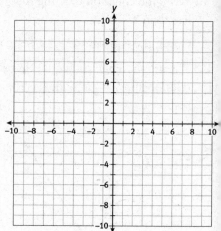

12. The table and the equation below represent different linear relationships. Which one has the greater rate of change? Explain your reasoning.

x	−2	−1	0	1	2
y	1	5	9	13	17

$y = 3x - 4$

13. How does the slope of a line relate to the steepness of the line?

14. Given the equations below, how can the steepness of the lines be determined without graphing the lines?
line A: $y = 8x$ line B: $y = -3x + 2$

15. Graph each equation.
- $y = \dfrac{1}{2}x$
- $y = x$
- $y = 2x$

a. State the slope of each equation.

b. **Reason quantitatively.** Which line is steepest? Justify your answer using the slope.

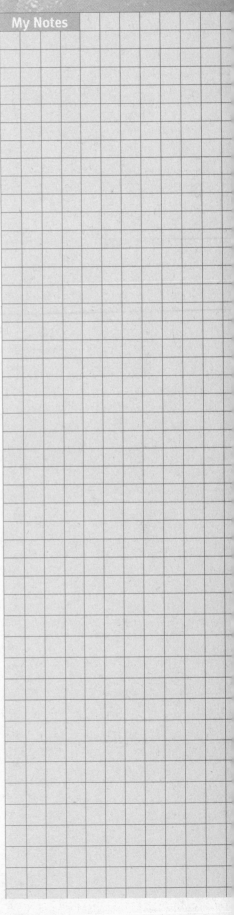

Learning Targets:

● Derive equations of the form $y = mx$ and $y = mx + b$ from their graphs.

● Graph linear relationships and identify and interpret the meaning of slope and y-intercept in graphs.

SUGGESTED LEARNING STRATEGIES: Close Reading, Discussion Groups, Sharing and Responding, Create Representations, Marking the Text

The **slope-intercept form** of a linear equation is $y = mx + b$ where m is the slope of the line and b is the y-intercept of the line.

1. For each linear equation below:
   - Make a table of values.
   - Graph on a blank grid like the one below, using a different color for each line.
   - Determine the slope and y-intercept.

   a. $y = \frac{1}{2}x$ **b.** $y = \frac{1}{4}x$ **c.** $y = \frac{1}{5}x$

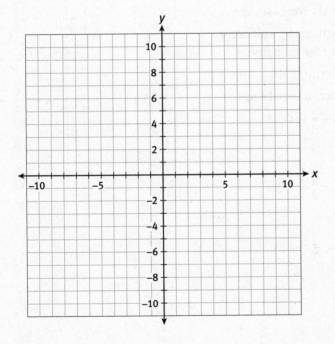

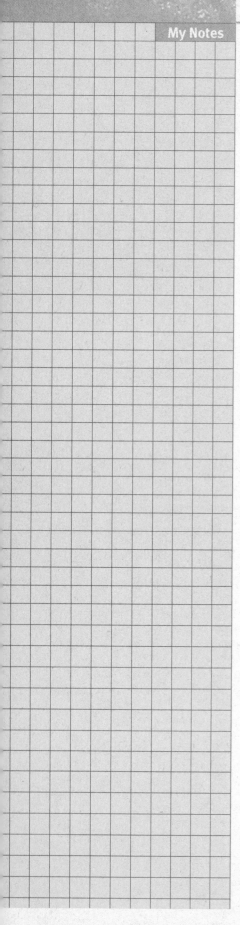

2. The equation and graph below represent different linear relationships. Identify the slope and y-intercept of both linear relationships.

$$y = \frac{1}{2}x + 4$$

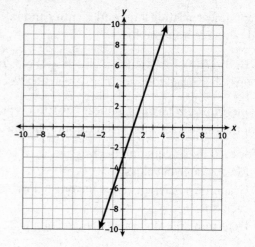

3. For each linear equation below:
- Make a table of values in the My Notes section.
- Graph using a different color for each line.
- Determine the y-intercept.
- Determine the slope.

a. $y = \frac{2}{3}x + 3$

b. $y = \frac{2}{3}x + 6$

c. $y = \frac{2}{3}x - 3$

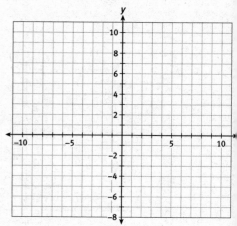

4. How is the *y*-intercept related to the constant term in the equations you just graphed?

5. Explain how to graph a line using the slope and *y*-intercept.

6. **Make use of structure.** Identify the slope and *y*-intercept in each of the following equations.

    a. $y = \frac{3}{2}x + 5$

    b. $y = -x + 1$

    c. $y = 4x - 3$

Check Your Understanding

7. Make a table of values and graph the equation $y = -3x + 2$. State the slope of the line. Give the coordinates of the *y*-intercept.

8. Write the equation of the line graphed.

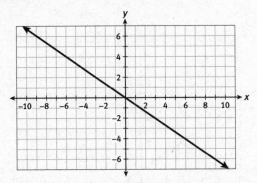

9. Graph each of the following linear equations using the *y*-intercept and the slope.

    a. $y = 2x + 4$ **b.** $y = -3x + 2$ **c.** $y = \frac{2}{3}x - 5$

10. Write an equation for the line graphed below.

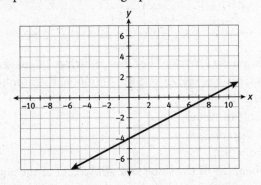

11. Explain two different ways to graph a linear equation of the form $y = mx + b$ where *m* and *b* represent any real number.

My Notes

LESSON 12-3 PRACTICE

12. Graph the following linear equations. State the slope and y-intercept for each.

   a. $y = 5x - 2$

   b. $y = 2x + 10$

   c. $y = -25x + 100$

13. What is the slope of the graph of $y = -2x + 6$?

   A. 2   **B.** 6   **C.** –2   **D.** –6

14. What is the y-intercept of the graph of $y = \frac{3}{5}x - 12$?

   A. $(0, -12)$ **B.** $\left(0, \frac{3}{5}\right)$ **C.** $(0, 12)$ **D.** $\left(0, -\frac{3}{5}\right)$

15. Graph each of the following linear equations. State the slope and y-intercept for each.

   a. $y = 5x$

   b. $y = -4x$

   c. $y = \frac{1}{5}x$

16. Make sense of problems. Write the equation of the line graphed below.

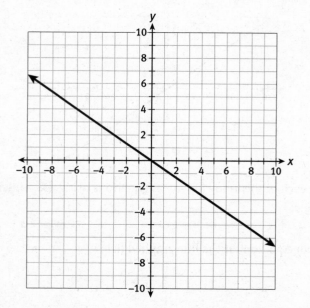

17. Celso is reading Lois Lowry's *The Giver*, which is 180 pages long. Celso reads 30 pages, on average, each hour. To model the number of pages he reads over time:

   a. Create a table of values.

   b. Construct a graph.

   c. Write an equation.

   d. State the meaning of the slope and y-intercept of the equation you wrote in part c.

ACTIVITY 12 PRACTICE
Write your answers on notebook paper.
Show your work.

Lesson 12-1

Owen found that he could use the equation $y = -3x + 24$ to model the amount of water, in mL, in his bottle after x seconds.

1. What is the slope and what does it represent in this problem situation? Be sure to include units.

2. What is the y-intercept and what does it represent in this problem situation? Be sure to include units.

3. Explain to Owen what would have to happen to the bottle for the slope to change to -4.

4. A line with a slope of -2 goes through the point $(3, 5)$. It also goes through the point $(-2, p)$. What is the value of p?
   A. $p = 15$ **B.** $p = 3$ **C.** $p = -1$

5. A line with a slope of 3 goes through the point $(-2, -4)$. It also goes through the point $(0, p)$. What is the value of p?

6. Find the slope of the line that passes through the data points in the table.
   A. -3 **B.** 3 **C.** 0

x	y
-4	-7
0	5
$\frac{1}{3}$	6

Lesson 12-2

7. What would happen to the slope of the graph of $y = \frac{2}{3}x - 3$ if the line were shifted 6 units up?

8. Explain how the slope of $y = 2x - 3$ can be used to graph the equation.

9. Compare and contrast the slopes for the equations $y = x$, $y = \frac{1}{3}x$, and $y = \frac{2}{3}x$. What conclusions can you draw about the slope of lines?

10. Write the equation of a line that is steeper than the line $y = \frac{1}{2}x$ but has a slope less than 1.

11. Write the equation of the line graphed below.

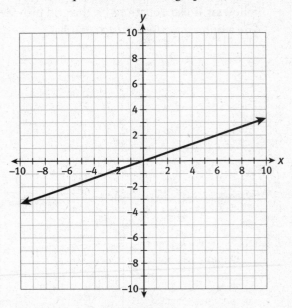

12. Two graphs are given below representing different linear relationships.

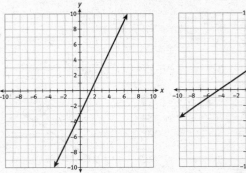 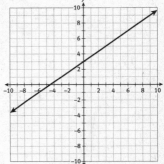

Which line has the larger slope? Explain your reasoning.

13. What is the slope of each line in Item 12? Explain the steps you used to find each slope.

Lesson 12-3

14. Identify and plot the y-intercept of the equation $y = \frac{1}{2}x + 3$. Then use the slope to determine and graph two more points on the line. Finally, sketch a line through the three points.

15. Explain how to graph the equation $y = 2x - 3$ without using a table of values.

16. Use the *y*-intercept and the slope to graph the following linear equations on the grid provided. Use a different color for each graph.

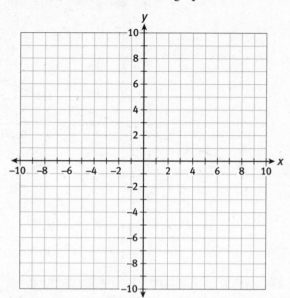

   a. $y = \frac{1}{3}x - 2$

   b. $y = -2x + 1$

   c. $y = -3x + 4$

17. Write an equation for the line graphed below.

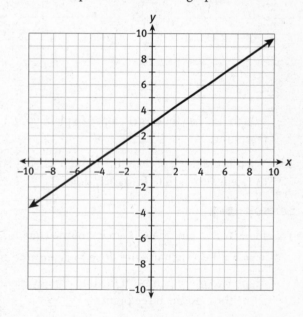

18. Identify the slope and *y*-intercept for the graph below.

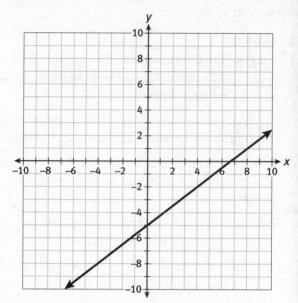

MATHEMATICAL PRACTICES
Make Sense of Problems

19. The graph and equation below represent different linear relationships.

$$y = \frac{1}{4}x + 2$$

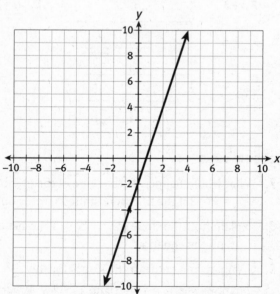

Identify the slope and *y*-intercept of both linear relationships.

Proportional Relationships
Vary Interesting
Lesson 13-1 Linear Proportional Relationships

Learning Targets:

- Represent linear proportional situations with tables, graphs, and equations.
- Identify slope and y-intercept in these representations and interpret their meaning in real-life contexts.

> **SUGGESTED LEARNING STRATEGIES:** Graphic Organizer, Marking the Text, Look for a Pattern, Create Representations, Construct an Argument

Scarlett is spending her summer afternoons as a junior lifeguard at a local pool. Each afternoon she works, she is paid $10.00 plus $2.00 per hour. In the evenings she is umpiring for a recreational softball league at the local community center. They pay her $4.00 for each hour she works.

1. **Construct viable arguments.** Which job do you think is better? Explain your reasoning.

2. Scarlett wants to determine how much money she can possibly save by the end of the summer. To do this, she creates tables to track her earnings.

   Complete each of the two tables below to track Scarlett's earnings for the first 5 hours she works at each job.

Lifeguarding	
Time in Hours	Earnings
0	
1	
2	
3	
4	
5	

Umpiring	
Time in Hours	Earnings
0	
1	
2	
3	
4	
5	

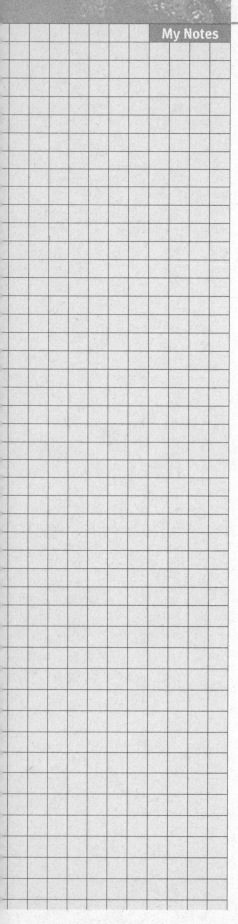

My Notes

3. Do the earnings from either job have a constant rate of change? Explain your response. Share your ideas with a partner or in your group. Use precise math terms and academic vocabulary. As you listen to your peers, make notes of new words and how they can be used to describe mathematical concepts.

4. Consider Scarlett's job as a junior lifeguard.
   a. Write an equation that could be used to determine the amount of money, y, that Scarlett would earn for x hours working at the pool.

   b. Identify the slope in the equation and explain its meaning in the problem situation.

   c. Identify the y-intercept in the equation and explain its meaning in the problem situation.

5. Consider Scarlett's job as an umpire.
   a. Write an equation that could be used to determine the amount of money, y, that Scarlett would earn for x hours working as an umpire.

   b. Identify the slope in the equation and explain its meaning in the problem situation.

   c. Identify the y-intercept in the equation and explain its meaning in the problem situation.

As you listen to group and class discussions, be sure to ask for clarification of terms you do not understand. Record the terms and make notes about them in your math notebook.

6. Describe the similarities and differences in the equations for the two jobs. How are these similarities and differences exemplified in the tables for the two jobs?

DISCUSSION GROUP TIPS

When working with a partner or in groups, listen as group members describe their ideas and understanding, and ask for clarification of concepts that are unclear.

7. Graph the lines representing Scarlett's two jobs on the grids provided. Be sure to label the axes and include a title for each graph.

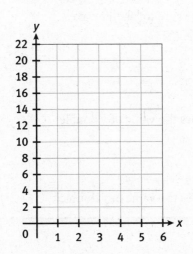
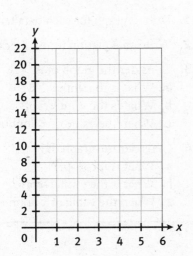

8. Compare and contrast the two graphs. How do the similarities and differences in the graphs relate to the equations and tables?

9. If Scarlett doubled the amount of time that she worked at the pool, would she double the amount of money that she made? Explain using examples.

10. If she doubled the amount of time she worked as an umpire at the community center, would Scarlett double the amount of money that she made? Explain using examples.

Check Your Understanding

Use the two data tables below for Items 11–14.

A.

x	1	2	3	4
y	4	7	10	13

B.

x	1	2	3	4
y	3	6	9	12

11. Draw a graph for each data table. Be sure to label the axes.

12. Write an equation for each graph.

13. Consider the graph of A.
   a. What is the slope?
   b. What is the y-intercept?
   c. When the value of x doubles, does the value of y double?

14. Consider the graph of B.
   a. What is the slope?
   b. What is the y-intercept?
   c. When the value of x doubles, does the value of y double?

LESSON 13-1 PRACTICE

Nina wants to sign up for swim classes. The school charges $6 per visit. The recreation center charges an initial fee of $15 plus $3 per visit.

15. Complete the tables to show the cost of lessons at the school and the center.

School Swim Classes

Visits	1	2	3	4
Cost (dollars)				

Recreation Center Swim Classes

Visits	1	2	3	4
Cost(dollars)				

16. a. Write an equation that can be used to find the total cost, y, for the number of visits, x, at the school swim classes from Item 15.
   b. Write an equation that can be used to find the total cost, y, for the number of visits, x, at the recreation center swim classes from Item 15.

7. a. Graph the equation you wrote for Item 16a. Be sure to label the axes.
   b. Graph the equation you wrote for Item 16b. Be sure to label the axes.

8. a. Use your graph from Item 17a to find its slope and *y*-intercept.
   b. Use your graph from Item 17b to find its slope and *y*-intercept.

9. Using the information from Items 15–18, where should Nina take her swim classes? Explain.

20. Critique the reasoning of others. Rayna wrote the equation for the graph shown as $y = \frac{1}{2}x$. Do you agree with Rayna? Explain your reasoning.

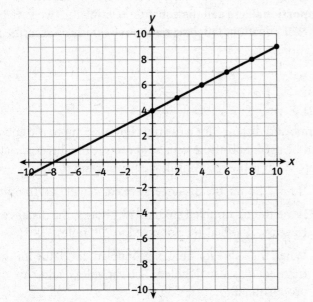

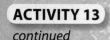

My Notes

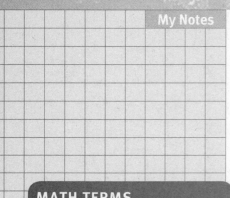

MATH TERMS

A **direct variation** is a relationship between two variables *x* and *y* that can be written in the form $y = kx$, where *k* is any constant other than 0.

Direct variation equations are *linear* equations.

Learning Targets:

● Solve problems involving direct variation.
● Distinguish between proportional and nonproportional situations using tables, graphs, and equations.

SUGGESTED LEARNING STRATEGIES: Vocabulary Organizer, Interactive Word Wall, Sharing and Responding, Look for a Pattern, Discussion Groups

If changing one variable in an equation by a factor causes the other variable to change by the same factor, we say the two variables are **directly proportional** and call the equation relating the two variables a *direct variation* equation. Direct variation relationships describe many real-life situations.

Example A

To relate time and distance for a car traveling at 55 mph, the equation $d = 55t$ can be used. Substitute values for *t* to see the direct variation relationship. What is the relationship between *d* and *t*?

Step 1:   If $t = 2$ hours, the distance traveled, *d*, will be 110 miles.

Step 2:   If the time is doubled so that $t = 4$ hours, the distance traveled, *d*, will also be doubled to 220 miles.

Solution: When the value for time, *t*, is doubled, the value for distance traveled, *d*, is also doubled. The variables *d* and *t* are directly proportional.

Try These A

Determine whether the relationship between the variables in the following equations is directly proportional or not. Explain your reasoning.
a. $y = 20x$

b. $y = 20 + x$

1. Consider the tables, graphs, and equations for Scarlett's two jobs in the previous lesson. Which of her jobs is an example of a directly proportional relationship? Justify your response with evidence from the table, graph, and equation.

2. a. Create a table, an equation, and a graph for each of the following situations.

Situation A: The distance Lili walks is 2 times the number of minutes she has been walking.

Situation B: The distance traveled by the rabbit in a critter race is consistently 1 inch more than twice the distance traveled by the iguana.

Situation C: The amount of water in the pitcher is half the time elapsed in seconds.

Situation A	
x	y
1	
2	
3	
4	
5	

Situation B	
x	y
1	
2	
3	
4	
5	

Situation C	
x	y
1	
2	
3	
4	
5	

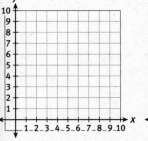

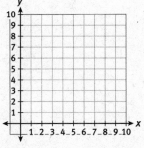

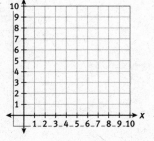

Equation: _____   Equation: _____   Equation: _____

b. Write a conjecture about the *y*-intercept of a directly proportional relationship.

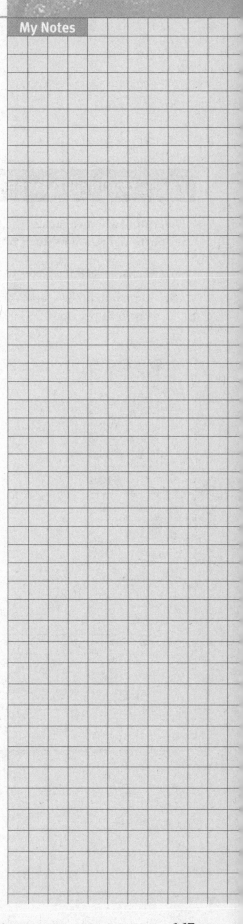

My Notes

3. Which of the situations in Item 2 are examples of directly proportional relationships? Justify your response.

Check Your Understanding

Determine whether each of the following is an example of a directly proportional relationship or not. Explain your reasoning.

4. Michael eats three pieces of fruit each day.

5. Admission to the school carnival costs $5.00 plus $0.75 per ride.

6. $y = x^2$

7.

x	y
2	32
4	128
6	288
8	512
10	800

8.

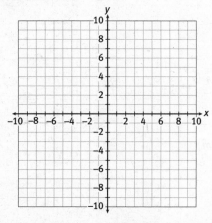

9. Kyra believes that the following graph shows a directly proportional relationship. Kwame disagrees. Who is correct? Justify your response.

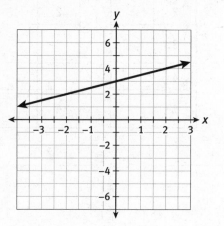

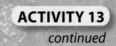
Direct variation equations can be written in the form $y = kx$. The value of k in the equation $y = kx$ is called the **constant of variation** or the **constant of proportionality**.

10. Use your tables, graphs, and equations from Item 2 to explain the relationship between the constant of variation, the rate of change, and the slope of a graph.

11. **Model with mathematics.** Direct variation equations are often used to solve real-world problems. In each of the following, determine the value of k, write an equation in the form $y = kx$ to represent the situation, and then use the equation to solve the problem.

   a. The Chumas family is driving from North Carolina to California on vacation. They drive 330 miles in 5.5 hours. How many hours would it take them to drive 720 miles?

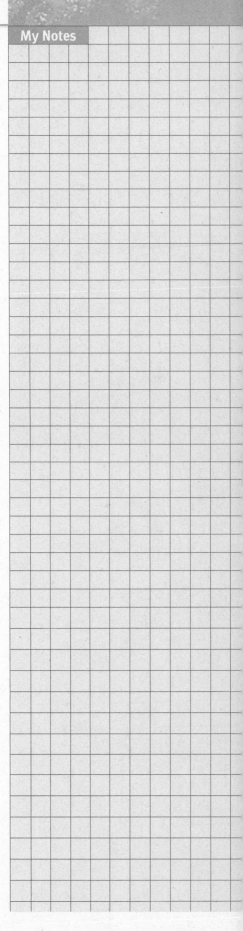

My Notes

b. Many animals age more rapidly than humans do. The chart below shows equivalent ages for dogs and humans. What is the equivalent dog age for a human who is 16 years old?

Dog Age	0	1	2	3	4	5
Human Age	0	7	14	21	28	35

Check Your Understanding

12. Ellen is training to compete in a half marathon. She currently runs at a rate of 4.5 miles per hour.
   a. Create a table and a graph showing Ellen's distance as it relates to the amount of time she runs.
   b. Write an equation to represent the relationship between the time she runs and the distance she runs.
   c. Is the equation from part b a direct variation equation? Explain your reasoning.
   d. If Ellen runs 13.1 miles to complete the half marathon, how long will it take her to finish the race?

LESSON 13-2 PRACTICE

For each representation below, tell whether the relationship is directly proportional or nonproportional.

13.

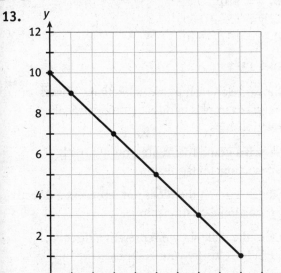

14.

a	b
0	0
2	200
4	400
6	600

15. $y = \frac{1}{3}x$

16. $d = 50 + 10h$

17.

x	0	5	10	15
y	1	26	51	76

18. Lupe reads 12 pages of her book every night.

19. Make sense of problems. Mrs. Tandy paid a $50 registration fee to join Fitness Club. She pays a monthly rate of $25. Write an equation to represent the total Mrs. Tandy pays for Fitness Club for *x* months. Determine if the equation you wrote represents a proportional relationship or a nonproportional relationship. Explain your reasoning.

ACTIVITY 13 PRACTICE
Write your answers on notebook paper.
Show your work.

Lesson 13-1

1. Consider the following equations.
   A: $y = 2x + 4$ B: $y = 2x$.
   a. What are the slope and y-intercept for equation A?
   b. What are the slope and y-intercept for equation B?

2. Kwame can type 25 words per minute.
   a. Create a table that represents the speed at which Kwame can type.
   b. Graph the data.
   c. Write an equation that that represents the relationship between the number of words Kwame can type and his typing speed.
   d. What is the slope in the equation you wrote in part c? What does the slope represent in this situation?
   e. What is the y-intercept in the equation you wrote in part c? What does the y-intercept represent in this situation?

3. Ashleigh is hiking at a rate of 4 miles per hour.
   a. Create a table to represent Ashleigh's distance after 1, 2, 3, 4, and 5 hours of hiking.
   b. Graph the data.
   c. Write an equation that represents the relationship between the time and her distance.
   d. What is the slope of the equation you wrote in part c? What does the slope represent in this situation?
   e. What is the y-intercept in the equation you wrote in part c? What does the y-intercept represent in this situation?

The tables show summer job earnings for Carolina and Monique. Use these tables for Item 4.

Carolina		Monique	
Hours	Earnings	Hours	Earnings
1	$55	1	$10
2	$60	2	$20
3	$65	3	$30
4	$70	4	$40
5	$75	5	$50

4. Which equation shows the relationship between the hours Carolina works, x, and her earnings, y?
   A. $y = \$5x$
   B. $y = \$10x$
   C. $y = \$5x + \$50$
   D. $y = 10x + \$10$

Lesson 13-2

5. Linear relationships are (*sometimes*, *always*, or *never*) examples of directly proportional relationships.

6. Sketch a graph that represents a directly proportional relationship.

7. Sketch a graph that does not represent a directly proportional relationship.

8. Does the table shown represent a direct variation? Justify your response.

x	y
4	7
6	8
9	11
12	14

9. Find the constant of variation for the directly proportional relationship represented by the data in the table. Then write the equation that describes the relationship.

x	y
1	0.2
4	0.8
8	1.6
12	2.4

10. Which of the equations below are examples of direct variation? Explain your choices.
    A. $y = 2x$
    B. $y = 3x + 5$
    C. $y = \dfrac{1}{2}x$
    D. $6x = y$

11. The number of cups of flour used in a recipe varies directly with the number of cups of milk used in the recipe. For each cup of milk used, 4 cups of flour are used. If *x* represents the number of cups of milk and *y* represents the number of cups of flour, which of the following graphs represents the relationship between cups of milk and cups of flour used in the recipe?

A.

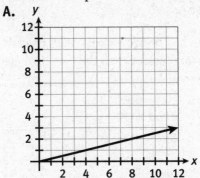

B.

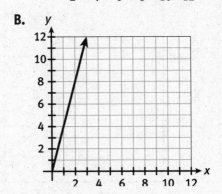

C.

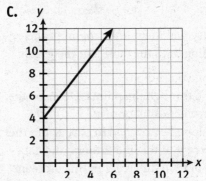

D.

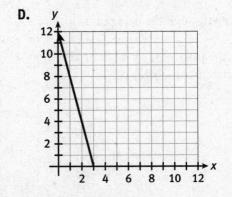

12. Tell whether the relationship shown is directly proportional or nonproportional. Explain your reasoning.

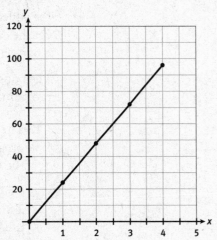

MATHEMATICAL PRACTICES
Reason Abstractly and Quantitatively

13. Explain how to recognize a directly proportional relationship in an equation, in a table, and in a graph. Use examples to support your responses.

The Athletic Booster Club at C. Brown High School publishes a fall sports program for the Athletic Department. The purpose of the program is to raise funds for a new scoreboard in the football stadium and to highlight each of the athletes participating in fall sports. The program contains interviews with coaches and athletes, schedules of games and other events, and brief biographies of each athlete and coach.

The booster club members must consider how much to charge for each program, and how much money can be raised.

1. The Finance Chairman has researched previous years' sales records and organized the results in the following table. Graph the data on a grid like the one shown.

Booster Club Program Sales	
Program Price	**Number of Programs Sold**
$2.50	1,625
$4.00	1,250
$5.00	1,000
$5.50	875
$7.50	375

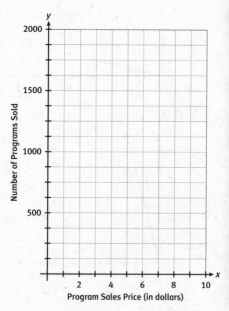

2. The relationship between the price and the number of programs sold is linear. Justify this statement using both the table and the graph.

3. Draw a line through the points on your graph.
   a. Determine the slope of the line through the points. Describe the meaning of the slope in this problem situation.
   b. Use the data in the table, the slope determined in part a, and the graph to determine the y-intercept of the line through the data points. Describe the meaning of the y-intercept in this problem situation.
   c. Write the equation of the line through the data points in slope-intercept form.
   d. Is the relationship between the price of the programs and the number of programs sold directly proportional? Justify your response.

4. Assume the slope of the line was changed to −425.
   a. Write the equation that could be used to represent this new relationship between the price of the programs and the number of programs sold.
   b. Describe the meaning of the slope in this new equation.
   c. Describe any changes in the graph that would result from this change in the slope.

5. Assume the y-intercept of the original line was changed to 3,000.
   a. Write the equation that could be used to represent this new relationship between the price of the programs and the number of programs sold.
   b. Describe the meaning of the y-intercept in this new situation.
   c. Describe any changes in the graph that would result from this change in the y-intercept.

6. L & L Printing will print the programs for $350 plus an additional $1.50 per program printed.
   a. Write the equation, in slope-intercept form, that could be used to determine the total cost, C, to the Booster Club for printing a given number of programs, p.
   b. Graph the equation on a grid like the one shown.

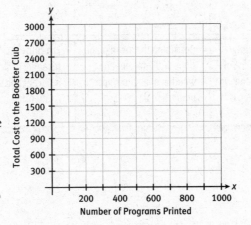

7. Red Baron Printing will print the programs for $1.82 each.
   a. If attendance for the football games averages 1,500 fans per game, which printing company should the Booster Club choose? Show your work and justify your response.
   b. Which printing company contract is an example of a direct variation? Justify your response.

Scoring Guide	Exemplary	Proficient	Emerging	Incomplete
	The solution demonstrates these characteristics:			
Mathematics Knowledge and Thinking (Items 1, 2, 3a-d, 4a-c, 5a-c, 6a-b, 7a-b)	• Precise and accurate understanding of linear equations, linear graphs, slope, intercept, and proportional relationships.	• Understanding of linear equations, linear graphs, slope, intercept, and proportional relationships.	• Some understanding of linear equations, linear graphs, slope, intercept, and proportional relationships, but with errors.	• Incorrect or incomplete understanding of linear equations, linear graphs, slope, intercept, and proportional relationships.
Problem Solving (Items 7a-b)	• An appropriate and efficient strategy that results in a correct answer.	• A strategy that may include unnecessary steps but results in a correct answer.	• A strategy that results in some incorrect answers.	• No clear strategy when solving problems.
Mathematical Modeling / Representations (Items 1, 3c, 4a, 5a, 6a-b)	• Clear and accurate representation of linear relationships with graphs and equations.	• Representing linear relationships with graphs and equations.	• Errors in representing linear relationships with graphs and equations.	• Inaccurate or incomplete representation of linear relationships with graphs and equations.
Reasoning and Communication (Items 2, 3a-b, 3d, 4b-c, 5b-c, 7a-b)	• Accurately and precisely describing the meaning of slope and intercept and whether a relationship is proportional.	• Describing the meaning of slope and intercept and whether a relationship is proportional.	• Errors in describing the meaning of slope and intercept and whether a relationship is proportional.	• An incomplete or inaccurate description of the meaning of slope and intercept and whether a relationship is proportional.

Graphing Systems of Linear Equations

Systems of Trees
Lesson 14-1 Understanding Solutions to Linear Systems

Learning Targets:

- Understand that solutions to systems of linear equations correspond to the points of intersection of their graphs.
- Solve systems of linear equations numerically and by graphing.
- Use systems of linear equations to solve real-world and mathematical problems.

SUGGESTED LEARNING STRATEGIES: Think-Pair-Share, Work Backwards, Graphic Organizer, Create Representations

Chip decided to upgrade the landscaping in his yard. He bought a 10-gallon mesquite tree and a 50-gallon desert willow and planted them. After one year he was shocked at the growth of both trees, so he measured their heights. The mesquite was 5 feet tall and the desert willow was 8 feet tall. The next year he measured again and found the mesquite was 6 feet, 6 inches tall and the desert willow was 8 feet, 8 inches tall.

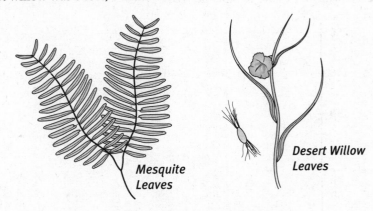

Mesquite Leaves

Desert Willow Leaves

1. List all the numerical information associated with each tree.

2. If the trees grew at a constant rate the first two years, how tall were they when Chip planted them?

3. Use the table below to help explain how the height of the mesquite tree compares to the height of the willow over time.

Year	Mesquite (in inches)	Willow (in inches)
0		
1		
2		
3		
4		
5		
6		
7		

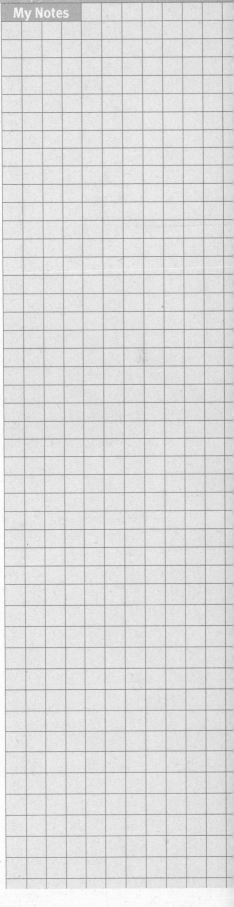

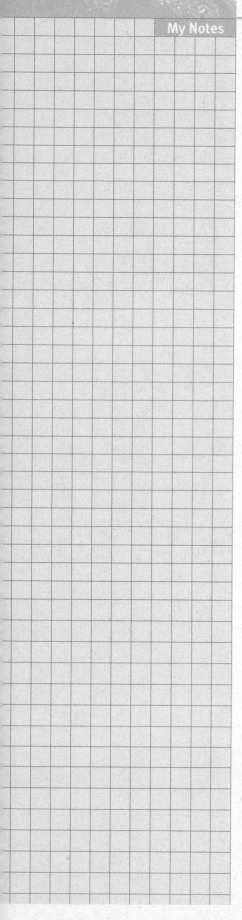

My Notes

4. Let *M* be the height of the mesquite tree in inches. Write a linear equation that could be used to determine the height of the tree in a given year, *t*.

5. Write a linear equation that could be used to determine the height, *W*, in inches of the desert willow in a given year, *t*.

6. **Model with mathematics.** Is it possible to use the equations you wrote to describe the growth of the two trees to predict the height of the trees at 1.5 years? Explain your reasoning.

7. Graph each of the equations on the grid below and use the graphs to determine in what year the mesquite will reach the same height as the desert willow. Be sure to label the axes.

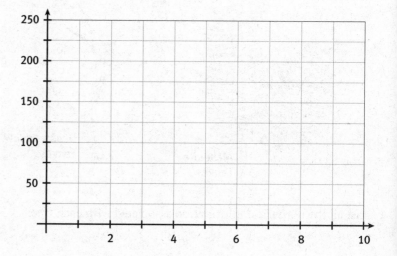

8. When the mesquite tree and the desert willow are the same height, what is true about the values of *W* and *M*?

9. Write and solve an equation to determine the value of t when the mesquite tree and the desert willow are the same height.

10. Describe the meaning of the value of t determined in Item 9.

11. How does the solution to the equation in Item 9 relate to the table in Item 3 and the graph in Item 7?

Equations M and W can together be described as a ***system of linear equations***. The ***solution to a system of linear equations*** will always be the point or set of points where the two lines intersect.

Systems of linear equations can also be solved numerically.

12. Create a table of values to determine the solution to the following system of equations.

$$\begin{cases} y = -x - 2 \\ y = \dfrac{2}{3}x + 3 \end{cases}$$

x	y_1	y_2
−6		
−5		
−4		
−3		
−2		
−1		
0		
1		

MATH TERMS

A **system of linear equations** is a collection of equations all considered simultaneously.

The word *linear* indicates that there will only be equations of lines in this collection.

A point, or set of points, is the **solution to a system of equations** in two variables when it makes both equations true.

READING MATH

y_1 is read "y sub 1" and refers to the y values from the first equation. y_2 refers to the y values from the second equation.

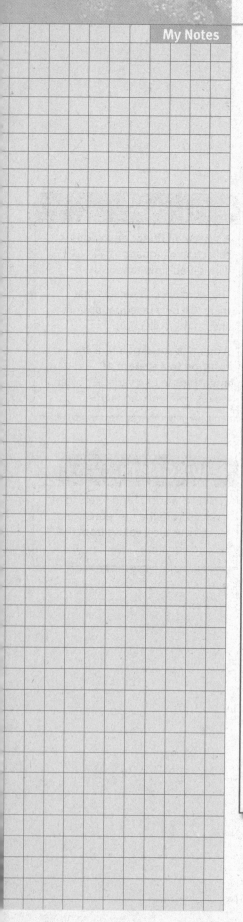

13. Determine which ordered pair in the set $\{(2, 2), (2, 3), (2, 4), (3,3)\}$ is the solution to the system of linear equations.

$$\begin{cases} y = -x + 5 \\ y = x + 1 \end{cases}$$

Check Your Understanding

14. Determine which of the points $\{(1, -2), (-1, 2), (1, 2), (-1, -2)\}$ are solutions to the system of equations.

$$\begin{cases} y = 3x - 5 \\ y = -\dfrac{1}{4}x - \dfrac{7}{4} \end{cases}$$

15. Create a table of values to determine the solution to the following system of equations.

$$\begin{cases} y = 5x + 4 \\ y = 2x + 1 \end{cases}$$

16. Complete the following table for each equation. Then graph each equation.

$$y = \frac{1}{2}x - 6 \quad \text{and} \quad y = -\frac{5}{3}x + \frac{8}{3}$$

x	y₁	y₂
−4		
−3		
−2		
−1		
0		
1		
2		
3		
4		

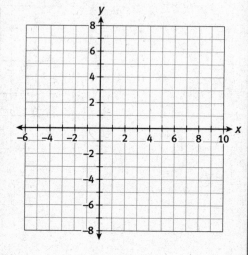

17. Use the table in Item 16 to determine at which value of x the values of y_1 and y_2 are the same.

18. Use the graph in Item 16 to determine at which value of x the values of y_1 and y_2 are the same.

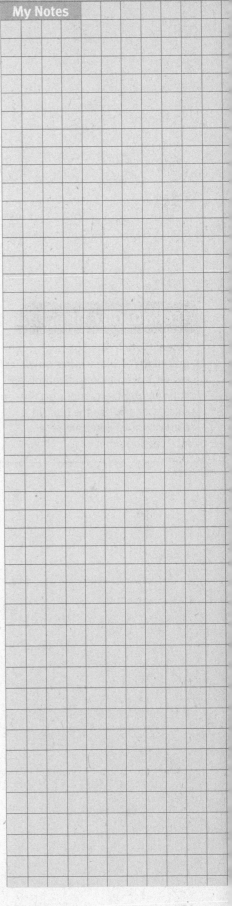

LESSON 14-1 PRACTICE

19. Create a table of values to determine the solution to the following system of equations.

$$\begin{cases} y = -x - 2 \\ y = \dfrac{2}{3}x + 3 \end{cases}$$

20. Determine which of the points $\{(1, -2), (-1, 2), (1, 2), (-1, -2)\}$, if any, are solutions to the system of equations.

$$\begin{cases} x = \dfrac{4}{5}y - 7 \\ 2x + y = -1 \end{cases}$$

21. Graph each of the equations below and use your graph to determine at which value of x the values of y are the same.

$$\begin{cases} 2x - 12y = -3 \\ x + 4y = -4 \end{cases}$$

The table below represents deposits to Joselyn's savings account and to Ben's savings account over the course of 5 weeks.

Week (W)	J's Account (in dollars)	B's Account (in dollars)
0	5	12
1	10	16
2	15	20
3	20	24

22. **a.** Let J be the amount of money in Joselyn's savings account. Write a linear equation that could be used to determine the amount of money in the account in a given week, W.
   b. **Reason abstractly.** Let B be the amount of money in Ben's savings account. Write a linear equation that could be used to determine the amount of money in the account in a given week, W.
   c. In what week will Joselyn and Ben have the same amount of money in their accounts? Explain your reasoning.

My Notes

Learning Targets:

- Convert linear equations into slope-intercept form.
- Solve systems of linear equations by graphing.
- Solve simple systems of linear equations by inspection.

SUGGESTED LEARNING STRATEGIES: Marking the Text, Create a Plan, Identify a Subtask, Discussion Group, Construct an Argument

The solution to a system of two linear equations will always be the point or points where the two lines intersect. So it is possible to solve systems of linear equations by graphing. To solve by graphing you must:

- Graph each line on the same coordinate plane.
- Determine the coordinates of the point where the lines cross.

1. Determine the solution to the following system of equations by graphing.

$$\begin{cases} y = 2x - 4 \\ y = -\frac{1}{2}x + 1 \end{cases}$$

TECHNOLOGY TIP

Often it is helpful to use a graphing calculator when solving systems of equations by graphing. You can graph equations on the calculator and use the built-in commands to determine the intersection point.

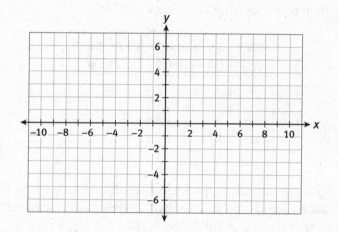

When graphing, it is helpful to have the equation in slope-intercept form: $y = mx + b$, where m is the slope and b is the y-intercept. When graphing an equation in this form, first plot the y-intercept $(0, b)$ and use the slope to move from the y-intercept and plot other points on the line. However, not all equations are written in slope-intercept form.

Example A

Solve $3x - 4y = 16$ for y.

Step 1: Use inverse operations. Subtract $3x$ from both sides.

$$3x - 4y = 16$$
$$\underline{-3x \qquad\quad -3x}$$
$$-4y = -3x + 16$$

Step 2: Use inverse operations. Divide both sides by -4.

$$\frac{-4y}{-4} = \frac{-3x}{-4} + \frac{16}{-4}$$

Solution: $y = \dfrac{3}{4}x - 4$

MATH TIP

To *solve for y* it is necessary to use inverse operations to isolate y on one side of the equal sign.

Try These A

Solve each of the following equations for y.

a. $x + y = 8$

b. $2x + y = 6$

c. $3y = -6x - 15$

d. $3x + 2y = 14$

e. $4x - 2y = 4$

2. Determine the solution to the following system of equations by graphing them on the grid provided.

$$\begin{cases} x + y = 4 \\ 4x - y = 1 \end{cases}$$

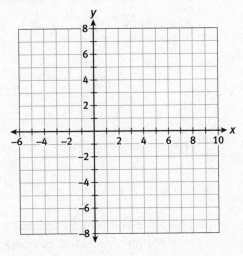

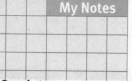

My Notes

3. Each of the three figures below is a graph of a system of equations. Identify each system of equations as having *one solution, no solution,* or *infinitely many solutions.* Justify your choices.

Graph 1

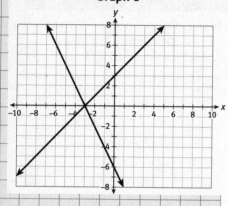

Graph 2

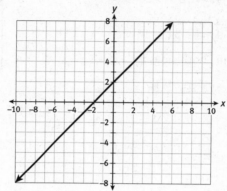

Graph 3

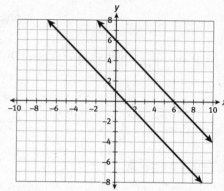

MATH TIP

Summarize in your own words how to use the slope and *y*-intercept of a pair of lines to determine if they intersect, coincide, or are parallel.

Often, it is possible to determine the solution to a system of equations by examining the equations carefully and *without* using a table or graphing.

4. For each system of equations shown below, carefully examine the system and make a conjecture as to the solution. Explain your reasoning.

a. $\begin{cases} 5x + 4y = 8 \\ 5x + 4y = -3 \end{cases}$

b. $\begin{cases} 3x + 2y = 4 \\ 6x + 4y = 8 \end{cases}$

c. Discuss in your groups and make a conjecture about the slopes and *y*-intercepts of lines that intersect.

d. Discuss in your groups and make a conjecture about the slopes and *y*-intercepts of lines that **coincide**.

ACADEMIC VOCABULARY

Coincide means to occur at the same time or to occupy the same place in space or time.

e. Discuss in your groups and make a conjecture about the slopes and *y*-intercepts of lines that are parallel.

My Notes

5. **Construct viable arguments.** Compare and contrast the advantages and disadvantages of using the numerical method and the graphing method to solve a system of equations. Given the option, which method would you choose? Why?

DISCUSSION GROUP TIPS

When discussing or presenting mathematical concepts with a partner or in a group, be sure to use precise terminology.

Check Your Understanding

Solve each of the following systems of equations by graphing.

6. $\begin{cases} y = -x - 1 \\ y = -5x - 17 \end{cases}$

7. $\begin{cases} y = \dfrac{1}{2}x + 4 \\ y = -\dfrac{3}{2}x - 4 \end{cases}$

8. Solve each of the following systems of equations without graphing. State your solution and the reason for the solution.

   a. $\begin{cases} x + y = 8 \\ x + y = 4 \end{cases}$

   b. $\begin{cases} 2x - 3y = -1 \\ y = \dfrac{2}{3}x + \dfrac{1}{3} \end{cases}$

9. Determine the solution to the following system of equations by graphing. Remember to solve each equation for y, if needed, before you begin.

$$\begin{cases} -3x + y = -4 \\ y = -x - 3 \end{cases}$$

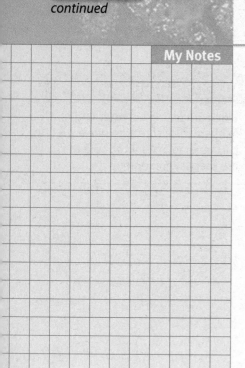

LESSON 14-2 PRACTICE

10. Solve by graphing.

$$\begin{cases} 2y = x + 8 \\ 2x - 4y = -16 \end{cases}$$

11. Explain (without graphing) why the system of equations below would not have infinitely many solutions.

$$\begin{cases} 2x - 4y = -1 \\ y = x - 1 \end{cases}$$

12. Graph the system of equations in Item 11 and verify that there is one unique solution.

13. Each of the three figures below is a graph of a system of equations. Identify each system of equations as having one *solution*, *no solution*, or *infinitely many solutions*. Justify your choices.

Graph 1

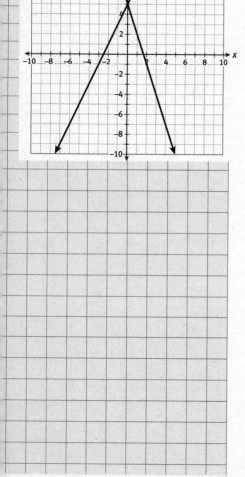

Graph 2

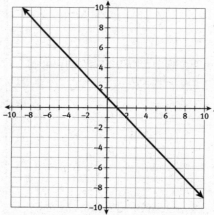

Graph 3

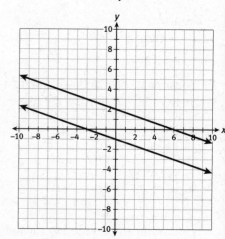

14. Use appropriate tools strategically. Create a table of values to determine the solution to the following system of equations.

$$\begin{cases} y = 5x - 3 \\ y = 2x - 6 \end{cases}$$

x	y_1	y_2
−4		
−3		
−2		
−1		
0		
1		
2		
3		

ACTIVITY 14 PRACTICE
Write your answers on notebook paper.
Show your work.

Lesson 14-1

Itmar was 63 inches tall in August at the start of eighth grade. His best friend, Megan, was 65 inches tall at that time. Itmar grew an average of one-half inch each month through May. Megan grew one-fourth of an inch each month through May.

1. Write two equations, one to show Itmar's height at any time during the school year and one to show Megan's. Use h for height and m to represent the number of months since August.

2. Graph each student's height from August to May.

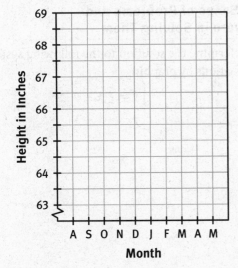

3. Will Itmar be taller than Megan by the end of eighth grade in May? Is there a time when their heights will be the same? Justify your reasoning.

4. Does the line through the points $(2, 2)$ and $(3, 4)$ intersect the line through the points $(-1, 5)$ and $(0, 7)$? Explain your response.

5. Determine which of the following points are solutions to the system of equations.
$$\begin{cases} 3x + 2y = 5 \\ x + 2y = 7 \end{cases}$$
   A. $(0, 3)$ **B.** $(-1, 4)$
   C. $(3, 0)$ **D.** $(4, -1)$

6. Determine which of the following points are solutions to the system of equations.
$$\begin{cases} 3x - y = -4 \\ 2x - 5y = 19 \end{cases}$$
   A. $(-3, 5)$ **B.** $(3, -5)$
   C. $(3, 5)$ **D.** $(-3, -5)$

7. Create a table of values to determine the solution to the following system of equations.

$$\begin{cases} y = 5x + 4 \\ y = 2x + 1 \end{cases}$$

x	y_1	y_2
−4		
−3		
−2		
−1		
0		
1		
2		
3		

Lesson 14-2

8. Solve each system of linear equations by graphing.

a. $\begin{cases} y = 3x + 2 \\ y = -2x - 8 \end{cases}$

b. $\begin{cases} x + y = -1 \\ 2x + 2y = 4 \end{cases}$

9. Determine the value of $x - y$ in the following system of equations.

$\begin{cases} 6x - 3y = 42 \\ 8x + 4y = -8 \end{cases}$

A. −5   **B.** 11
C. 5   **D.** −11

10. Solve $2y = 3x + 12$ for y.

11. Solve the following system of equations without graphing. State your solution and the reason for the solution.

$\begin{cases} x - 6y = -3 \\ 2x + 3y = 9 \end{cases}$

12. Determine the solution to the following system of equations by graphing. Remember to solve each equation for y before you begin.

$\begin{cases} 6x + 2y = -4 \\ 2x + y = -4 \end{cases}$

MATHEMATICAL PRACTICES
Make Sense of Problems and Persevere in Solving Them

13. Determine the solution to the following system of equations by graphing.

$\begin{cases} y = \dfrac{1}{3}x + 2 \\ y = -x - 3 \end{cases}$

What's the Point?

Lesson 15-1 Solving Linear Systems Algebraically

Learning Targets:

- Connect solutions to systems of linear equations to the points of intersection of their graphs.
- Solve systems of linear equations algebraically.

> **SUGGESTED LEARNING STRATEGIES:** Shared Reading, Marking the Text, Summarizing, Note Taking, Identify a Subtask, Discussion Group

The solution to a system of linear equations is the point where the two lines intersect. The intersection point is a solution to both equations in the system. Algebraically, this point can be determined by calculating when the two expressions for y will be equal to each other.

Example A

Solve the system of equations algebraically.
$$\begin{cases} y = 0.25x - 1 \\ y = -x + 4 \end{cases}$$

Step 1: Set the expressions equal to each other.

$$0.25x - 1 = -x + 4$$

Step 2: Solve for x.

$$0.25x - 1 = -x + 4$$
$$\underline{+ x \qquad\qquad + x}$$
$$1.25x - 1 = 4$$
$$\underline{\quad + 1 \quad + 1}$$
$$\frac{1.25x}{1.25} = \frac{5}{1.25}$$
$$x = 4$$

Step 3: Substitute x into one of the original equations, and solve for y.

$$y = 0.25(4) - 1$$
$$y = 1 - 1$$
$$y = 0$$

Step 4: Check your solution using the other equation.

$$y = -x + 4$$
$$0 = -4 + 4$$
$$0 = 0$$

Solution: Write the solution as an ordered pair.

(4, 0); The lines intersect at the point (4, 0).

My Notes

Try These A

Solve each system of equations algebraically. Show all steps. Remember to write the solution as an ordered pair.

a. $\begin{cases} y = \dfrac{3}{2}x + 1 \\ y = 2x + 2 \end{cases}$ **b.** $\begin{cases} y = 4x + 1 \\ y = -2x - 5 \end{cases}$ **c.** $\begin{cases} y = 5x + 1 \\ y = -4 \end{cases}$

Another method for solving systems of equations involves **substitution**. This method is similar to the algebraic method you learned in the last example.

> **MATH TIP**
>
> Solve for a variable with a coefficient of 1.

Example B

Solve the system of equations using substitution.

$$\begin{cases} x + y = 8 \\ 3x + 2y = 14 \end{cases}$$

Step 1:   Solve one equation for one of the variables.

$$\begin{array}{r} x + y = 8 \\ -x \qquad -x \\ \hline y = -x + 8 \end{array}$$

Step 2:   Substitute this expression into the other equation.

$$3x + 2y = 14$$
$$3x + 2(-x + 8) = 14$$

Step 3:   Solve the resulting equation for the remaining variable.

$$3x + 2(-x + 8) = 14$$
$$3x - 2x + 16 = 14$$
$$x + 16 = 14$$
$$\begin{array}{r} -16 \qquad -16 \\ \hline x = -2 \end{array}$$

Step 4:   Substitute into one of the original equations to find the corresponding value of the other variable.

$$\begin{array}{r} -2 + y = 8 \\ +2 \qquad +2 \\ \hline y = 10 \end{array}$$

Step 5:   Check the solution in both equations.

$$\begin{array}{ll} x + y = 8 & \qquad 3x + 2y = 14 \\ -2 + 10 = 8 & \qquad 3(-2) + 2(10) = 14 \\ 8 = 8 & \qquad -6 + 20 = 14 \\ & \qquad 14 = 14 \end{array}$$

Solution: Write the solution as an ordered pair.
$(-2, 10)$; The lines intersect at the point $(-2, 10)$.

My Notes

Try These B
Use substitution to solve the systems.

a. $\begin{cases} y = 5x \\ x + y = -6 \end{cases}$

b. $\begin{cases} x + 2y = 8 \\ 3x - 4y = 4 \end{cases}$

Systems of linear equations can also be solved using *elimination*. In the elimination method, one variable is *eliminated*, creating an equation in one variable that can be solved using inverse operations.

> **MATH TIP**
>
> The *elimination method* is sometimes called *linear combination*.

Example C

Solve the system of equations using elimination. $\begin{cases} 7x + 5y = -1 \\ 4x - y = -16 \end{cases}$

Step 1: Decide which variable to eliminate. Then, use multiplication to create equations in which at least two variable terms are opposites. Select y to eliminate, and multiply the second equation by 5 so that the y terms are opposites.

$\begin{cases} 7x + 5y = -1 \\ 4x - y = -16 \end{cases}$ → $\begin{cases} 7x + 5y = -1 \\ 5(4x - y) = 5(-16) \end{cases}$ → $\begin{cases} 7x + 5y = -1 \\ 20x - 5y = -80 \end{cases}$

> **MATH TIP**
>
> Keep the equation balanced by multiplying the factor with each term in the equation.

Step 2: Add the two equations and solve for the remaining variable.

$$7x + 5y = -1$$
$$\underline{20x - 5y = -80}$$
$$27x + 0y = -81$$

Step 3: Solve the resulting equation.

$$27x + 0y = -81$$
$$\frac{27x}{27} = \frac{-81}{27}$$
$$x = -3$$

Step 4: Substitute into one of the original equations to determine the value of the second variable.

$$7x + 5y = -1$$
$$7(-3) + 5y = -1$$
$$-21 + 5y = -1$$
$$\underline{+21 \qquad\quad +21}$$
$$\frac{5y}{5} = \frac{20}{5}$$
$$y = 4$$

Step 5: Check the solution in both equations.

$$7x + 5y = -1 \qquad\qquad 4x - y = -16$$
$$7(-3) + 5(4) = -1 \qquad 4(-3) - 4 = -16$$
$$-21 + 20 = -1 \qquad\quad -12 - 4 = -16$$
$$-1 = -1 \qquad\qquad\quad -16 = -16$$

Solution: Write the solution as an ordered pair.

$(-3, 4)$; The lines intersect at the point $(-3, 4)$.

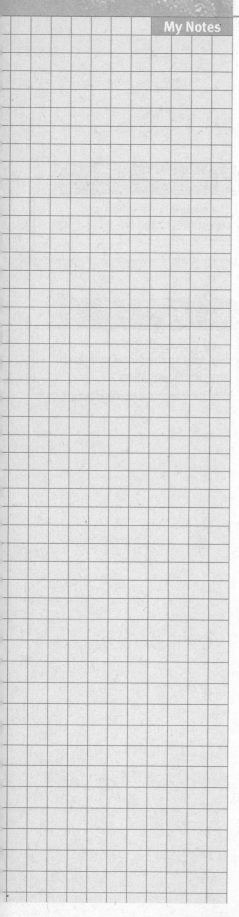

My Notes

Try These C

Use elimination/linear combination to solve the following.

a. $\begin{cases} 3x + 4y = 17 \\ 5x - 4y = 7 \end{cases}$

b. $\begin{cases} 3x - 4y = 12 \\ 5x + 8y = 20 \end{cases}$

c. $\begin{cases} 18x + 36y = -42 \\ 11x + 9y = -30 \end{cases}$

Check Your Understanding

Solve each system. Explain why you chose a particular solution method.

1. $\begin{cases} y = 3x - 4 \\ 3x + y = -4 \end{cases}$

2. $\begin{cases} 4x + 3y = 19 \\ 3x - 4y = 8 \end{cases}$

3. Sara solved a system of equations algebraically. Her result was $7 = -4$. All of her work was correct. Describe the graph of the system of equations. Explain your reasoning.

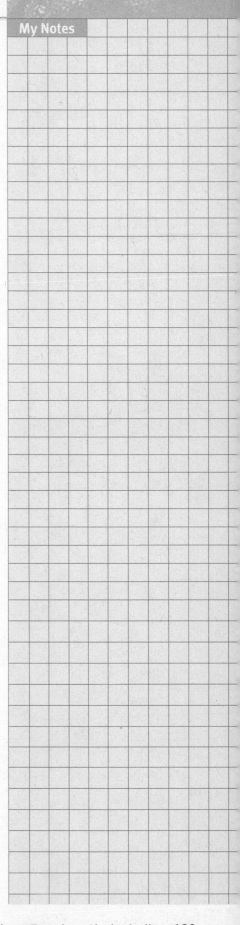

LESSON 15-1 PRACTICE

4. Solve by elimination/linear combination:

$$\begin{cases} 3x + 7y = -1 \\ 4x - 3y = 11 \end{cases}$$

5. Solve by substitution:

$$\begin{cases} y = -3x \\ 2x - 3y = 22 \end{cases}$$

6. Solve using the method of your choice (numerical, graphing, substitution, elimination/linear combination):

$$\begin{cases} y = \frac{1}{2}x - 8 \\ 2x + 5y = -13 \end{cases}$$

7. Write a system of linear equations with no solution. Describe the appearance of the graph.

8. **Reason abstractly.** Write a system of linear equations that has a solution of (2, 7). Explain how you determined such a system.

My Notes

Learning Targets:
- Write linear systems to solve real-world and mathematical problems.
- Solve systems of linear equations algebraically.

SUGGESTED LEARNING STRATEGIES: Shared Reading, Close Reading, Marking the Text, Summarizing, Note Taking, Identify a Subtask, Discussion Group

Systems of linear equations can also be used to solve real-world and mathematical problems.

Example A

A group of 6 youths and 5 adults sign up to take a karate class for a total cost of $147. Another group of 4 youths and 4 adults pay a total cost of $108. What was the cost for 1 adult and the cost for 1 youth to take the class?

Step 1: Define your variables.
Let x = cost for 1 youth; y = cost for 1 adult

Step 2: Write one equation to represent the first karate class.
$$6x + 5y = 147$$

Write another equation to represent the second karate class.
$$4x + 4y = 108$$

Step 3: Solve the system. Select y to eliminate. The LCM of the coefficients of the y terms is 20, so multiply the first equation by -4 and the second equation by 5.

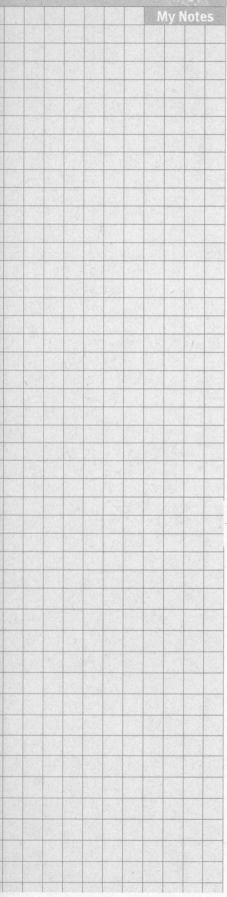

$$\begin{cases} 6x + 5y = 147 \\ 4x + 4y = 108 \end{cases} \longrightarrow \begin{cases} -4(6x + 5y) = -4(147) \\ 5(4x + 4y) = 5(108) \end{cases} \longrightarrow \begin{cases} -24x - 20y = - \\ 20x + 20y = 540 \end{cases}$$

$$\begin{array}{ll} -24x - 20y = -588 & 6x + 5y = 147 \\ \underline{20x + 20y = 540} & 6(12) + 5y = 147 \\ \dfrac{-4x}{-4} = \dfrac{-48}{-4} & 72 + 5y = 147 \\ & \underline{-72 \qquad\quad -72} \\ x = 12 & \dfrac{5y}{5} = \dfrac{75}{5} \\ & y = 15 \end{array}$$

Step 4: Check the solution in both equations.

$$6x + 5y = 147 \qquad\qquad 4x + 4y = 108$$
$$6(12) + 5(15) = 147 \qquad 4(12) + 4(15) = 108$$
$$72 + 75 = 147 \qquad\qquad 48 + 60 = 108$$
$$147 = 147 \qquad\qquad\qquad 108 = 108$$

Solution: Interpret the solution in the context of the problem. It costs $12 for a youth to take the class and $15 for an adult to take the class.

Try These A

Use a system of linear equations to solve the following.

a. During a sale on winter clothing, Jody bought 2 scarves and 4 pairs of gloves for $43. Amanda bought 2 scarves and 2 pairs of gloves for $30. How much does one scarf cost? How much for one pair of gloves?

b. Peter placed an order with an online nursery for 6 apple trees and 5 azaleas and the order came to $147. The next order for 3 apple trees and 4 azaleas came to $96. What was the cost for each apple tree and for each azalea?

c. At the end of the 2010 baseball season, the Cincinnati Reds and the New York Yankees together had won a total of 32 World Series. At the end of that season, the Yankees had won 5.4 times as many World Series as the Reds. How many World Series did each team win?

d. Complementary angles are two angles whose measures have a sum of 90 degrees. Angles x and y are complementary. The measure of angle x is 24 degrees greater than the measure of angle y. Determine the measures of angles x and y.

Check Your Understanding

1. Mara bought 8 boxes of pencils and 3 packages of pens for $24. At the same store, Elaine bought 4 boxes of pencils and 6 packages of pens for $30. How much does one box of pencils cost? How much does one package of pens cost?

2. The difference of two numbers is 18. The sum of the numbers is 84. What is the larger number? What is the smaller number?

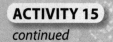

My Notes

LESSON 15-2 PRACTICE

Use a system of linear equations to solve each problem.

3. A group of 3 adults and 5 children pay a total of $52 for movie tickets. A group of 2 adults and 4 children pay a total of $38 for tickets. What is the cost of one adult ticket? What is the cost of one child ticket?

4. The sum of two angle measures is 130 degrees. The difference in the two angle measures is 12 degrees. What are the two angle measures?

5. Mandy buys 5 reams of paper and 3 ink cartridges for $131. Kevin buys 2 reams of paper and 5 ink cartridges for $174. How much does one ream of paper cost? How much does one ink cartridge cost?

6. Carlisle thinks of two numbers. One number is 14 less than twice the other number. The two numbers sum to 160. What is the smaller number?

7. **Critique the reasoning of others.** Jacob is asked to solve the problem below:

Kayla is 9 years older than twice Hannah's age. If the difference in their ages is 16, how old is Kayla? How old is Hannah?

Jacob finds Hannah's age to be 16 years. Is he correct? Explain.

Solving Systems of Linear Equations Algebraically
What's the Point?

ACTIVITY 15
continued

ACTIVITY 15 PRACTICE

Write your answers on notebook paper.
Show your work.

Lesson 15-1

1. Solve by substitution.

a. $\begin{cases} y = -\dfrac{1}{2}x + 5 \\ 3x - y = 2 \end{cases}$

b. $\begin{cases} y = -3x + 6 \\ 3x + y = 5 \end{cases}$

c. $\begin{cases} 2x + y = 8 \\ 2x - 3y = 24 \end{cases}$

2. Solve by elimination/linear combination.

a. $\begin{cases} 3x + 4y = 17 \\ 5x - 4y = 7 \end{cases}$

b. $\begin{cases} 8x - 2y = 2 \\ 6x + y = -6 \end{cases}$

c. $\begin{cases} 2x + 2y = 14 \\ x - 3y = -1 \end{cases}$

3. Solve using the method of your choice.

a. $\begin{cases} 3x + 4y = 8 \\ y = -\dfrac{3}{4}x + 2 \end{cases}$

b. $\begin{cases} y = -\dfrac{1}{2}x + 5 \\ 3x - y = 2 \end{cases}$

c. $\begin{cases} 4x - 7y = 10 \\ 3x + 2y = -7 \end{cases}$

4. Describe when a linear system is easiest to solve by each method.
   a. setting expressions equal to each other
   b. the substitution method
   c. elimination/linear combination

5. The system below is not a linear system, but it can still be solved using the methods from this activity.

$$\begin{cases} \dfrac{3}{x} + \dfrac{1}{y} = 4 \\ \dfrac{6}{x} - \dfrac{2}{y} = -2 \end{cases}$$

   a. Let $u = \dfrac{1}{x}$ and $v = \dfrac{1}{y}$. Rewrite the system above using the variables u and v. Is the resulting system linear?
   b. Solve the system from part a for u and v.
   c. What is the solution to the original system? Explain how you determined the solution.

6. The solution to a linear system is $(3, 0)$. One of the equations of the system is $x - y = 3$. Which could be the other equation?
   A. $y = x + 3$
   B. $3x - y = 6$
   C. $x + y = 3$
   D. $-y = 3 - x$

Lesson 15-2

7. The Adventure Shoe Company manufactures two types of shoes, athletic shoes and hiking shoes. The cost of manufacturing 20 pairs of athletic shoes and 10 pairs of hiking shoes is $750. If 25 pairs of athletic shoes and 20 pairs of hiking shoes were manufactured, the cost would be $1,200. How much does it cost to manufacture each type of shoe?
    A. $20 for each pair of athletic shoes and $35 for each pair of hiking shoes
    B. $25 for each pair of athletic shoes and $30 for each pair of hiking shoes
    C. $24 for each pair of athletic shoes and $27 for each pair of hiking shoes
    D. $35 for each pair of athletic shoes and $20 for each pair of hiking shoes

8. The sum of two numbers is 24. The difference between the greater number and twice the smaller number is 18. Find the *greater* number.

9. Michael buys 3 notebooks and 4 packages of highlighters for $12. Amy buys 6 notebooks and 2 packages of highlighters for $15. What is the cost of one notebook? What is the cost of one package of highlighters?

10. Karen buys 5 cups of coffee and 2 bagels for $26. Kenneth buys 3 cups of coffee and 3 bagels for $21. How much does one cup of coffee cost? How much does one bagel cost?

11. Judy pays $29 for 8 gallons of gas and 2 bottles of water. Carmen pays $45 for 12 gallons of gas and 4 bottles of water. How much does one gallon of gas cost? How much does one bottle of water cost?

12. Christie's average monthly expenses are $450 less than half of her monthly income. If the sum of her average monthly expenses and monthly income is $3,600, what is her monthly income?

13. Today, Hector is 22 years older than his sister. In 5 years, he will be 3 times as old as she will be. How old are Hector and his sister today?

14. A jar is full of 100 coins. All of the coins are either nickels or dimes.
    a. The value of the coins is $6.35. Write a linear system representing this situation.
    b. Solve the system to determine how many of each type of coin is in the jar.
    c. Suppose the value of the coins was $6.30. Explain how you can determine the number of each type of coin without solving another system of equations.
    d. Suppose the value of the coins was $6.40. Explain how you can determine the number of each type of coin without solving another system of equations.

15. Consider the jar of 100 coins from Item 14. Suppose that the coins were all dimes and quarters, with a value of $15.75.
    a. Write a system to represent this situation.
    b. Solve the system. Explain how the solution of the system shows that the coins cannot have the value as described.

MATHEMATICAL PRACTICES
Reason Abstractly and Quantitatively

16. Explain how a linear system that represents a real-world situation can have a solution, but the corresponding situation has no solution. Give an example and describe why the numerical solution does not make sense in the context of the situation.

Solving Systems of Linear Equations

SUPPLY AND DEMAND

When something is popular and many people need or want to buy it, the price goes up. Items that no one wants are marked down to a lower price.

The change in an item's price and the amount available to buy are the basis of the concept of *supply and demand* in economics. Demand is the number of things people are willing to buy at a particular price. Supply refers to the number of things the manufacturer is willing to make at a particular price. The price that the customer pays is based on both supply and demand.

Suppose that during a six-month period, the supply and demand for a popular gaming system in a certain city has been tracked and approximated by the following system of equations, where x represents the number of gaming systems (in thousands) and y represents the price per gaming system.

- Demand equation: $0.7x + y = 340$
- Supply equation: $-1.5x + y = 320$

1. Solve the system algebraically to determine the balance point between supply and demand.

2. At about what price do the supply and demand balance?

3. About how many gaming systems is the manufacturer willing to supply at that price?

During the same 6-month period in a different city, the supply and demand for the same gaming system is represented by the following system of equations.

- Demand equation: $1.4x + 2y = 800$
- Supply equation: $-1.5x + y = 320$

4. Solve the system by graphing to determine the balance point between the supply and demand in this city.

5. At about what price do the supply and demand balance?

6. About how many gaming systems is the manufacturer willing to supply at that price?

The manufacturer will supply gaming systems to a third city based on the supply equation shown below.

- Supply equation for first two cities: $-1.5x + y = 320$
- Supply equation for third city: $3x - 2y = 370$

7. At what price will the manufacturer supply all three cities with the same number of gaming systems? You may solve either algebraically or graphically. Show all work and explain your response.

Scoring Guide	Exemplary	Proficient	Emerging	Incomplete
	The solution demonstrates these characteristics:			
Mathematics Knowledge and Thinking (Items 1, 2, 3, 4, 5, 6, 7)	• Precise and accurate understanding of solving systems of linear equations algebraically or by graphing.	• An understanding of solving systems of linear equations algebraically or by graphing.	• Some understanding of solving systems of linear equations algebraically or by graphing.	• Incorrect or incomplete understanding of solving systems of linear equations algebraically or by graphing.
Problem Solving (Items 1, 4)	• An appropriate and efficient strategy that results in a correct answer.	• A strategy that may include unnecessary steps but results in a correct answer.	• A strategy that results in some incorrect answers.	• No clear strategy when solving problems.
Mathematical Modeling / Representations (Items 4, 7)	• Clear and accurate representation of systems of linear equations with graphs and equations.	• Representing systems of linear equations with graphs and equations.	• Errors in representing systems of linear equations with graphs and equations.	• Inaccurate or incomplete representation of systems of linear equations.
Reasoning and Communication (Items 2, 3, 5, 6, 7)	• Accurately and precisely communicating the numerical or graphical solution as a real-world result.	• Describing the numerical or graphical solution as a real-world result.	• Errors in describing the numerical or graphical solution as a real-world result.	• An incomplete or inaccurate description of the numerical or graphical solution as a real-world result.

Geometry

Unit Overview

In this unit you will continue your study of angles and triangles and explore the Pythagorean Theorem. You will investigate 2- and 3-dimensional figures and apply formulas to determine the area and volume of those figures. You will explore rigid transformations of figures, including translations, rotations, and reflections of two-dimensional figures.

Key Terms

As you study this unit, add these and other terms to your math notebook. Include in your notes your prior knowledge of each word, as well as your experiences in using the word in different mathematical examples. If needed, ask for help in pronouncing new words and add information on pronunciation to your math notebook. It is important that you learn new terms and use them correctly in your class discussions and in your problem solutions.

Academic Vocabulary

- alternate
- transform

Math Terms

- angle
- ray
- complementary angles
- supplementary angles
- congruent
- transversal
- alternate exterior angles
- alternate interior angles
- corresponding angles
- vertical angles
- exterior angle of a triangle
- remote interior angle
- diagonal
- transformation
- preimage
- image
- translation
- reflection
- line of reflection
- equidistant
- rotation
- center of rotation
- composition of transformations
- similar figures
- similarity statement
- proportion
- scale factor
- dilation
- center of dilation
- scale factor of dilation
- hypotenuse
- legs
- Pythagorean Theorem
- surface area
- lateral area

ESSENTIAL QUESTIONS

? What are transformations and how are they useful in solving real-world problems?

? How are two- and three-dimensional figures related?

EMBEDDED ASSESSMENTS

These assessments, following activities 17, 19, 21, 24, and 26, will give you an opportunity to demonstrate how you can use your understanding of angles, triangles, transformation, and geometric formulas to solve problems.

Embedded Assessment 1:

Angle Measures   p. 229

Embedded Assessment 2:

Rigid Transformations   p. 263

Embedded Assessment 3:

Similarity and Dilations   p. 293

Embedded Assessment 4:

The Pythagorean Theorem   p. 325

Embedded Assessment 5:

Surface Area and Volume   p. 353

Getting Ready

**Write your answers on notebook paper.
Show your work.**

1. Give the coordinates of points *A*, *B*, *C*, and *D* on the graph below.

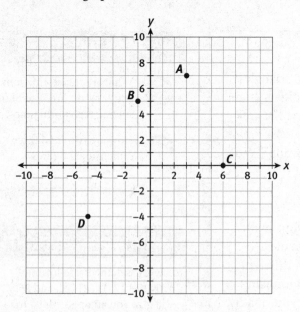

2. On the grid below, draw a square that has (−2, 4) and (3, −1) as two of its vertices. Label the other two vertices.

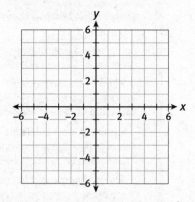

3. Define the following terms:
   a. acute triangle
   b. right triangle
   c. obtuse triangle

4. Write three ratios equivalent to $\frac{2}{5}$.

5. Find the value of *x* in each of the following.
   a. $\frac{2}{3} = \frac{6}{x}$ b. $\frac{4}{7} = \frac{x}{21}$

6. Find the perimeter or circumference of each of the figures below.

   a.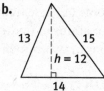

   b.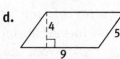

   c.
   d.

7. Find the area of each figure in Item 6.

8. Explain using specific formulas how you could find the area of the shaded area of the figure below.

Angle-Pair Relationships

The Winning Angle

Lesson 16-1 Complementary and Supplementary Angles

Learning Targets:

- Identify and determine the measure of complementary angles.
- Identify and determine the measure of supplementary angles.

> **SUGGESTED LEARNING STRATEGIES:** Visualization, Create Representations, Graphic Organizer, Identify a Subtask

Bob Toose, football coach and geometry teacher at Johnny Unitas High School, names his football plays after different geometric terms. He knows that the players from other schools won't know what is coming at them with these names.

Coach Toose gives playbook quizzes to make sure his players know their plays. A portion of one of his quizzes is below.

1. Match each play shown at the right with the mathematical term that best describes it. Draw a line to connect the plays and the terms.

   Angle

   Perpendicular Lines

   Parallel Lines

   Right Angle

My Notes

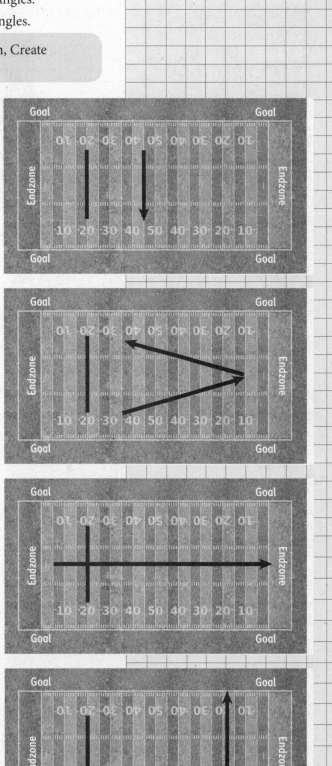

My Notes

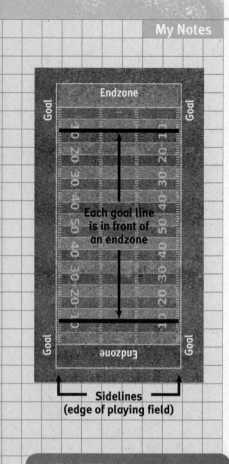

Each goal line is in front of an endzone

Sidelines
(edge of playing field)

MATH TERMS

An **angle** is the union of two rays with a common endpoint called the vertex.

A ray is part of a line with one endpoint. It extends indefinitely in one direction.

X ●————————●→ Y

Ray *XY* can be written $\overrightarrow{XY}$. Its endpoint is *X* and it extends forever through point *Y*.

Coach Toose is very particular about the routes that his players run. He told his receiver that this "corner" route needed to be run at a 50° angle to the sideline of the end zone.

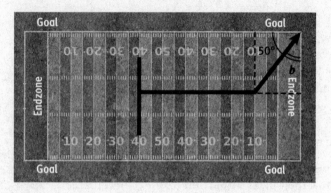

2. What is the measure of angle *b* in the diagram above?

3. Two angles are ***complementary*** if the sum of their measures is 90°. Explain why these two angles can be classified as complementary.

4. Coach Toose wanted his players to run other corner routes as well. Identify the ***angle*** complementary to the one listed. Draw a diagram to illustrate the angle and its complement.
  a. 20°   **b.** 73°

5. **Make use of structure.** Shown below is an example of two pairs of angles. Compare and contrast the angle pairs.

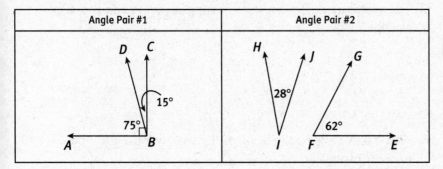

Angle Pair #1	Angle Pair #2

Make notes about the math terms and academic vocabulary used in Example A below and other examples that follow. Review your notes and use new vocabulary when you write and discuss your responses to items.

Example A

The measure of angle A is $(3x)°$ and the measure of its complement, angle B, is $(x + 6)°$. Determine the measures of the angles.

Step 1: Write an equation that shows the relationship between $\angle A$ and $\angle B$.

The sum of the angle measures is $90°$. $m\angle A + m\angle B = 90°$.
Substitute the expressions for the
angle measures. $3x + x + 6 = 90$

Step 2: Solve the equation.

Original equation $3x + x + 6 = 90$
Combine like terms. $4x + 6 = 90$
Subtract 6 from both sides. $4x + 6 - 6 = 90 - 6$
Simplify. $4x = 84$
Divide both sides by 4. $\dfrac{4x}{4} = \dfrac{84}{4}$
Simplify. $x = 21$

Step 3: Determine the measure of the two angles.

$$m\angle A = (3x)° = (3 \cdot 21)° = 63°$$
$$m\angle B = (x + 6)° = (21 + 6)° = 27°$$

Solution: $m\angle A = 63°$, and $m\angle B = 27°$.

Try These A

Angle P and angle Q are complementary. Determine the measures of the angles.

a. $m\angle P = (2x - 5)°$ and $m\angle Q = (x + 20)°$
b. $m\angle P = (x + 4)°$ and $m\angle Q = (5x - 4)°$

My Notes

Another route that Coach Toose has his players run is a "post" route. The route can be used to show *supplementary* angles.

6. Tell what it means for angles to be supplementary and sketch an example below.

7. This "post" route is seen below as it passes over the goal line. Give the measure of angle *d*.

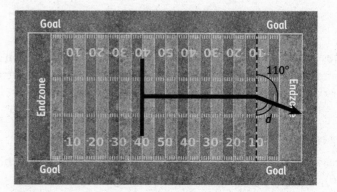

8. Coach Toose's team runs a variety of "post" routes. Identify the angle supplementary to the one listed. Draw a diagram to illustrate the angle and its supplement.

a. 20°   **b.** 153.1°

9. One of Coach Toose's players claims that two angles do not need to be adjacent to be supplementary. Draw a pair of nonadjacent supplementary angles and explain why they are supplementary.

10. The measures of two supplementary angles are $(x + 1)°$ and $(2x - 1)°$.
    a. Write an equation that shows the relationship between the two angle measures and determine the value of x.

    b. Determine the measure of the two angles.

Check Your Understanding

11. Determine the complement and/or supplement of each angle. If it is not possible, explain.
    a. $57.2°$ b. $93°$

12. Determine whether angles with measures $47°$ and $53°$ are complementary. Explain why or why not.

13. Determine whether angles with measures $37°$ and $143°$ are supplementary. Explain why or why not.

LESSON 16-1 PRACTICE

14. Determine the measure of two *congruent*, complementary angles.

15. Draw a pair of adjacent, complementary angles.

16. Angle C and angle D are complementary. The measure of angle C is $(2x)°$ and the measure of angle D is $(3x)°$. Determine the measure of the two angles. Show the work that leads to your answer.

17. Angle E and angle F are supplementary. The measure of angle E is $(x + 10)°$ and the measure of angle F is $(x + 40)°$. Determine the measure of the two angles. Show the work that leads to your answer.

18. **Construct viable arguments.** Determine whether the following statement is true or false. Justify your reasoning. "Two right angles are always supplementary."

> **MATH TERMS**
>
> Angles that have the same measure are called **congruent**.

My Notes

Learning Targets:

- Determine the measure of angles formed by parallel lines and transversals.
- Identify angle pairs formed by parallel lines and transversals.

SUGGESTED LEARNING STRATEGIES: Predict and Confirm, Think-Pair-Share, Interactive Word Wall, Graphic Organizer

The coach uses a diagram like the one below to show plays to his team. Your teacher will give you tape to recreate these same play lines on your desk or on a piece of paper.

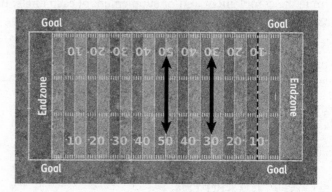

Now using the tape, add a "slant" route to your diagram and label the angles as seen below.

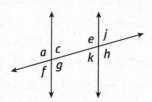

Coach Toose calls this route the "*transversal*."

1. On the above diagram, mark each of the eight angles formed by the parallel lines and the transversal as acute or obtuse.

2. Measure angle *j* on your diagram.

3. Without measuring, predict which other angles are the same size as angle *j* and list them below.

4. Now measure these angles. Were your predictions correct?

5. What is true about the measures of the remaining angles?

MATH TERMS

A **transversal** is a line that intersects two or more other lines to form eight or more angles.

6. Using the diagram that you made on your desk and your observations in the previous items, what can you say about the measures of the angles formed by two parallel lines cut by a transversal?

In the diagram, $\overline{CD} \parallel \overline{EG}$.

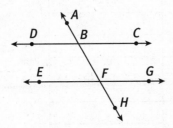

7. Determine whether each pair of angles is congruent or supplementary.
   a. $\angle ABD$ and $\angle CBH$
   b. $\angle ABD$ and $\angle EFH$
   c. $\angle DBH$ and $\angle CBF$
   d. $\angle ABC$ and $\angle BFG$
   e. $\angle CBF$ and $\angle EFB$

8. Critique the reasoning of others. In the diagram, $m\angle CBF = (x + 10)°$ and $m\angle EFB = (3x - 54)°$. Students were asked to determine the value of x. One student's solution is shown below. Determine whether or not the solution is correct. If it is correct, explain the reasoning used by the student. If it is incorrect, identify the student's error and explain to the student how to correctly solve the problem.

$$x + 10 + 3x - 54 = 180$$
$$4x - 44 = 180$$
$$4x = 224$$
$$x = 56$$

READING MATH

The symbol $\parallel$ is used to indicate parallel lines. $\overline{CD} \parallel \overline{EG}$ is read "line CD is parallel to line EG."

READING MATH

To read this angle, say "angle *ABC*," "angle *CBA*," or "angle *B*."

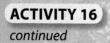

My Notes

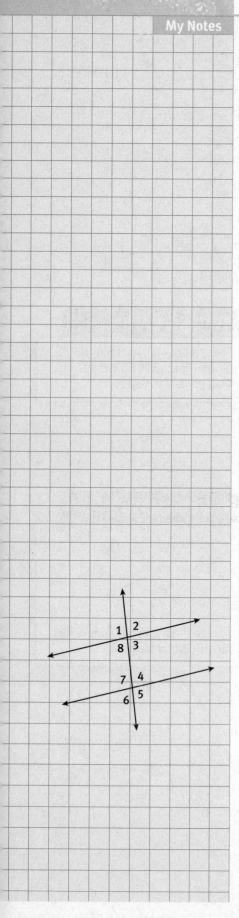

Check Your Understanding

9. In the diagram, $\overline{JC} \parallel \overline{SO}$. Copy and complete the table to find the missing angle measures.

Angle	Measure
∠RHC	125°
∠JHK	
∠RHJ	
∠CHK	
∠HKS	
∠SKU	
∠OKU	
∠HKO	

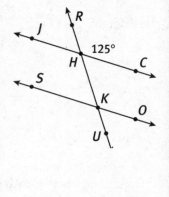

Each diagram shows parallel lines cut by a transversal. Solve for the value of x.

10.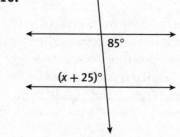

11.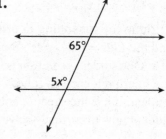

12. Refer to the diagram in the My Notes section.
   a. What does the term *exterior* mean in everyday language? Give at least two examples.

   b. Which angles in the figure do you think are exterior angles? Explain.

   c. What does the term *interior* mean in everyday language? Give at least two examples.

   d. Which angles in the figure do you think are interior angles? Explain.

My Notes

13. Alternate angles are on opposite sides of the transversal and have a different vertex. There are two pairs of angles in the diagram that are referred to as **alternate exterior angles** and two pairs of angles that are referred to as **alternate interior angles**.

a. Explain what it means for angles to be *alternate exterior angles*.

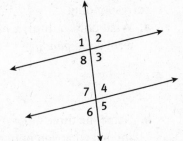

b. Name the two pairs of alternate exterior angles in the diagram.

ACADEMIC VOCABULARY

As a verb, the word **alternate** means to shift back and forth between one state and another.

c. Explain what it means for angles to be *alternate interior angles*.

d. Name the two pairs of alternate interior angles in the diagram.

14. The above diagram shows a pair of parallel lines cut by a transversal.
a. If the measure of ∠2 is 70°, determine the measures of the other angles.

b. What relationship do you notice about the measures of the alternate exterior angles?

c. What relationship do you notice about the measures of the alternate interior angles?

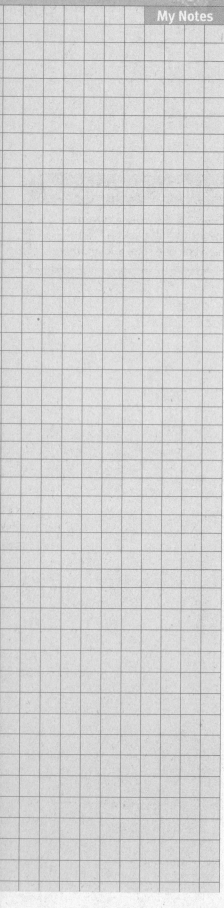

My Notes

15. Another classification for angle pairs that exist when two lines are cut by a transversal is **corresponding angles**. In the diagram, ∠2 and ∠4 are corresponding.

   a. What do you think is meant by the term *corresponding*?

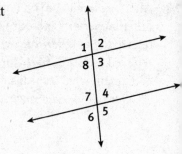

   b. Name the three other pairs of corresponding angles in the diagram and tell what you notice about the measures of these angles.

16. In Figure A, two parallel lines are cut by a transversal. The measure of ∠1 = 42°. Find *m*∠2 and describe the relationship that helped you determine the measure.

Figure A

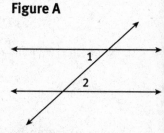

17. In Figure B, two parallel lines are cut by a transversal. The measure of ∠1 = 138°. Find *m*∠2 and describe the relationship that helped you determine the measure.

Figure B

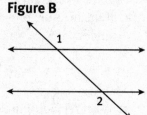

18. In Figure C, two parallel lines are cut by a transversal. The measure of ∠1 = 57°. Find *m*∠2 and describe the relationship that helped you determine the measure.

Figure C

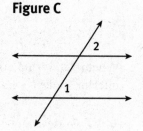

My Notes

19. Two pairs of **vertical angles** are formed when two lines intersect. They share a vertex but have no common rays. List the pairs of vertical angles in the diagram and tell what you notice about the measures of these angles.

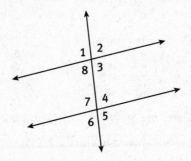

Check Your Understanding

20. Identify each pair of angles as alternate interior, alternate exterior, corresponding, or vertical.
 a. ∠RHJ and ∠RKS
 b. ∠CHK and ∠SKH
 c. ∠OKU and ∠HKS
 d. ∠CHK and ∠UKO
 e. ∠RHJ and ∠OKU

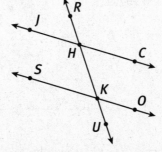

21. Angles *ABC* and *ADF* are alternate interior angles. The measure of ∠*ABC* = $(8x + 4)°$ and the measure of ∠*ADF* = $(10x - 20)°$. Determine the measure of each of the angles.

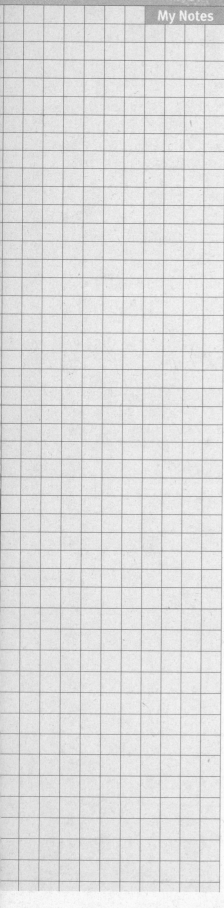

My Notes

LESSON 16-2 PRACTICE

The figure shows a pair of parallel lines that are intersected by a transversal. Use the figure for Items 22–26.

22. Name all pairs of vertical angles in the figure.

23. Name all of the angles in the figure that are supplementary to ∠8.

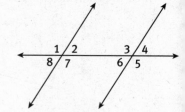

24. If $m\angle2 = 57°$, find $m\angle3$ and $m\angle4$.

25. If $m\angle6 = (5x + 1)°$ and $m\angle8 = (7x - 23)°$, find $m\angle6$ and $m\angle8$.

26. Suppose ∠9, which is not shown in the figure, is complementary to ∠4. Given that $m\angle1 = 153°$, what is $m\angle9$?

27. Two parallel lines are intersected by a transversal. The transversal forms four right angles with one of the parallel lines. Can you conclude that the transversal forms four right angles with the other parallel line? Justify your answer.

28. **Model with mathematics.** DeMarco is designing a skateboard ramp as shown in the figure. He wants the sides $\overline{AB}$ and $\overline{CD}$ to be parallel to each other. He also wants the measure of ∠A to be five times the measure of ∠D. Explain how he can find the correct measures of these two angles.

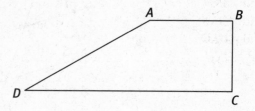

ACTIVITY 16 PRACTICE

Write your answers on notebook paper.
Show your work.

Lesson 16-1

1. Are angles with measures of 11° and 89° complementary? Why or why not?

2. Can two obtuse angles be supplementary? Explain why or why not.

3. What is the measure of an angle that is supplementary to an angle that measures 101°?

4. What is the measure of an angle that is complementary to an angle that measures 75°?

5. The measures of two complementary angles are $(3y - 1)°$ and $(4y + 7)°$.
   a. Determine the value of y.
   b. Calculate the measure of each of the angles.

6. The measures of two supplementary angles are $\left(\frac{1}{2}x\right)°$ and $(x + 30)°$.
   a. Determine the value of x.
   b. Calculate the measure of each of the angles.

7. In the figure below, determine the value of x.

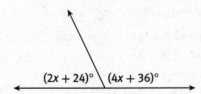

8. Suppose $\angle A$ is complementary to $\angle B$ and $\angle B$ is supplementary to $\angle C$. If $m\angle A$ is 21°, find $m\angle C$.

9. A student determined the value of x as shown. Explain the student's error.

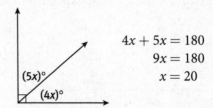

$$4x + 5x = 180$$
$$9x = 180$$
$$x = 20$$

10. $\angle 1$ and $\angle 2$ are supplementary. Which of the following statements cannot be true?
    A. $\angle 1$ is obtuse and $\angle 2$ is acute.
    B. $\angle 1$ and $\angle 2$ are adjacent angles.
    C. $\angle 1$ and $\angle 2$ are congruent angles.
    D. $\angle 1$ and $\angle 2$ are complementary.

11. $\angle A$ and $\angle B$ are complementary angles. The measure of $\angle A$ is 4 times the measure of $\angle B$. Which of these is the measure of $\angle B$?
    A. 18°   B. 22.5°
    C. 36°   D. 72°

Lesson 16-2

12. The diagram below shows parallel lines cut by a transversal. Determine the measures of $\angle 1$ through $\angle 7$.

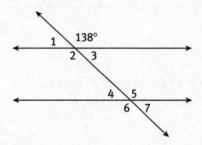

13. Name a pair of alternate interior angles in the above figure.

14. Two parallel lines are cut by a transversal as shown below. Find each of the following measures if $m\angle 2 = 82°$. Explain your answers.

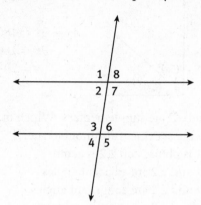

   a. $m\angle 6$ b. $m\angle 7$
   c. $m\angle 4$ d. $m\angle 8$

15. The figure shows parallel lines cut by a transversal. Find the value of y.

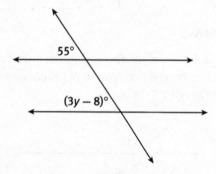

16. The figure shows parallel lines cut by a transversal. Find the value of w.

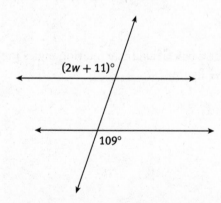

Draw and label a figure to match each statement.

17. Parallel lines are cut by a transversal and a pair of alternate interior angles are right angles.

18. Parallel lines are cut by a transversal and a pair of corresponding angles are complementary.

19. The figure shows several parking spaces at a mall. The parking spaces were created by drawing four parallel lines and a transversal.

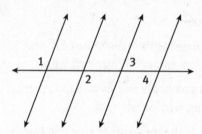

   a. If $m\angle 1 = 111°$, find $m\angle 4$.
   b. If $m\angle 2 = (3x - 15)°$ and $m\angle 3 = (2x - 30)°$, find the value of x.

Determine whether each statement is always, sometimes, or never true.

20. When two parallel lines are intersected by a transversal, all of the corresponding angles are right angles.

21. When two parallel lines are intersected by a transversal, every pair of angles are either congruent or supplementary.

22. When two parallel lines are intersected by a transversal, there is one pair of alternate exterior angles that are not congruent.

23. If $\angle Q$ and $\angle R$ are vertical angles, then $\angle Q$ is congruent to $\angle R$.

MATHEMATICAL PRACTICES
Make Sense of Problems

24. The figure shows rectangle *EDFA*. The opposite sides of the rectangle are parallel. Also, $\overline{AB} \parallel \overline{CD}$. If $m\angle EBA = 50°$, is it possible to determine $m\angle DCF$? If so, explain how. If not, explain why not.

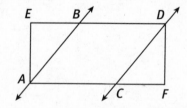

Angles of Triangles and Quadrilaterals

The Parallel Chute
Lesson 17-1 Angles in a Triangle

Learning Targets:

- Describe the relationship among the angles of a triangle.
- Write and solve equations involving angles of a triangle.

> **SUGGESTED LEARNING STRATEGIES:** Look for a Pattern, Graphic Organizer, Create Representations, Think-Pair-Share

Chip designs games for his computer. One of his current projects is called Parallel Chute. In the game, triangles appear at the top of a long chute that has parallel sides and slowly descend to rest at the bottom. The object of the game is to completely fill the region between the parallel sides of the chute.

As the triangle descends in the chute, the player is allowed to change the position of the triangle with the following commands: flip, slide, and turn.

The figure shows a triangle that has come to rest at the bottom of the chute.

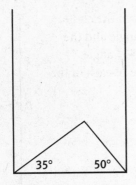

1. Work with your group. Use the triangular pieces given to you by your teacher to fill in the rectangular chute you have. Is there more than one way to fill the chute? Explain.

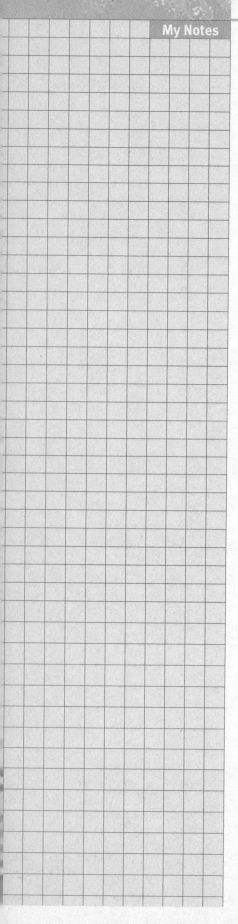

During the game, before each triangle appears, the player must select the measure (in degrees) of one angle in the triangle.

2. In one game, Chip's first triangle with a 90° angle came to rest and displayed the measure of ∠CAB to be 32°.

   a. Determine the measure of ∠CAD.

   b. Explain why the measure of ∠CAD must equal the measure of ∠ACB.

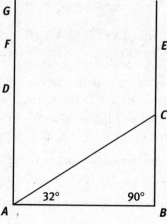

3. When △ACD came down the chute, Chip selected the 58° angle and the computer selected the 43° angle. Determine the measure of each of the following angles.

   a. ∠ECD
   b. ∠CDA
   c. ∠FDC

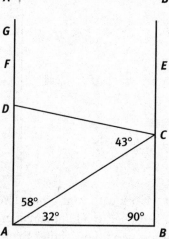

4. List the measures of the three angles in △ACD. Then list the measures of the three nonoverlapping angles whose vertex is at C. How do the two lists compare?

My Notes

5. Find the measure of each of the
following angles.
   a. ∠FCE
   b. ∠CFD
   c. ∠EFG
   d. ∠CEF
   e. ∠FGE

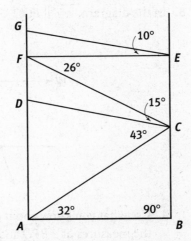

6. Every triangle has three sides and three angles. Use your responses to
Items 2, 3, and 5 to complete the following table. For each triangle, list
the angle measures and find the sum of the measures of the three angles.

Triangle Name	Angle Measures	Sum of Angle Measures
△ ABC	90°, 32°, 58°	
△ ACD		
△ DCF		
△ ACF		
△ CEF		
△ GEF		

7. Express regularity in repeated reasoning. Write a conjecture
about the sum of the measures of the angles of a triangle.

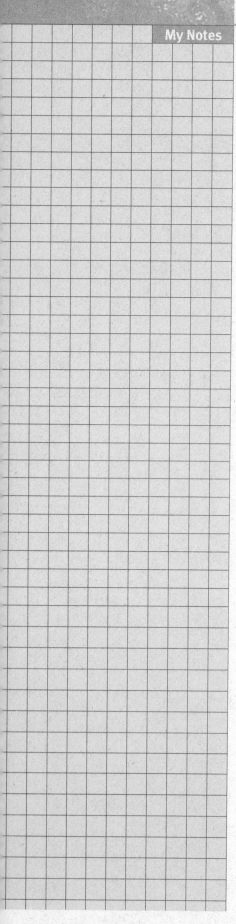

8. In the diagram, $\overrightarrow{WT} \parallel \overline{PQ}$.

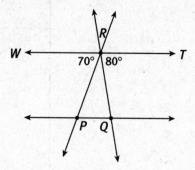

a. Use what you know about parallel lines and transversals to determine the measures of $\angle RPQ$ and $\angle RQP$.

b. Explain how this diagram supports your conjecture in Item 7.

9. Determine the measure of the unknown angle in the triangle below.

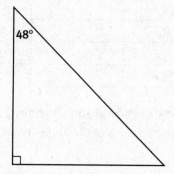

10. Chip has discovered an error in the programming of the game. Before a triangle appeared, a player selected an angle with measure 100° and the computer selected 82° for a different angle measure. Explain how Chip knew there was an error.

11. The measures of the three angles in a triangle are $x°$, $(2x + 4)°$ and $(2x − 9)°$.
   a. Write an equation based on the relationship between the three angle measures and then solve for x.

   b. Determine the measures of the three angles of the triangle.

Check Your Understanding

12. If one of the acute angles of a right triangle has a measure of 22°, calculate the measure of the other acute angle.

13. Suppose the measures of the angles in a triangle are given in the figure. Write an equation, solve for x, and determine the measure of each angle.

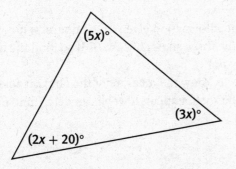

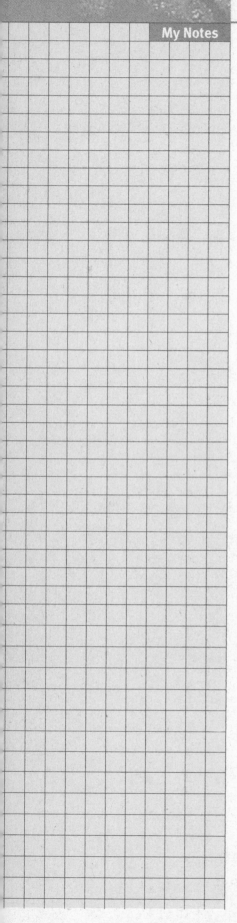

My Notes

LESSON 17-1 PRACTICE

In Items 14 and 15, the measures of two angles of a triangle are given. Find the measure of the third angle of the triangle.

14. $23°, 78°$

15. $105°, 40°$

16. The measures of the three angles in a triangle are $(4x)°$, $(3x - 3)°$, and $(5x + 3)°$. Write an equation, solve for x, and determine the measure of each angle.

17. In $\triangle ABC$, $\angle A$ and $\angle B$ have the same measure. The measure of $\angle C$ is twice the measure of $\angle A$. Find the measures of the angles in the triangle.

18. Eliana claimed that she drew a triangle with two right angles. Draw a sketch of such a triangle or explain why it is not possible.

19. Model with mathematics. Brian is building a brace for a shelf. The figure shows the plans for the brace.

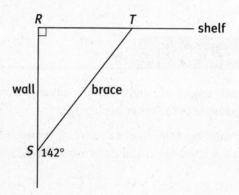

a. Based on the information given in the figure, is it possible to determine the three angles of $\triangle RST$? If so, find the measures. If not, explain why not.

b. Brian wants to know the measure of the obtuse angle formed by the brace and the shelf. Explain how he can determine this.

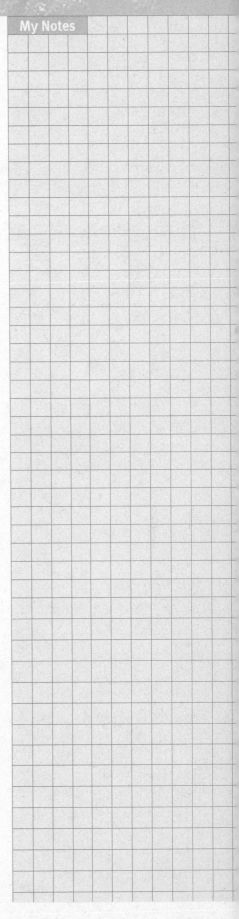

My Notes

Learning Targets:

- Describe and apply the relationship between an exterior angle of a triangle and its remote interior angles.
- Describe and apply the relationship among the angles of a quadrilateral.

> **SUGGESTED LEARNING STRATEGIES:** Vocabulary Organizer, Look for a Pattern, Visualization, Create Representations, Think-Pair-Share

An *exterior angle* of a triangle is formed by extending a side of the triangle. The vertex of the exterior angle is a vertex of the triangle. The sides of the exterior angle are determined by a side of the triangle and the extension of the adjacent side of the triangle at the vertex.

1. Use △SRQ below.
    a. Extend side $\overline{SQ}$ of the triangle by drawing $\overrightarrow{SP}$ through point Q to create exterior angle RQP.

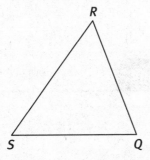

    b. Describe the relationship between the measures of ∠RQP and ∠RQS.

2. An exterior angle has been drawn at each of the three vertices of △SBM.
    a. Determine the measure of each of the three exterior angles.

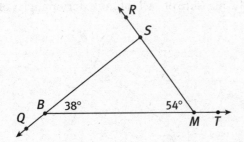

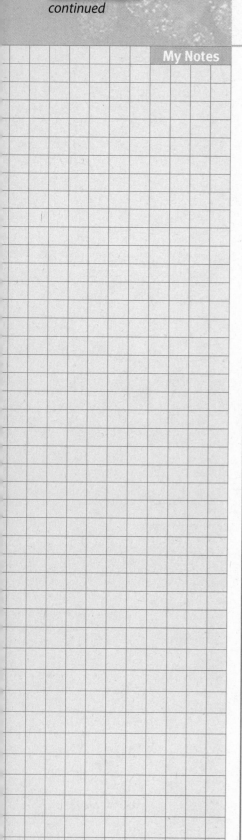

My Notes

b. For each exterior angle of a triangle, the two nonadjacent interior angles are its **remote interior angles**. Name the two remote interior angles for each exterior angle of △SBM.

Exterior Angle	Two Remote Interior Angles
∠SMT	
∠RSB	
∠QBM	

c. Chip claims that there is a relationship between the measure of an exterior angle and its remote interior angles. Examine the measures of the exterior angles and the measures of their corresponding remote interior angles to write a conjecture about their relationship.

Check Your Understanding

3. Determine the value of x.

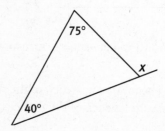

4. Determine the measure of each of the exterior angles of △YAX.

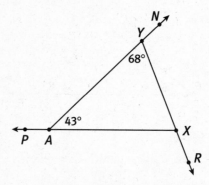

5. The measures of two interior angles of a triangle are 75° and 65°. Determine the measure of the largest exterior angle.

6. Now consider quadrilaterals.
  a. Draw a *diagonal* from *one* vertex in each quadrilateral.

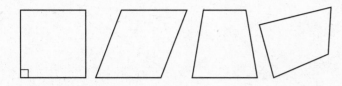

My Notes

MATH TERMS

A **diagonal** of a polygon is a line segment connecting two nonconsecutive vertices.

  b. Construct viable arguments. What is the sum of the measures of the interior angles in any quadrilateral? Explain your reasoning.

7. Find the unknown angle measure in quadrilateral *MATH*.

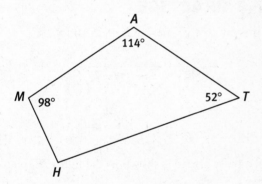

8. Determine the value of *x* in the quadrilateral.

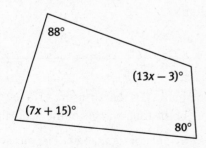

My Notes

Check Your Understanding

9. Determine the value of x.

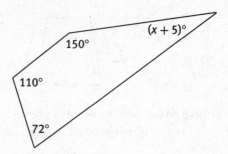

10. In quadrilateral *RSTU*, all of the angles of the quadrilateral are congruent. What can you conclude about the angles? What can you conclude about the quadrilateral?

LESSON 17-2 PRACTICE

11. Determine the value of y. Then find $m\angle S$ and $m\angle T$.

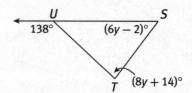

12. A portion of a truss bridge is shown in the figure. Explain how to determine the measure of $\angle AEB$.

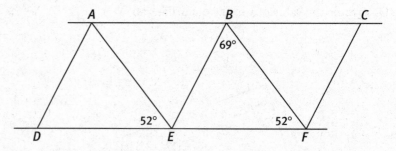

13. A quadrilateral contains angles that measure 47°, 102°, and 174°. What is the measure of the fourth angle of the quadrilateral?

14. In quadrilateral *DEFG*, $\angle D$ is a right angle. The measure of $\angle E$ is half the measure of $\angle D$. The measure of $\angle F$ is three times the measure of $\angle E$. Sketch the quadrilateral and label the measure of each angle.

15. **Make use of structure.** Can an exterior angle of a triangle ever be congruent to one of its remote interior angles? Justify your answer.

ACTIVITY 17 PRACTICE
Write your answers on notebook paper.
Show your work.

Lesson 17-1

1. Two angles of a triangle measure 32° and 70°. Find the measure of the third angle.

2. In the diagram below, $\overleftrightarrow{AC} \parallel \overleftrightarrow{DF}$. Determine the measure of each of the angles in $\triangle BDE$.

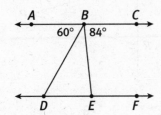

3. Determine the value of b.

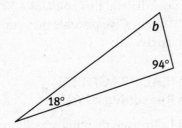

4. Write an equation, solve for x, and determine the measure of each angle in $\triangle PAT$.

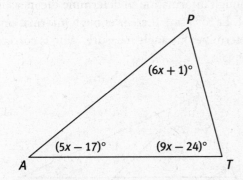

5. The measures of the three interior angles of a triangle are 85°, 20°, and 75°. Determine the measures of the three exterior angles.

6. The measures of two angles of a triangle are 38° and 47°. What is the measure of the third angle?
   A. 85° B. 95°
   C. 133° D. 142°

7. In $\triangle DEF$, the measure of $\angle D = (3x - 6)°$, the measure of $\angle E = (3x - 6)°$, and the measure of $\angle F = (2x)°$. Which of the following is the measure of $\angle F$?
   A. 24° B. 46°
   C. 48° D. 66°

8. In $\triangle PQR$, $\angle P$ is an obtuse angle. Which of the following statements about the triangle must be true?
   A. The other two angles must be congruent.
   B. The other two angles must be acute angles.
   C. One of the other two angles could be a right angle.
   D. One of the other two angles could also be an obtuse angle.

9. The figure shows a rectangular lawn at a civic center. Over time, people have cut across the lawn to walk from the library to city hall and made a straight path in the lawn, as shown. What is the measure of $\angle 1$ in the figure?

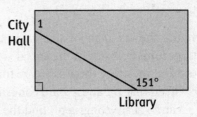

Lesson 17-2

In Items 10–12, determine the value of x.

10.

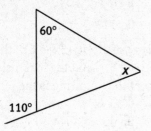

11.

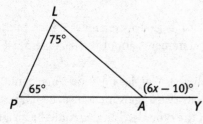

12.

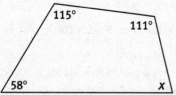

13. Determine the measure of each angle in quadrilateral $DEFG$ with $m\angle D = (12x - 4)°$, $m\angle E = (18x + 4)°$, $m\angle F = (15x + 10)°$, and $m\angle G = (5x)°$.

14. The figure shows a plan for a corral in the shape of a trapezoid. One side of the corral is formed by a house and the other three sides are formed by a fence. Given that $\angle 1$ and $\angle 2$ are congruent, and that $\angle 3$ and $\angle 4$ are congruent, find the measures of the four angles.

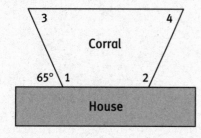

15. In quadrilateral $ABCD$, $m\angle A = (5x - 5)°$, $m\angle B = (9x)°$, $m\angle C = (12x + 15)°$, and $m\angle D = (15x - 60)°$. Which angle has the greatest measure?

   A. $\angle A$ **B.** $\angle B$
   C. $\angle C$ **D.** $\angle D$

16. Which expression represents the measure of $\angle P$?

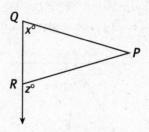

   A. $(z + x)°$ **B.** $(z - x)°$
   C. $(x - z)°$ **D.** $z°$

17. Sketch a quadrilateral that contains a $50°$ angle and a $170°$ angle. Give possible measures for the other two angles.

MATHEMATICAL PRACTICES
Critique the Reasoning of Others

18. Nick and LaToya are painting a backdrop of a mountain for a stage set. A sketch for the backdrop is shown below. Nick says there is not enough information to determine the measure of $\angle 1$. LaToya says there is enough information to determine this angle measure. Who is correct? Explain.

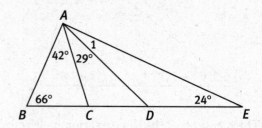

A beam of light and a mirror can be used to study the behavior of light. When light hits the mirror it is reflected so that the angle of incidence and the angle of reflection are congruent.

1. Name a pair of nonadjacent complementary angles in the diagram.

2. Name a pair of adjacent supplementary angles in the diagram.

3. In the diagram, $m\angle CBD = (4x)°$ and $m\angle FBD = (3x - 1)°$.
   a. Solve for the value of x.
   b. Determine $m\angle CBD$, $m\angle FBD$, and $m\angle DBE$.

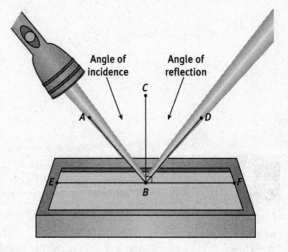

Light rays are bent as they pass through glass. Since a block of glass is a rectangular prism, the opposite sides are parallel and a ray is bent the same amount entering the piece of glass as exiting the glass.

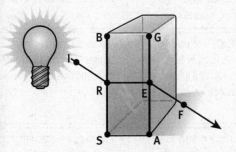
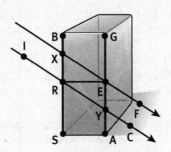

This causes $\overleftrightarrow{XF}$ to be parallel to $\overleftrightarrow{RY}$, as shown.

4. If the measure of $\angle YEX$ is $130°$, determine the measure of each of the following angles. Explain how you arrived at your answer.
   a. $\angle BXE$ b. $\angle GEF$ c. $\angle SRY$

5. If $m\angle CYA = (5x)°$ and $m\angle SRY = (6x - 10)°$, then the value of x is _____.

6. If $m\angle XRE = 90°$ and $m\angle REX = 30°$, then $m\angle RXE = $ _____. Explain how you arrived at your answer.

7. The measures of the angles of a triangle are $(2x)°$, $(x + 14)°$, and $(x - 38)°$. Determine the value of x and the measures of each of the three angles.

8. One of the quadrilaterals in a mural design is shown below. Determine the measure of the missing angle.

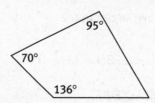

Scoring Guide	Exemplary	Proficient	Emerging	Incomplete
	The solution demonstrates these characteristics:			
Mathematics Knowledge and Thinking (Items 1, 2, 3a-b, 4a-c, 5, 6, 7, 8)	• Clear and accurate understanding of angle relationships, and finding angle measures in a triangle and quadrilateral.	• An understanding of angle relationships and finding angle measures in a triangle and quadrilateral.	• Partial understanding of angle relationships and finding angle measures in a triangle and quadrilateral.	• Little or no understanding of angle relationships and finding angle measures in a triangle and quadrilateral.
Problem Solving (Items 3a-b, 4a-c, 5, 6, 7, 8)	• Interpreting a problem accurately in order to find missing angle measures.	• Interpreting a problem to find missing angle measures.	• Difficulty interpreting a problem to find missing angle measures.	• Incorrect or incomplete interpretation of a problem.
Mathematical Modeling / Representations (Items 1, 2, 3a-b, 4a-c, 5, 6, 7, 8)	• Accurately interpreting figures in order to characterize angle pairs and find angle measures.	• Interpreting figures in order to find angle pairs and find missing angle measures.	• Difficulty interpreting figures in order to find angle pairs and find missing angle measures.	• Incorrectly interpreting figures in order to find angle pairs and find missing angle measures.
Reasoning and Communication (Items 4a-c, 6)	• Precise use of appropriate terms to describe finding angle measures.	• An adequate description of finding of missing angle measures.	• A confusing description of finding missing angle measures.	• An inaccurate description of finding missing angle measures.

Introduction to Transformations

Move It!
Lesson 18-1 What Is a Transformation?

Learning Targets:
- Recognize rotations, reflections, and translations in physical models.
- Explore rigid transformations of figures.

SUGGESTED LEARNING STRATEGIES: Visualization, Create Representations, Vocabulary Organizer, Paraphrasing

A *transformation*, such as a flip, slide, or turn, changes the position of a figure. Many graphic artists rely on graphic design software to transform images to create logos or promotional materials.

A *preimage* is a figure before it has been transformed and the *image* is its position after the transformation. You can tell whether a figure has been transformed if the preimage can be moved to coincide with its image.

1. Each set of pictures below shows the preimage and image of some familiar objects. Use the terms *flip, slide,* and *turn* to describe what transformation will make the two objects coincide.

a. 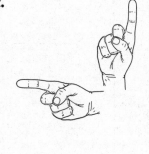   b.    c.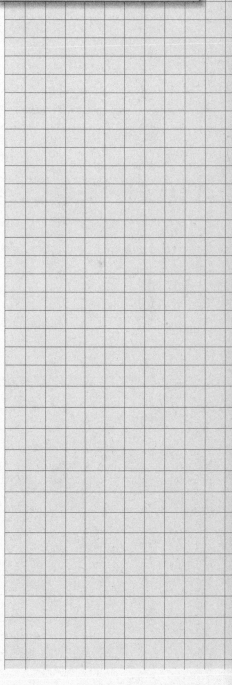

2. Make a conjecture about the preimage and image of a transformed object based on your observations of the pictures.

ACADEMIC VOCABULARY

The word *transform* means "to change."

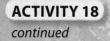

My Notes

3. **Make use of structure.** The table below shows the proper name for transformations and the corresponding definition. Match each transformation with the words *flip*, *slide*, and *turn*.

Transformation	Definition	Example
Translation	Each point of a figure is moved the same distance in the same direction.	
Reflection	Each point of a figure is reflected over a line, creating a mirror image.	line of reflection
Rotation	Each point of a figure is rotated through a given angle in a given direction around a fixed point.	

4. For each capital letter shown below, visualize the movement the letter takes while being transformed. Identify the transformation by its proper name.

a.

P q

b.

L L

c.

B

B

Check Your Understanding

Tell what single transformation, translation, reflection, or rotation will make the figures coincide. Explain how you determined your answers.

5.

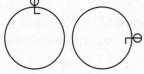

6.

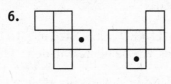
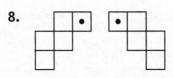

7.

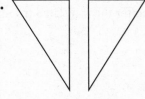

8.

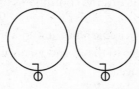

9. **Construct viable arguments.** How do the sides of the image of a triangle after a translation, reflection, or rotation compare with the corresponding sides of the original figure? How do you know?

LESSON 18-1 PRACTICE

Each set of figures shows the preimage and image of an object after a single transformation. Describe how the object was transformed using the proper name.

10.

11.

12.

13.

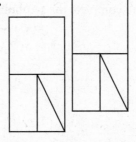

14. **Reason abstractly.** Which of the three transformations do you most commonly see in the world around you? Give examples to support your answer.

My Notes

Learning Targets:

● Determine the effect of translations on two-dimensional figures using coordinates.
● Represent and interpret translations involving words, coordinates, and symbols.

SUGGESTED LEARNING STRATEGIES: Visualization, Discussion Groups, Create Representations, Identify a Subtask, Interactive Word Wal

A *translation* changes only a figure's position. A verbal description of a translation includes words such as *right, left, up,* and *down.*

1. Consider the triangle shown on the coordinate plane.

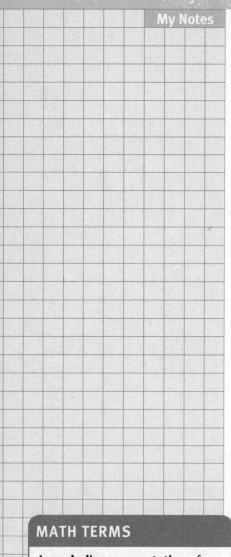

Coordinates of Triangle	Coordinates of Image

a. Record the coordinates of the vertices of the triangle in the table.
b. Translate the triangle down 2 units and right 5 units. Graph the translation.
c. Record the coordinates of the vertices of the *image* in the table.

A *symbolic representation* of a transformation is an algebraic way to show the changes to the *x*- and *y*-coordinates of the vertices of the original figure, or *preimage*.

d. **Make use of structure.** Use the information in the table to help you complete the symbolic representation for the translated triangle:
$$(x, y) \rightarrow (x + 5, y - 2)$$

MATH TERMS

A **symbolic representation** of a transformation is an algebraic way to show the changes to the *x*- and *y*-coordinates of the vertices of the original figure, or preimage.

A **preimage** is a figure before it has been transformed and the **image** is its position after the transformation.

2. Figure 2 is the image of Figure 1 after a translation, as shown in the coordinate plane.

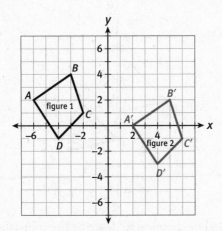

READING MATH

A prime symbol (′) is placed after the letter for the original point to show that the new point is its image.

Example: Point A' is the image of point A.

a. Record the coordinates of the vertices of the preimage and image.

Figure 1: Preimage		Figure 2: Image	
A		A′	
B		B′	
C		C′	
D		D′	

b. **Make sense of problems.** Refer to the table and graph.
   Was the figure translated up or down? _____ By how much? _____

   Was the figure translated to the left or right? _____ By how much? _____

c. Write a verbal description to describe the translation.

d. Describe the translation using a symbolic representation.
   symbolic representation: $(x, y) \rightarrow (x + 8, y - 2)$

My Notes

3. The coordinate plane shows △P′Q′R′ after △PQR undergoes a translation.

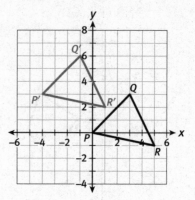

a. Write a verbal description to describe the translation.

b. Describe the translation using a symbolic representation.
  symbolic representation: $(x, y) \rightarrow (x - 4, y + 3)$

Check Your Understanding

4. The triangle shown on the coordinate plane is translated according to the following symbolic representation: $(x, y) \rightarrow (x + 1, y + 6)$.

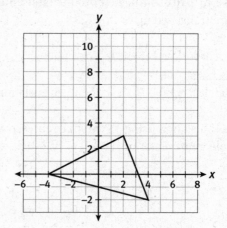

a. Describe how the symbolic representation can be used to determine if the triangle is translated left or right, and up or down.

b. Write a verbal description of the translation.

c. **Attend to precision.** Sketch the image of the triangle according to the symbolic representation.

5. **Construct viable arguments.** Explain how the change in the coordinates of a translated point is related to the symbolic representation.

LESSON 18-2 PRACTICE

6. Triangle *ABC* is shown along with its image △*A'B'C'* on the coordinate plane below.
   a. Write a verbal description of the translation.
   b. Show the translation using symbolic representation.

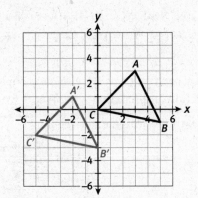

7. Determine the coordinates of the vertices for each image of △*GEO* after each of the following translations is performed.

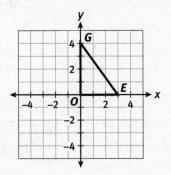

   a. 3 units to the left and 3 units down
   b. $(x, y) \rightarrow (x, y - 4)$
   c. $(x, y) \rightarrow (x - 2, y + 1)$
   d. $(x, y) \rightarrow (x - 4, y)$

8. **Critique the reasoning of others.** Quadrilateral *QRST* has vertices $Q(0, 0)$, $R(4, 0)$, $S(4, 4)$, and $T(0, 4)$. Eric states that the image of this quadrilateral after a given translation has vertices $Q'(0, 0)$, $R'(2, 0)$, $S'(2, 2)$, and $T'(0, 2)$. Do you agree or disagree with Eric's statement? Justify your reasoning.

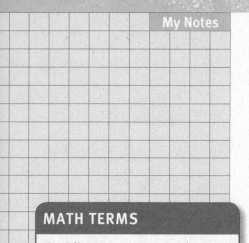

My Notes

MATH TERMS

Equidistant means to be the same distance from a given point or line.

CONNECT TO AP

Translations and reflections of figures in the coordinate plane are preparing you to successfully translate and reflect graphs of functions. This is a helpful tool for visualizing and setting up the graphs for many problems you will solve in calculus.

Learning Targets:

- Determine the effect of reflections on two-dimensional figures using coordinates.
- Represent and interpret reflections involving words, coordinates, and symbols.

SUGGESTED LEARNING STRATEGIES: Visualization, Create Representations, Interactive Word Wall, Construct an Argument, Summarizing

To perform a **reflection**, each point of a preimage is copied on the opposite side of the line of reflection and remains **equidistant** from the line.

1. $\triangle GHI$ is shown on the coordinate plane below.

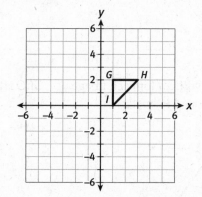

Coordinates of Triangle	Coordinates of Image

a. Record the coordinates of the vertices of $\triangle GHI$ in the table.

b. Sketch the reflection of $\triangle GHI$ over the x-axis.

c. Record the coordinates of the vertices of the image $\triangle G'H'I'$ in the table.

The symbolic representation for this transformation is $(x, y) \rightarrow (x, -y)$.

d. Explain how the change in the coordinates of the vertices is related to the symbolic representation for this transformation.

My Notes

2. Figure 2 is the image of figure 1 after a reflection, as shown in the coordinate plane.

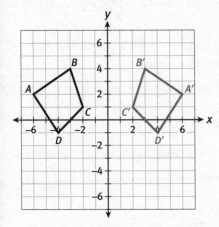

	Preimage: Figure 1		Image: Figure 2	
A		A′	
B		B′	
C		C′	
D		D′	

a. Record the coordinates of the vertices of the preimage and image.

b. The line across which an object is reflected is called the **line of reflection**. Identify the line of reflection in the transformation of Figure 1.

c. A verbal description of a reflection includes the line of reflection. Write a verbal description of the reflection.

d. Describe the reflection using a symbolic representation.
Symbolic Representation: $(x, y) \rightarrow$

Check Your Understanding

3. Triangle *ABC* and its reflected image are shown on the coordinate plane.

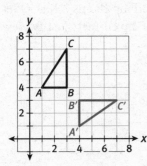

Coordinates of △ABC		Coordinates of △A′B′C′	
A		A′	
B		B′	
C		C′	

a. Complete the table.
b. Identify the line of reflection. Write a verbal description of the transformation.
c. Describe the reflection using symbolic representation.

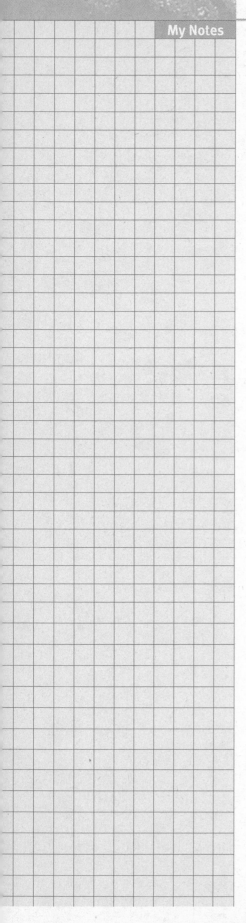

4. **Express regularity in repeated reasoning.** Write a summary statement describing which coordinate stays the same when a figure is reflected over the *y*-axis.

5. Modify your statement in Item 4 describing which coordinate stays the same when a figure is reflected over the *x*-axis.

LESSON 18-3 PRACTICE

6. Triangle *BAM* is shown along with its image △*B'A'M'* on the coordinate plane below.

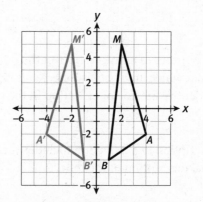

   a. Write a verbal description of the reflection.
   b. Describe the reflection using symbolic representation.

7. Suppose △*CDF*, whose vertices have coordinates *C*(−2, 1), *D*(4, 5), and *F*(5, 3), is reflected over the *x*-axis.
   a. Explain a way to determine the coordinates of the vertices of △*C'D'F'*.
   b. Find the coordinates of △*C'D'F'*.

8. **Critique the reasoning of others.** Filip claims △*N'P'Q'* is a reflection of △*NPQ* over the *x*-axis. Is Filip correct? Justify your answer.

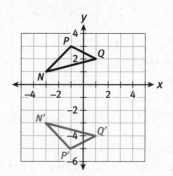

Learning Targets:

- Determine the effect of rotations on two-dimensional figures using coordinates.
- Represent and interpret rotations involving words, coordinates, and symbols.

SUGGESTED LEARNING STRATEGIES: Visualization, Create Representations, Look for a Pattern, Interactive Word Wall

A *rotation* is a transformation that describes the motion of a figure about a fixed point. To perform a rotation, each point of the preimage travels along a circle the same number of degrees.

1. The point (3, 1) is rotated in a counterclockwise direction about the origin 90°, 180°, and 270°.

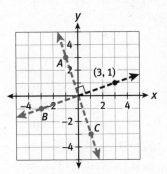

Image Point	Coordinates	Measure of Angle of Rotation
A		
B		
C		

a. Write the coordinates of each image point *A, B,* and *C* in the table.

b. Complete the table by giving the angle of rotation for each image point.

c. **Reason abstractly.** Describe in your own words why the origin is the *center of rotation* in this rotation transformation.

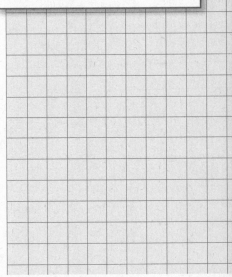

MATH TIP

If the direction of a rotation is counterclockwise, the measure of the angle of rotation is given as a positive value. If the direction of a rotation is clockwise, the measure of the angle of rotation is given as a negative value.

d. **Construct viable arguments.** Make a conjecture about the changes of the *x*- and *y*-coordinates when a point is rotated counterclockwise 90°, 180°, and 270° about the origin.

e. What are the coordinates of the point (3,1) after a 360° rotation about the origin? Explain your answer.

2. Figure 2 is a 90° counterclockwise rotation about the origin of figure 1.

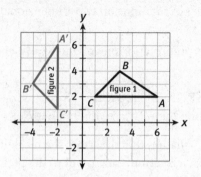

Determine the coordinates of the vertices for each figure.

Preimage: Figure 1		Image: Figure 2	
A		A′	
B		B′	
C		C′	

3. Make sense of problems. Complete the summary statement:

When a figure in Quadrant I of the coordinate plane is rotated 90° counterclockwise about the origin, its image is located in Quadrant _____.

My Notes

4. **Use appropriate tools strategically.** Consider $\triangle DEF$ shown on the coordinate plane.

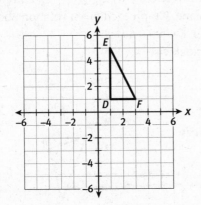

a. Trace $\triangle DEF$ and the positive x-axis on a piece of tracing paper. Label the vertices and the axis.

b. Rotate the triangle 90° counterclockwise by aligning the origin and rotating the tracing paper until the positive x-axis coincides with the positive y-axis.

c. Record the coordinates of the vertices of the image in the table.

Preimage	$D(1, 1)$	$E(1, 5)$	$F(3, 1)$
Image	$D'($ $)$	$E'($ $)$	$F'($ $)$

d. Sketch $\triangle D'E'F'$ on the coordinate plane above.

Check Your Understanding

5. **Make use of structure.** Use your results from Items 1, 2, and 3 to write a symbolic representation for a 90° counterclockwise rotation.
$(x, y) \rightarrow ($ $,$ $)$

6. **Critique the reasoning of others.**
Sven recognized the 180° rotation of $\triangle DEF$ about the origin in the coordinate plane and determined the symbolic representation to be $(x, y) \rightarrow (-x, -y)$.

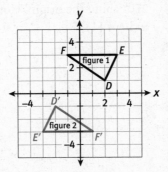

Determine whether the symbolic representation is correct. Justify your answer.

7. A point with coordinates (x, y) is rotated 360° in a counterclockwise direction about the origin. Write the symbolic representation for this transformation:
$(x, y) \rightarrow ($ $,$ $)$.

What does the symbolic representation indicate?

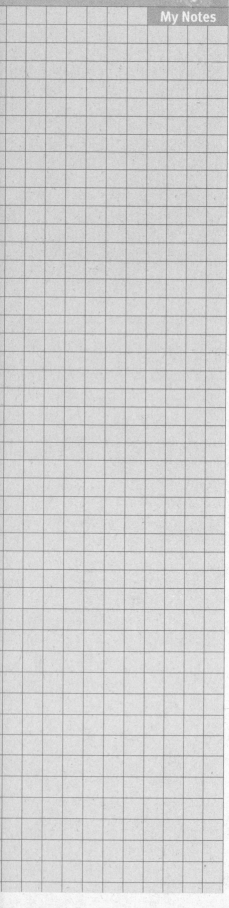

LESSON 18-4 PRACTICE

8. Triangle *PQR* with vertices $P(1, 3)$, $Q(3, -2)$, and $R(4, 2)$ is shown on the coordinate plane. Graph each given rotation about the origin.
   a. 90° counterclockwise
   b. 180° counterclockwise

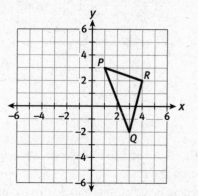

9. The preimage of point *A* is located at $(-1, 5)$. What are the coordinates of the image, A', after a 270° counterclockwise rotation?

10. Complete the summary statements:
    a. When a figure in Quadrant I of the coordinate plane is rotated 180° counterclockwise about the origin, its image is located in Quadrant _____.
    b. When a figure in Quadrant I of the coordinate plane is rotated 270° counterclockwise about the origin, its image is located in Quadrant _____.

11. **Reason quantitatively.** Use your answer from Item 9 to write a conjecture about the symbolic representation for a 270° counterclockwise rotation.

12. Draw a figure on a coordinate plane. Rotate the figure counterclockwise 270° about the origin. How does your drawing confirm your conjecture in Item 11?

ACTIVITY 18 PRACTICE
Write your answers on notebook paper.
Show your work.

Lesson 18-1
For Items 1–3, the shaded figure is the preimage and the unshaded figure is the image. Identify the single transformation that will make the figures coincide.

1.
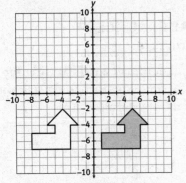

2.
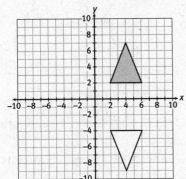

3.
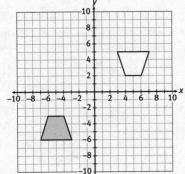

Lesson 18-2
4. Figure *B* is the image of figure *A* after a transformation, as shown in the coordinate plane.

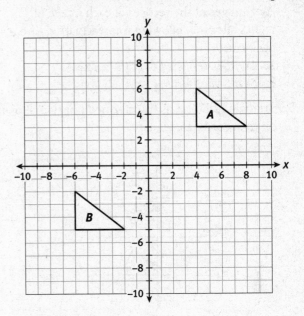

a. Write a verbal description of the transformation.
b. Write a symbolic representation of the transformation.

5. The vertices of △*MOV* are located at $M(-2, -2)$, $O(4, -2)$, and $V(4, 3)$. Determine the coordinates of the vertices of the image after △*MOV* is translated 3 units up and 2 units to the right.

6. Which symbolic representation describes the transformation shown on the coordinate plane?

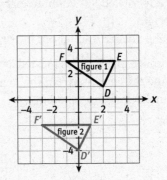

A. $(x, y) \rightarrow (x + 2, y - 5)$
B. $(x, y) \rightarrow (x - 2, y - 5)$
C. $(x, y) \rightarrow (x - 2, y + 5)$
D. $(x, y) \rightarrow (x + 2, y + 5)$

Lesson 18-3

7. The vertices of △QRS are located at Q(2, 2), R(−4, 2), and S(−4, −4). Determine the coordinates of the vertices of each image of △QRS after the following transformations are performed:
   a. △QRS is reflected over the x-axis.
   b. △QRS is reflected over the y-axis.

8. Triangle *FED* and its transformed image is shown on the coordinate plane.

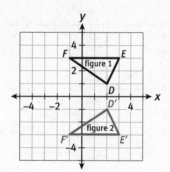

   a. Identify the line of reflection.
   b. Write a verbal description of the transformation.
   c. Write a symbolic representation of the transformation.

Lesson 18-4

9. The vertices of △XYZ are located at X(−2, −2), Y(4, −2), and Z(4, 3). Determine the coordinates of the vertices of each image of △XYZ after the following transformations are performed:
   a. △XYZ is rotated 90° counterclockwise about the origin.
   b. △XYZ is rotated 180° about the origin.

10. The preimage of point B is located at (−1, 4). Determine the coordinates of the image, B′, for each counterclockwise rotation.
    a. 90°
    b. 180°
    c. 270°

11. Triangle ABC has vertices A(2, 4), B(5, 7), and C(−1, 5). If △ABC is rotated 270° counterclockwise about the origin, in what quadrant(s) would you find the image of △ABC?
    A. Quadrant I
    B. Quadrant III
    C. Quadrants II and III
    D. Quadrants I and IV

MATHEMATICAL PRACTICES
Make Use of Structure

12. Determine the coordinates of the vertices for each image of △GEO after each of the following transformations is performed.

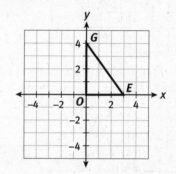

    a. Translate △GEO 2 units to the left and reflect over the x-axis.
    b. Reflect △GEO over the x-axis and translate 2 units to the left.

13. Does the order in which multiple transformations, such as rotations, reflections, and translations, are performed on a preimage have an effect on the image?

Rigid Transformations and Compositions

All the Right Moves

Lesson 19-1 Properties of Transformations

Learning Targets:

- Explore properties of translations, rotations, and reflections on two-dimensional figures.
- Explore congruency of transformed figures.

SUGGESTED LEARNING STRATEGIES: Visualization, Identify a Subtask, Create Representations, Critique Reasoning, Predict and Confirm

Skip and Kate are designing a skateboard park for their neighborhood. They want to include rails, a grindbox, a quarter-pipe, and a ramp. They are deciding where to place the equipment. Kate sketches her plan for the layout on a coordinate plane.

Using the origin as the center of their park, Kate sketched figures to represent the equipment on the coordinate plane, as shown below.

MATH TIP

The coordinates of the origin on a coordinate plane are (0, 0).

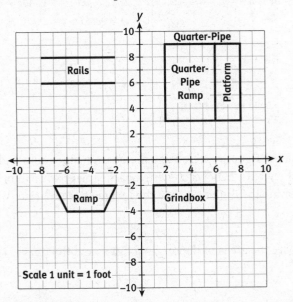

Kate uses the layout on the coordinate plane to determine the dimensions and the area of each figure.

1. **Model with mathematics.** Use the scale on Kate's layout to complete the table of dimensions for each piece of equipment.

MATH TIP

The area of a trapezoid can be found using the formula

$\text{Area} = \frac{1}{2}h(b_1 + b_2)$, where h is the height and b_1 and b_2 are the bases.

Equipment	Base (ft)	Height (ft)	Area (ft²)
Quarter-Pipe (ramp and platform)			
Ramp	base 1: base 2:		
Grindbox			

My Notes

Skip reviewed Kate's plan for the skateboarding park. To improve the layout, Skip suggested transformations for each piece of equipment as described.

2. The original placement of the quarter-pipe is shown on the coordinate plane.

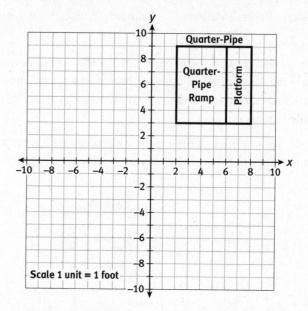

a. Reflect the figure representing the quarter-pipe ramp and platform over the *y*-axis. Label each vertex of the image with an ordered pair.

b. Determine the dimensions of the image, in feet.

c. Compare the areas of the original figure and the image.

d. Explain why the image is congruent to the original figure.

My Notes

3. The original placement of the ramp is shown on the coordinate plane.

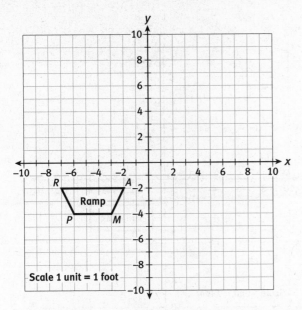

Scale 1 unit = 1 foot

a. Rotate the figure representing the ramp 90° counterclockwise about the origin. Label the vertices of the image R', A', M', and P'.

b. **Critique the reasoning of others.** Kate states that this rotation will change the shape and size of the figure. Skip reassures her that the image is congruent to the original figure. With whom do you agree? Justify your reasoning.

Congruent figures have corresponding angles as well as corresponding sides.

c. List the pairs of corresponding angles in trapezoids $RAMP$ and $R'A'M'P'$.

d. **Construct viable arguments.** Make a conjecture about the corresponding angles of congruent figures.

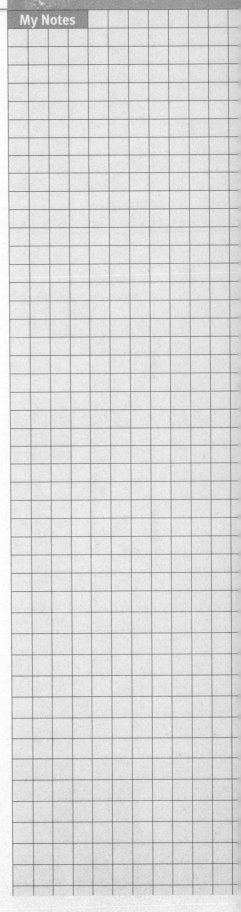

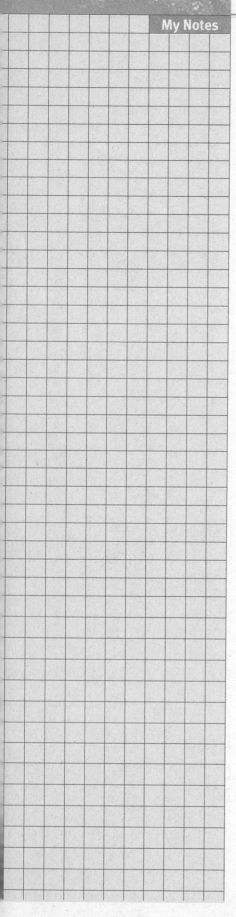

4. The original placement of the grindbox is shown on the coordinate plane.

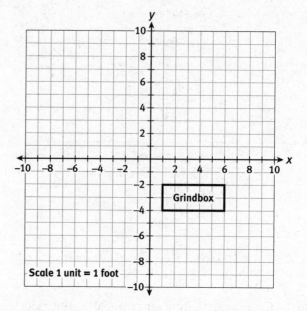

a. Plot the image of this figure using the transformation whose symbolic representation is $(x, y) \rightarrow (x + 2, y + 9)$.

b. Write a verbal description of the transformation.

c. Is the image of the grindbox congruent to the preimage of the grindbox? Justify your answer.

5. **Reason abstractly.** After using reflections, rotations, and translations to create images of figures, what can you infer about the preimage and its image under all of these transformations?

Check Your Understanding

Consider △NTR shown on the coordinate grid.

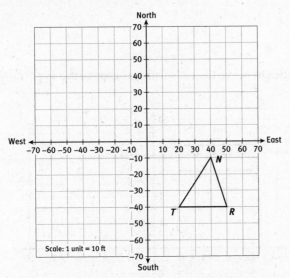

Scale: 1 unit = 10 ft

My Notes

MATH TIP

The area of a triangle can be found using the formula
$$\text{Area} = \frac{1}{2} \times \text{base} \times \text{height}.$$

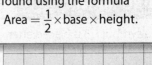

6. Rotate △NTR 180° about the origin. Label the vertices T', R', and N'.

7. Find the area, in square units, of △NTR and △N'T'R'. Show the calculations that led to your answer.

8. Write a supporting statement justifying how you know that △NTR and △N'T'R' are congruent triangles.

9. **Express regularity in repeated reasoning.** Could your statement in Item 8 be used to support other types of transformations of △NTR? Explain.

Finally, Skip decides to move the location of the rails. The original placement of the rails is shown on the coordinate plane.

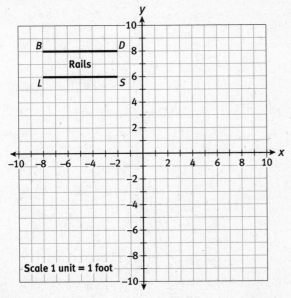

Scale 1 unit = 1 foot

MATH TERMS

Performing two or more transformations on a figure is called a **composition of transformations**.

READING MATH

A prime symbol (′) is placed after the letter of the original point to show that the new point is its image. Two prime symbols (″) are placed after the letter of the original point to show that the new point has been transformed twice.

10. **Construct viable arguments.** Skip claims that the rails are parallel and that moving them, using a reflection, rotation, or translation, will not affect this relationship. Confirm or contradict Skip's claim. Use examples to justify your answer.

11. Skip decides to move the rails using a *composition of transformations*.

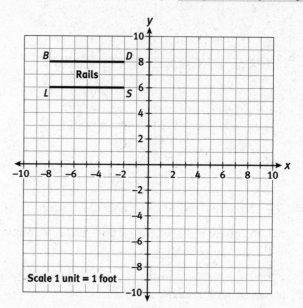

a. Reflect the graph of each rail, $\overline{BD}$ and $\overline{LS}$, over the x-axis. Label the image points B', D', L', and S'.

b. Then, translate the reflected image 3 feet up and 1 foot left. Label the image points B'', D'', L'', and S''.

Check Your Understanding

12. Refer to Item 11. Describe a method to determine if $\overline{B''D''}$ and $\overline{L''S''}$ are congruent to $\overline{BD}$ and $\overline{LS}$.

13. Describe how the rails in Item 11 would differ in orientation if the translation in Item 11b was changed to a counterclockwise rotation 90° about the origin.

14. Do you agree with the statement that congruency is preserved under a composition of transformations involving translations, reflections, and rotations? If not, provide a counterexample.

LESSON 19-1 PRACTICE

15. Quadrilateral *ABCD* is reflected across line *m* as shown in the diagram.

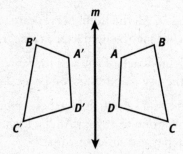

a. Name the side that corresponds to $\overline{CD}$ and explain the relationship between the lengths of these two segments.

b. Name the angle that corresponds to angle *C* and explain the relationship between the measures of these two angles.

16. Draw a coordinate plane on grid paper. Create and label a triangle having vertices *D*(3, 5), *H*(0, 8), and *G*(3, 8). Perform each transformation on the coordinate plane.

a. Reflect △*DHG* across the *x*-axis.

b. Rotate △*DHG* 90° counterclockwise about the origin.

c. Translate △*DHG* 4 units right.

d. Which of the transformed images above are congruent to △*DHG*?

My Notes

Learning Targets:

- Explore composition of transformations.
- Describe the effect of composition of translations, rotations, and reflections on two-dimensional figures using coordinates.

> **SUGGESTED LEARNING STRATEGIES:** Self Revision/Peer Revision, Visualization, Discussion Groups, Create Representations, Close Reading

To explore composition of transformations, you and a partner will play a game called All the Right Moves. Cut out the five All the Right Moves cards on page 259 and two game pieces. You and your partner will use only one set of All the Right Moves game cards to play the game, but you both need a game piece.

DISCUSSION GROUP TIPS

As you read and discuss the rules of All the Right Moves, ask and answer questions to be sure you have a clear understanding of not only all the terminology used, but also how the game is to be played.

All the Right Moves Rules

1. As partners, lay out the 5 All the Right Moves cards face down.

2. Take turns choosing an All the Right Moves card. You will each take 2 cards. The extra card may be used later as a tiebreaker.

3. Working independently, each of you will use your All the Right Moves cards to complete the two game sheets on pages 255 and 256.

4. To complete the first game sheet, follow these steps:
   a. Record the number of one of your All the Right Moves cards on your game sheet. You may use either one first.
   b. Plot and label the points for Position 0 on the grid. Then use those points as the vertices to draw a triangle.
   c. Follow the directions on the All the Right Moves card to find the coordinates of the vertices for Position 1.
   d. Record the new coordinates on your game sheet, plot the new points on the coordinate plane, and draw a triangle. Use your game piece to identify the transformation you made and record its name on your game sheet.
   e. Continue until you have moved the figure to all 5 positions on the All the Right Moves card. Then record the coordinates of the composition of transformations, which is Position 5.

5. Repeat the process with your other All the Right Moves card for the second game sheet.

6. When you and your partner have completed your two cards, exchange game sheets and check each other's work.

7. Score your game sheets: You get 2 points for each transformation you correctly identify and 5 points for the correct coordinates of each composition of transformations.

8. The player with the greater number of points wins the game.

All the Right Moves
Game Sheet

Player: _____

All the Right Moves **Card:** _____

Position 0: A( ), B( ), C( )	Type of Transformation
Position 1: A( ), B( ), C( )	
Position 2: A( ), B( ), C( )	
Position 3: A( ), B( ), C( )	
Position 4: A( ), B( ), C( )	
Position 5: A( ), B( ), C( )	

Composition of Transformations:

A(   ), B(   ), C(   )

Points Earned for All the Right Moves **Card:** _____

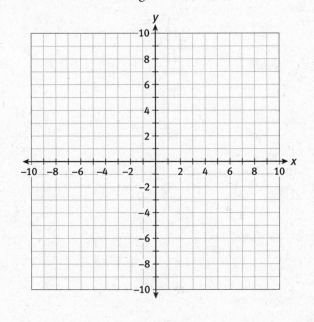

My Notes

All the Right Moves
Game Sheet

Player: _____

All the Right Moves **Card:** _____

Position 0: A( ), B( ), C( )	Type of Transformation
Position 1: A( ), B( ), C( )	
Position 2: A( ), B( ), C( )	
Position 3: A( ), B( ), C( )	
Position 4: A( ), B( ), C( )	
Position 5: A( ), B( ), C( )	

Composition of Transformations:

$A($ $), B($ $), C($ $)$

Points Earned for All the Right Moves **Card:** _____

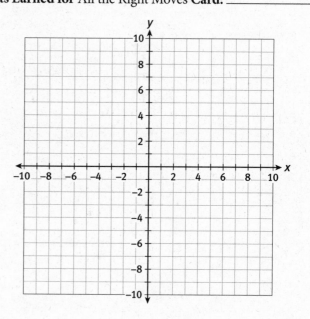

Total Points Earned: _____

9. **Model with mathematics.** Work with your partner to discover a composition of transformations that has the same result as one from the All the Right Moves game but takes fewer transformations.

    a. Select one of the All the Right Moves game cards.

    b. Follow the instructions on the card and use the coordinate plane below to draw the locations of Position 0 and Position 5.

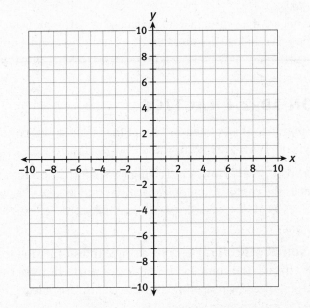

    c. Use what you know about reflections, translations, and rotations to move the game piece from Position 0 to Position 5 in four or fewer steps.

    d. Write the directions for the moves you found in Item 9c on a separate sheet of paper. Then trade directions with your partner and follow each other's directions to see whether the new transformation is correct.

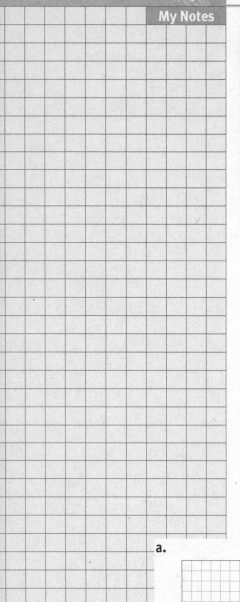

Check Your Understanding

10. The point $T(5, -1)$ is reflected across the x-axis, then across the y-axis. What are the coordinates of T' and T''?

11. $\triangle ABC$ has vertices $A(-5, 2)$, $B(0, -4)$, and $C(3, 3)$.
  a. Determine the coordinates of the image of $\triangle ABC$ after a translation 2 units right and 4 units down followed by a reflection over the y-axis.
  b. What are the coordinates of the image of $\triangle ABC$ after a reflection over the y-axis followed by a translation 2 units right and 4 units down?

LESSON 19-2 PRACTICE

12. The point $(1, 3)$ is rotated $90°$ about the origin and then reflected across the y-axis. What are the coordinates of the image?

13. Attend to precision. Find a single transformation that has the same effect as the composition of translations $(x, y) \rightarrow (x - 2, y + 1)$ followed by $(x, y) \rightarrow (x + 1, y + 3)$. Use at least three ordered pairs to confirm your answer.

14. Reason abstractly. Describe a single transformation that has the same effect as the composition of transformations reflecting over the x-axis followed by reflecting over the y-axis. Use at least three ordered pairs to confirm your answer.

15. Write a composition of transformations that moves figure A so that it coincides with figure B.

a.

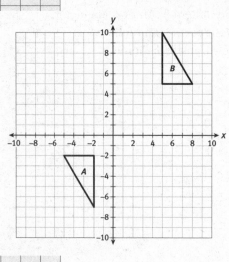

b.

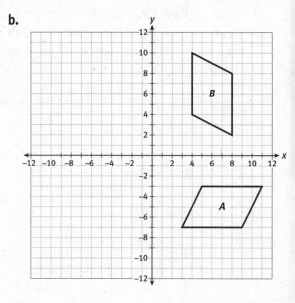

All the Right Moves Game Cards

All the Right Moves Card 1	All the Right Moves Card 2	All the Right Moves Card 3
Position 0: $A(3, 4)$, $B(3, 1)$, $C(7, 1)$	**Position 0:** $A(1, 1)$, $B(1, -2)$, $C(5, -2)$	**Position 0:** $A(-5, 0)$, $B(-5, -3)$, $C(-1, -3)$
Position 1: $(x, y) \rightarrow (-x, y)$	**Position 1:** $(x, y) \rightarrow (x + 2, y)$	**Position 1:** $(x, y) \rightarrow (-y, x)$
Position 2: $(x, y) \rightarrow (x + 3, y + 4)$	**Position 2:** $(x, y) \rightarrow (-x, y)$	**Position 2:** $(x, y) \rightarrow (-x, y)$
Position 3: $(x, y) \rightarrow (x, -y)$	**Position 3:** $(x, y) \rightarrow (x, 4 - y)$	**Position 3:** $(x, y) \rightarrow (-6 - x, y)$
Position 4: $(x, y) \rightarrow (x - 1, y)$	**Position 4:** $(x, y) \rightarrow (-y, x)$	**Position 4:** $(x, y) \rightarrow (x + 3, y + 4)$
Position 5: $(x, y) \rightarrow (-y, x)$	**Position 5:** $(x, y) \rightarrow (x - 1, y)$	**Position 5:** $(x, y) \rightarrow (-y, x)$

All the Right Moves Card 4	All the Right Moves Card 5	Game Pieces
Position 0: $A(-3, -4)$, $B(-3, -7)$, $C(1, -7)$	**Position 0:** $A(0, -1)$, $B(0, -4)$, $C(4, -4)$	Cut out one game piece for each partner.
Position 1: $(x, y) \rightarrow (-x, y)$	**Position 1:** $(x, y) \rightarrow (y, -x)$	
Position 2: $(x, y) \rightarrow (x + 5, y)$	**Position 2:** $(x, y) \rightarrow (x, 2 - y)$	
Position 3: $(x, y) \rightarrow (x + 2, y - 1)$	**Position 3:** $(x, y) \rightarrow (x, -y)$	
Position 4: $(x, y) \rightarrow (4 - x, y)$	**Position 4:** $(x, y) \rightarrow (x + 2, y)$	
Position 5: $(x, y) \rightarrow (y, -x)$	**Position 5:** $(x, y) \rightarrow (-x, -y)$	

This page is intentionally blank.

ACTIVITY 19 PRACTICE

Write your answers on notebook paper.
Show your work.

Lesson 19-1

Each figure in Items 1–4 is an image of the figure shown on the coordinate plane below. Describe the transformations that were performed to obtain each image.

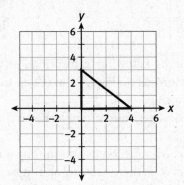

1.

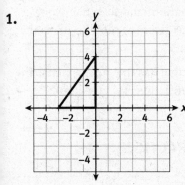

2.

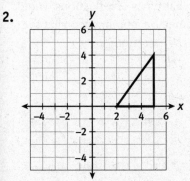

3.

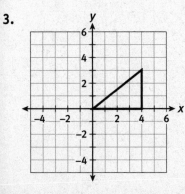

4.

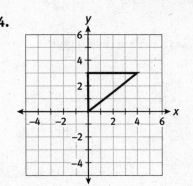

5. Compare the figures in Items 1–4.
   a. How do the areas of each figure compare to the area of the original figure?
   b. What can you determine about the corresponding sides of each figure?
   c. What can you determine about the corresponding angles of each figure?
   d. Can you determine if the images of each figure are congruent to the original figure? Provide reasoning for your answer.

6. The coordinate plane below shows △ABC and a 90° clockwise rotation of △ABC about the origin.

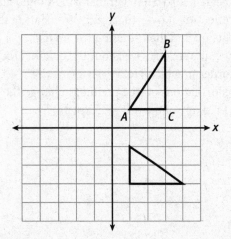

   a. Sketch the 180° clockwise rotation of △ABC.
   b. Sketch the 90° counterclockwise rotation of △ABC.
   c. How do the images compare with △ABC?

Lesson 19-2

7. The preimage of a triangle is shown on the coordinate plane.

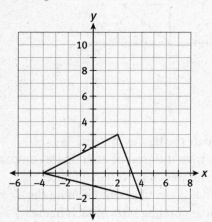

Which of the following types of transformation results in an image where corresponding angles and sides are NOT congruent?

A. reflection

B. rotation

C. translation

D. none of the above

8. To create a logo, Henry transforms a quadrilateral by reflecting it over the x-axis, translating it 4 units up and then rotating the image 270° counterclockwise about the origin. Does the order in which Henry performs the transformations on the preimage change the size or shape of the image? Explain.

9. Figure 1 shows the preimage of a figure.

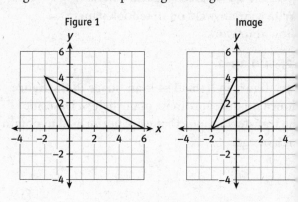

Which of the following transformation(s) have been performed on Figure 1 to obtain the image?

A. Rotate 180°.

B. Shift down 2 units and reflect over the line $y = 2$.

C. Reflect over the x-axis and shift up 4 units.

D. Reflect over the y-axis and shift up 4 units.

10. List two transformations and then name one transformation that gives the same result as the two transformations.

11. Find a translation that has the same effect as the composition of translations $(x, y) \rightarrow (x + 7, y - 2)$ followed by $(x, y) \rightarrow (x - 3, y + 2)$.

MATHEMATICAL PRACTICES
Reason Abstractly

12. How many and what types of reflections would have to be performed on a preimage to get the same image as a 180° rotation?

In medieval times, a person was rewarded with a coat of arms in recognition of noble acts. In honor of your noble acts so far in this course, you are being rewarded with a coat of arms. Each symbol on the coordinate plane below represents a special meaning in the history of heraldry.

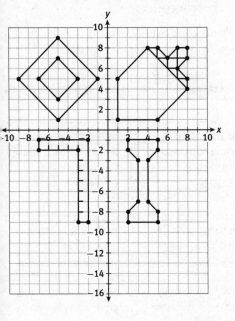

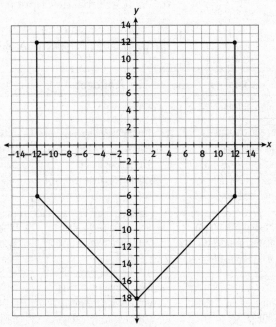

Transform the figures from their original positions to their intended positions on the shield above using the following descriptions.

1. The **acorn** in Quadrant I stands for antiquity and strength and is also the icon used in the SpringBoard logo.
   a. Reflect the acorn over the *x*-axis. Sketch the image of the acorn on the shield.
   b. Write the symbolic representation of this transformation.

2. The **mascle** in Quadrant II represents the persuasiveness you have exhibited in justifying your answers.
   a. Rotate the mascle 270° counterclockwise about the origin. Sketch the image of the mascle on the shield.
   b. Write the symbolic representation of this transformation.

3. The **carpenter's square** in Quadrant III represents your compliance with the laws of right and equity. The location of the carpenter's square is determined by a composition of transformations. Rotate the carpenter's square 90° counterclockwise about the origin followed by a reflection over the *y*-axis.
   a. Copy and complete the table by listing the coordinates of the image after the carpenter's square is rotated 90° counterclockwise about the origin.
   b. Sketch the image of the carpenter's square after the composition of transformations described.

Preimage	Image
(−7, −1)	
(−7, −2)	
(−2, −1)	
(−3, −2)	
(−3, −9)	
(−2, −9)	

4. Finally, the **column** in Quadrant IV represents the determination and steadiness you've shown throughout your work in this course.
   a. Sketch the column using the transformation given by the symbolic representation $(x, y) \rightarrow (x - 9, y + 10)$.
   b. Write a verbal description of the transformation.

5. Explain why each of the symbols on your coat of arms is congruent to the preimage of the symbol on the original coordinate plane.

Scoring Guide	Exemplary	Proficient	Emerging	Incomplete
	The solution demonstrates these characteristics:			
Mathematics Knowledge and Thinking (Items 1a-b, 2a-b, 3a-b, 4a-b, 5)	• Clear and accurate understanding of reflections, rotations, and translations in the coordinate plane.	• An understanding of reflections, rotations, and translations in the coordinate plane with few errors.	• Partial understanding of reflections, rotations, and translations in the coordinate plane.	• Incorrect understanding of reflections, rotations, and translations in the coordinate plane.
Problem Solving (Items 1a-b, 2a-b, 3a-b, 4a-b)	• Interpreting a problem accurately in order to carry out a transformation.	• Interpreting a problem to carry out a transformation.	• Difficulty interpreting a problem to carry out a transformation.	• Incorrect or incomplete interpretation of a transformation situation.
Mathematical Modeling / Representations (Items 1a, 2a, 3a, 4a)	• Accurately transforming pre-images and drawing the images.	• Transforming pre-images and drawing the images with few, if any, errors.	• Difficulty transforming pre-images and drawing the images.	• Incorrectly transforming pre-images and drawing the images.
Reasoning and Communication (Items 4b, 5)	• A precise explanation of congruent transformations.	• An understanding of transformations that retain congruence.	• A confusing explanation of congruent transformations.	• An inaccurate explanation of congruent transformations.

Similar Triangles

Mirrors and Shadows
Lesson 20-1 Exploring Similarity

Learning Targets:

- Identify similar triangles.
- Identify corresponding sides and angles in similar triangles.

> **SUGGESTED LEARNING STRATEGIES:** Look for a Pattern, Visualization, Create Representations, Group Discussion

Thales of Miletus was a Greek philosopher, mathematician, and scientist who lived in 600 B.C.E. Two thousand six hundred years ago, he wondered about the height of the Great Pyramid in Egypt. Thales noticed that the sun's shadows fell from every object in the desert at the same angle, creating similar triangles from every object. Thales's research allowed him to use similar triangles to measure the height of the pyramids of Egypt and the distance to a ship at sea.

Thales used shadows in his work; however, a mirror placed on the floor can also be used to determine measures indirectly. When the mirror is placed at a particular distance from the wall, the distance that an observer stands from the mirror determines the reflection that the observer sees in the mirror.

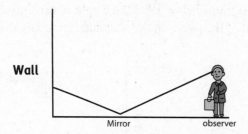

1. Use the table on the next page to record results for each of the steps below.
   - Find a spot on the floor 20 feet away from one of the walls of your classroom.
   - Place a mirror on the floor 4 feet from that wall.
   - Each group member should take a turn standing on the spot 20 feet from the wall and look into the mirror. Other group members should help the observer locate the point on the wall that the observer sees in the mirror and then measure the height of this point above the floor.
   - Before moving the mirror, each group member should take a turn as the observer.
   - Repeat the same process by moving the mirror to locations that are 8 feet and 10 feet away from the wall.

My Notes

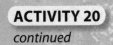

My Notes

Distance from the Wall to the Mirror (in feet)	Height of the Point on the Wall Reflected in the Mirror (in feet)			
	Person A	Person B	Person C	Person D
4				
8				
10				

2. Measure the eye-level height for each member of the group and record it in the table below.

Eye-Level Height for Each Group Member			
Person A	Person B	Person C	Person D

3. Consider the data collected when the mirror was 4 feet from the wall.
   a. On the diagrams below, label the height of each group member and the height of the point on the wall determined by the group member.

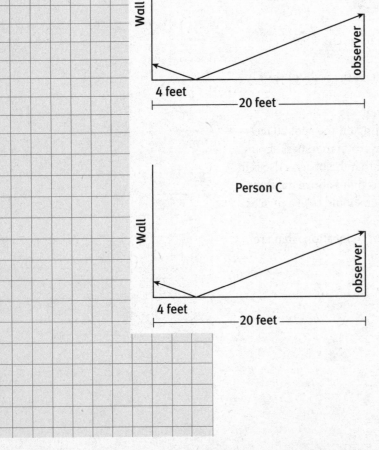

Person A

Wall

4 feet

20 feet

observer

Person B

Wall

4 feet

20 feet

observer

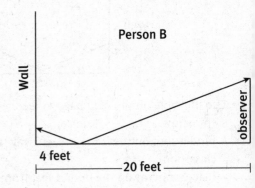

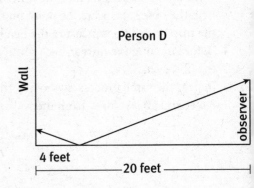

Person C

Wall

4 feet

20 feet

observer

Person D

Wall

4 feet

20 feet

observer

My Notes

b. For each person in the group, determine the ratio of the height of the point on the wall to the eye-level height of the observer.

Ratio of height of the point on the wall to eye level of observer		Person A	Person B	Person C	Person D
	Ratio as a fraction				
	Ratio as a decimal				

c. **Express regularity in repeated reasoning.** What appears to be true about the ratios you found?

4. If the eye-level height of a five-year-old observer is 3.6 feet, what height can you predict for the point on the wall? Explain your reasoning.

5. Consider the data collected when the mirror was 8 feet from the wall. For each group member, determine the ratio of the height of the point on the wall to the eye-level height of the observer. What appears to be true?

6. Consider the data collected when the mirror was 10 feet from the wall. For each group member, determine the ratio of the height of the point on the wall to the eye-level height of the observer. What appears to be true?

MATH TERMS

Similar polygons are polygons in which the lengths of the corresponding sides are in proportion, and the corresponding angles are congruent.

MATH TERMS

When two ratios are equivalent, then they form a **proportion**. For example, the ratios $\frac{3}{7}$ and $\frac{12}{28}$ are equivalent. Setting these ratios equal generates the proportion $\frac{3}{7} = \frac{12}{28}$.

WRITING MATH

The symbol $\sim$ is used to denote two similar figures.

Similar polygons are polygons in which the lengths of the corresponding sides are in **proportion**, and the corresponding angles are congruent.

For example, in the following triangles, the corresponding angles are congruent, and the corresponding sides are in proportion. Therefore, the triangles are similar.

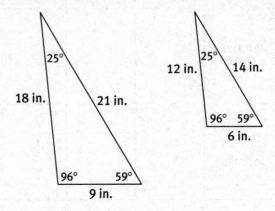

A similarity statement for the triangles below is $\triangle PWM \sim \triangle EFM$. A **similarity statement** indicates that the corresponding angles are congruent, and the corresponding sides are proportional.

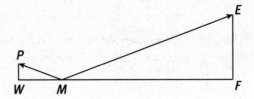

My Notes

7. The diagram below shows two similar triangles like the triangles you worked with in Item 3.

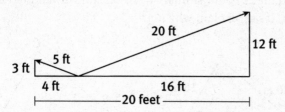

20 ft

12 ft

5 ft

3 ft

4 ft   16 ft

20 feet

a. Use the lengths of the three pairs of corresponding sides to create three ratios in the form $\dfrac{\text{side length in small triangle}}{\text{corresponding length in large triangle}}$

b. Compare the ratios written in part a. Then explain how these ratios relate to the ratios you created in Item 3.

Check Your Understanding

8. Are the triangles shown below similar? If so, explain why and write a similarity statement. If not, explain why not.

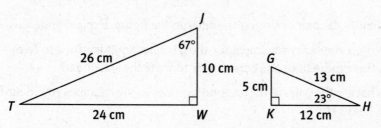

J

67°

26 cm

10 cm   G

5 cm   13 cm

T   23°

24 cm   W   K   12 cm   H

9. In the figure, $\triangle ABC \sim \triangle DEF$. Complete the following.

a. $m\angle F = \underline{\hspace{2cm}}$

b. $\dfrac{AB}{DE} = \dfrac{\square}{DF}$

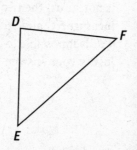

A

D

F

C

B

E

My Notes

LESSON 20-1 PRACTICE

10. Are the triangles below similar? If so, explain why and write a similarity statement. If not, explain why not.

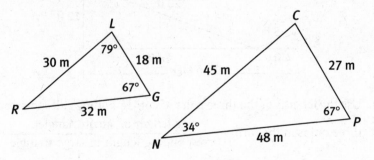

Use the figure below for Items 11–13.

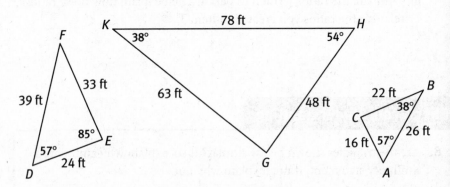

11. Identify the pair of similar triangles in the figure. Explain your answer.

12. Write a similarity statement for the triangles you identified in Item 11. Is there more than one correct way to write the statement?

13. What are the pairs of corresponding sides in the triangles you identified in Item 11?

14. Construct viable arguments. Malia is a jewelry designer. She created two silver triangles that she would like to use as earrings, but she is not sure if the two triangles are similar. One triangle has angles that measure 51° and 36°. The other triangle has angles that measure 36° and 95°. Is it possible to determine whether or not the triangles are similar? Justify your answer.

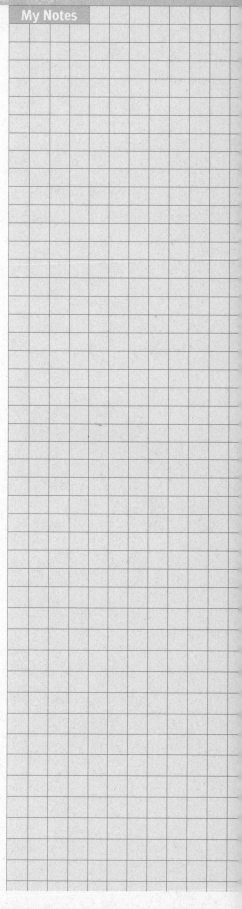

Learning Targets:

- Determine whether triangles are similar given side lengths or angle measures.
- Calculate unknown side lengths in similar triangles.

SUGGESTED LEARNING STRATEGIES: Look for a Pattern, Create Representations, Identify a Subtask, Visualization

Two figures are similar if the corresponding angles are congruent and the corresponding sides are proportional. However, only one of these conditions is necessary in order to conclude that figures are congruent.

> **Necessary Condition for Similarity**
> When two triangles satisfy at least one of the following conditions, then they are similar.
> (1) The corresponding angles are congruent.
> (2) The corresponding sides are proportional.

The ratio of two corresponding sides of similar triangles is called the **scale factor**.

1. What appears to be the scale factor for the similar triangles you created In Lesson 20-1 using the data collected when the mirror was 8 feet from the wall? Support your answer using corresponding sides for the similar triangles.

2. The triangles shown here are similar.

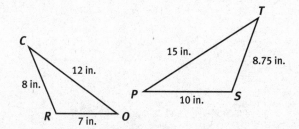

a. Name the transformation that can help you identify the corresponding parts of the triangles.

b. Write a similarity statement for the triangles.

c. Determine the scale factor for the two similar triangles. Show your calculations.

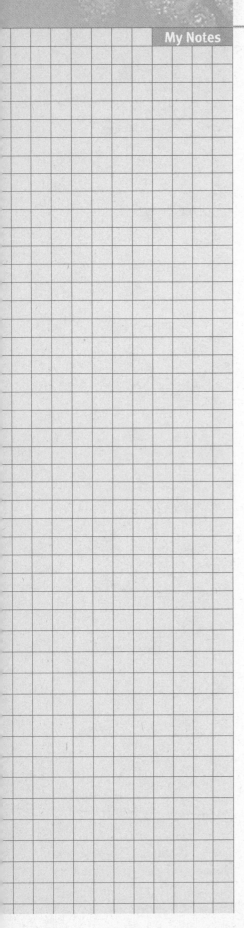

3. Consider the three triangles below.

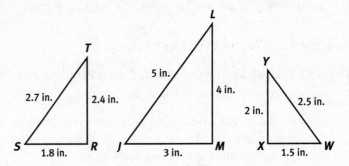

a. Compare ratios to identify any similar triangles.

b. Write a similarity statement to identify the similar triangles.

c. State the scale factor for the similar triangles.

d. What are the pairs of corresponding angles of the similar triangles?

Lesson 20-2
Properties and Conditions of Similar Triangles

The scale factor can be used to determine an unknown side length in similar figures.

Example A

Solve for x if $\triangle AIM \sim \triangle LOW$.

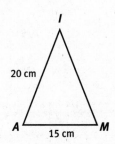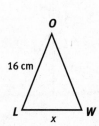

Step 1: Find the scale factor using known corresponding lengths.

The scale factor is $\dfrac{20 \text{ cm}}{16 \text{ cm}}$ or $\dfrac{5}{4}$.

Step 2: Write a proportion using the scale factor.

$$\frac{5}{4} = \frac{15 \text{ cm}}{x}$$

Step 3: Solve the proportion.

$$5x = 60.$$
$$x = 12$$

Solution: $x = 12$ cm

Try These A

Given $\triangle TIN \sim \triangle CAN$.

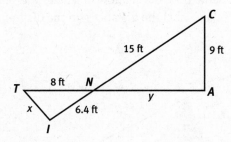

a. Determine the scale factor.

b. Solve for x and y.

4. Suppose that a fly has landed on the wall and a mirror is lying on the floor 5 feet from the base of the wall. Fiona, whose eye-level height is 6 feet, is standing 3 feet away from the mirror and 8 feet away from the wall. She can see the fly reflected in the mirror.

   a. Use the information provided to label the distances on the diagram.

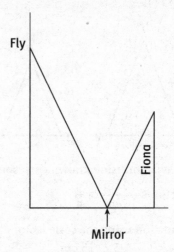

   b. Show how to use the properties of similar triangles to calculate the distance from the floor to the observed fly.

5. **Model with mathematics.** In his research, Thales determined that the height of the Great Pyramid could easily be calculated by the using the length of its shadow relative to the length of Thales's own shadow. Assume Thales was 6 feet tall and the shadow of the pyramid was 264 feet at the same time the shadow of Thales was 3.5 feet.

   a. Using these data, label the distances on the diagram.

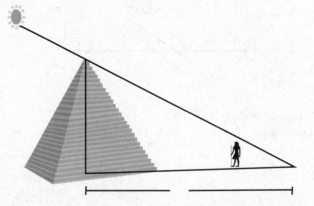

   b. Determine the height of the Great Pyramid. Round your answer to the nearest tenth.

6. In $\triangle JKL$, $m\angle J = 32°$ and $m\angle K = 67°$. In $\triangle PQR$, $m\angle P = 32°$ and $m\angle Q = 67°$. Is $\triangle JKL \sim \triangle PQR$? Explain.

Check Your Understanding

7. Are the two triangles shown below similar? If so, write a similarity statement and determine the scale factor. If not, explain why not.

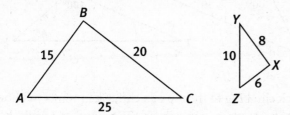

8. Given $\triangle ABC \sim \triangle DEF$. Determine the value of x and y.

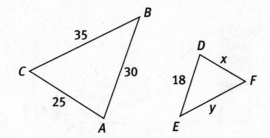

9. Given $\triangle TUS \sim \triangle TVW$. Determine the value of x and y.

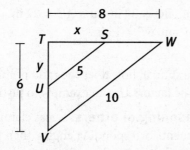

My Notes

LESSON 20-2 PRACTICE

10. Write similarity statements to show which triangles are similar.

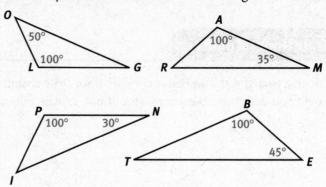

11. Before rock climbing to the top of a cliff, Chen wants to know how high he will climb. He places a mirror on the ground and walks backward until he sees the top of the cliff in the mirror, as shown in the figure. What is the height of the cliff?

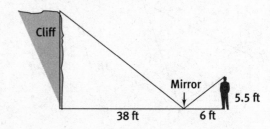

12. Given: △*ABC* ~ △*RST*
    AB = 44 in., *BC* = 33 in., and *AC* = 22 in.
    RS = 20 in. and *ST* = 15 in.
Find *RT*.

13. If two triangles are similar, how does the ratio of their perimeters compare to the scale factor? Use an example to justify your answer.

14. Critique the reasoning of others. Lucas claims, "If triangles have two pairs of congruent corresponding angles, then the third angles must also be congruent and the triangles must be similar." Is Lucas correct? Justify your answer.

ACTIVITY 20 PRACTICE
Write your answers on notebook paper.
Show your work.

Lesson 20-1

1. Determine whether the triangles are similar. If so, write a similarity statement. If not, explain why not.

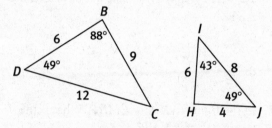

2. If $\triangle JOE \sim \triangle AMY$, find the measure of each of the following angles.

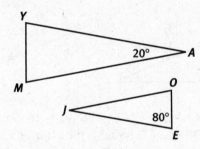

   a. $m\angle J$ b. $m\angle O$
   c. $m\angle Y$ d. $m\angle M$

3. $\triangle ABC$ has side lengths 15 cm, 20 cm, and 25 cm. What could be the side lengths of a triangle similar to $\triangle ABC$?
   A. 7 m, 8 m, and 9 m
   B. 6 m, 8 m, and 10 m
   C. 5 cm, 10 cm, and 15 cm
   D. 30 mm, 40 mm, and 55 mm

4. In $\triangle PQR$, $m\angle P = 27°$ and $m\angle R = 61°$. In $\triangle XYZ$, $m\angle Y = 92°$.
   a. Is it possible for $\triangle PQR$ to be similar to $\triangle XYZ$? Explain your reasoning.
   b. Can you conclude that $\triangle PQR$ is similar to $\triangle XYZ$? Why or why not?

5. Given that $\triangle ABC$ is similar to $\triangle GHJ$, which of the following statements must be true?
   A. Both triangles have the same side lengths.
   B. If $\triangle ABC$ has a right angle, then $\triangle GHJ$ has a right angle.
   C. The perimeter of $\triangle ABC$ is greater than the perimeter of $\triangle GHJ$.
   D. If $\triangle ABC$ has a side of length 2 cm, then $\triangle GHJ$ has a side of length 2 cm.

Lesson 20-2
For Items 6 and 7, determine whether the triangles shown are similar. If so, write a similarity statement for the triangles and determine the scale factor. If not, explain why not.

6.

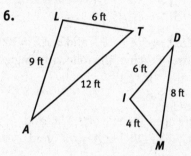

7.

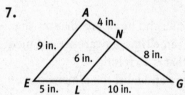

8. Given $\triangle SIX \sim \triangle TEN$, find a and b.

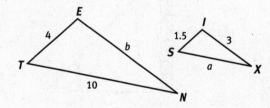

9. Given $\triangle CAN \sim \triangle CYR$, find p and q.

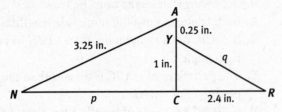

10. Given: $\triangle JKL \sim \triangle QRS$. Determine the value of x.

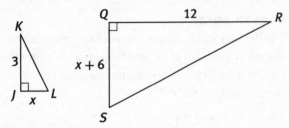

11. $\triangle MON \sim \triangle WED$, $m\angle M = 37°$, and $m\angle E = 82°$. Find the measure of each of the following angles.
   a. $\angle O$ **b.** $\angle W$
   c. $\angle N$ **d.** $\angle D$

12. Tell the measure of each angle of $\triangle ABC$ and $\triangle PQR$ if $\triangle ABC \sim \triangle PQR$, $m\angle A = 90°$, and $m\angle B = 56°$.

13. Aaron is 6.25 ft tall, and he casts a shadow that is 5 ft long. At the same time, a nearby monument casts a shadow that is 25 ft long.
   a. Copy the figure and label the dimensions on the figure.

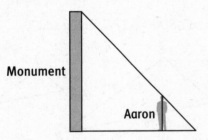

   b. Determine the height of the monument.

14. $\triangle ABC \sim \triangle DEF$ and the scale factor of $\triangle ABC$ to $\triangle DEF$ is $\frac{4}{3}$. If $AB = 60$, what is DE?

15. Sonia is 124 centimeters tall and casts a shadow that is 93 centimeters long. She is standing next to a tree that casts a shadow that is 135 meters long. How tall is the tree?

16. $\triangle STU \sim \triangle XYZ$, $ST = 6$, $SU = 8$, $XZ = 12$, and $YZ = 15$. What is the scale factor of $\triangle STU$ to $\triangle XYZ$?
   A. $\frac{2}{5}$ **B.** $\frac{1}{2}$
   C. $\frac{8}{15}$ **D.** $\frac{2}{3}$

17. In the figure, $\triangle JKL \sim \triangle MNP$. What is the perimeter of $\triangle MNP$?

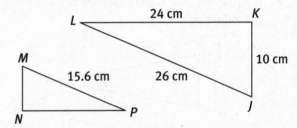

18. $\triangle ABC \sim \triangle DEF$. $AB = 12$, $AC = 16$, $DE = 30$, and $DF = x + 5$. What is the value of x?
   A. 30   **B.** 35
   C. 40   **D.** 45

MATHEMATICAL PRACTICES
Look For and Make Use of Structure

19. An equiangular triangle is a triangle with three congruent angles. Explain why all equiangular triangles are similar.

Dilations

Alice's Adventures in Shrinking and Growing
Lesson 21-1 Stretching and Shrinking Geometric Figures

Learning Targets:

- Investigate the effect of dilations on two-dimensional figures.
- Explore the relationship of dilated figures on the coordinate plane.

> **SUGGESTED LEARNING STRATEGIES:** Look for a Pattern, Predict and Confirm, Create Representations, Visualization

In the story *Alice's Adventures in Wonderland* written by Lewis Carroll, Alice spends a lot of time shrinking and growing in height. The height changes occur when she drinks a potion or eats a cake.

1. Complete the table by finding Alice's new height after she eats each bite of cake or drinks each potion.

Starting Height (inches)	Change in Height	New Height (inches)
56	$\frac{1}{8}$ times as tall	
60	$\frac{2}{5}$ times as tall	
60	1.5 times as tall	
24	$\frac{5}{3}$ times as tall	
30	2.2 times as tall	

CONNECT TO LITERATURE

Alice's Adventures in Wonderland is a novel published in 1865. It is the story of a young girl named Alice who wants to escape being bored by adulthood. In a dream she follows a white rabbit and falls down a deep tunnel and the adventure begins.

2. Each change in height resulted in a decrease or increase to Alice's starting height.

   a. Alice's starting height decreased when it was multiplied by which two factors?

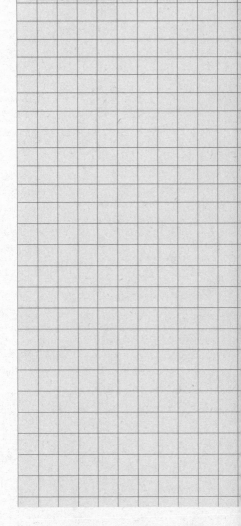

My Notes

b. Write a conjecture regarding the number you multiply by to decrease Alice's height.

c. Confirm your conjecture by providing two additional examples that show that Alice's starting height decreases.

d. Write a conjecture regarding the number you multiply by to increase Alice's starting height.

e. Confirm your conjecture regarding Alice's increase in height by providing two additional examples that show that Alice's starting height increases.

Alice's height changes—shrinking and growing—are a type of transformation known as a dilation.

A **dilation** is a transformation where the image is *similar* to the preimage; the size of the image changes but the shape stays the same.

3. **Use appropriate tools strategically.** Given the preimage of $\triangle PQR$ below, use a ruler to draw the image of $\triangle PQR$ if it is dilated:

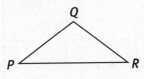

a. by a factor of 2

b. by a factor of $\frac{1}{2}$

4. Rectangles $ABCD$ and $A'B'C'D'$ are shown on the coordinate plane with the **center of dilation** at the origin, O.

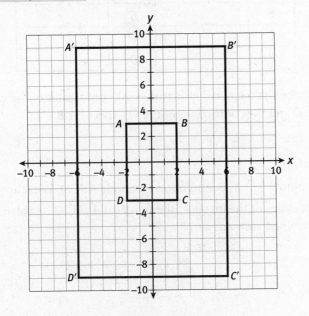

MATH TERMS

A **dilation** is a transformation that changes the size but not the shape of an object.

MATH TERMS

The **center of dilation** is a fixed point in the plane about which all points are expanded or reduced. It is the only point under a dilation that does not move.

My Notes

a. Determine the length of each side of rectangles *ABCD* and *A'B'C'D'*.

Side	Length (in units)
$\overline{AB}$	
$\overline{BC}$	
$\overline{CD}$	
$\overline{AD}$	

Side	Length (in units)
$\overline{A'B'}$	
$\overline{B'C'}$	
$\overline{C'D'}$	
$\overline{A'D'}$	

b. Describe the relationship between the side lengths of rectangle *ABCD* and rectangle *A'B'C'D'*.

c. Determine the coordinates of each of the vertices of both rectangles.

Rectangle *ABCD*		Rectangle *A'B'C'D'*	
A		A'	
B		B'	
C		C'	
D		D'	

d. Describe the relationship between the coordinates of the vertices of *ABCD* and the coordinates of the vertices of *A'B'C'D'*.

e. The point $\left(\frac{1}{3}, -3\right)$ is a point on rectangle *ABCD*. What are the coordinates of the image of the point on *A'B'C'D'*? Explain how you determined your answer.

Example A

Quadrilateral *SQRE* is dilated to quadrilateral *S'Q'R'E'* as shown on the coordinate plane. What is the relationship between the side lengths, perimeter, and area of the two figures?

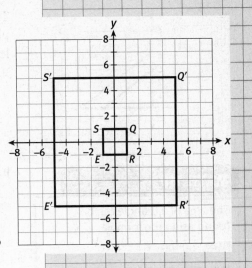

Step 1: Compare the side lengths of corresponding sides of quadrilateral *S'Q'R'E'* to quadrilateral *SQRE*.

$$\frac{S'Q'}{SQ} = \frac{10}{2} = \frac{5}{1}; \quad \frac{S'E'}{SE} = \frac{10}{2} = \frac{5}{1}$$

$$\frac{E'R'}{ER} = \frac{10}{2} = \frac{5}{1}; \quad \frac{R'Q'}{RQ} = \frac{10}{2} = \frac{5}{1}$$

The side lengths of quadrilateral *S'Q'R'E'* are 5 times as great as the side lengths of quadrilateral *SQRE*.

Step 2: Find the perimeter of each quadrilateral. Then write the ratio of the perimeter of quadrilateral *S'Q'R'E'* to the perimeter of quadrilateral *SQRE*.

Perimeter of quadrilateral *SQRE* = 8 units
Perimeter of quadrilateral *S'Q'R'E'* = 40 units

$$\text{ratio}: \frac{\text{Perimeter of } S'Q'R'E'}{\text{Perimeter of } SQRE} = \frac{40}{8} = \frac{5}{1}$$

Solution: The perimeter of quadrilateral *S'Q'R'E'* is 5 times as great as that of quadrilateral *SQRE*.

Step 3: Find the area of each quadrilateral. Then write the ratio of the area of quadrilateral *S'Q'R'E'* to the area of quadrilateral *SQRE*.

Area of quadrilateral *SQRE* = 4 square units
Area of quadrilateral *S'Q'R'E'* = 100 square units

$$\text{ratio}: \frac{\text{Area of } S'Q'R'E'}{\text{Area of } SQRE} = \frac{100}{4} = \frac{25}{1}$$

Solution: The area of quadrilateral *S'Q'R'E'* is 25 times as great as that of quadrilateral *SQRE*.

READING MATH

The fraction bar in a ratio is read aloud as "to." For example, the ratio $\frac{4}{1}$ is read as "4 to 1."

As you discuss Example A, make notes about the notation and vocabulary used so you can review them later to aid your understanding of dilating geometric figures.

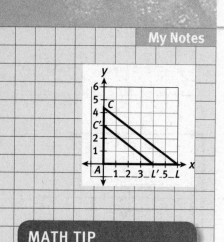

My Notes

MATH TIP

The area of a triangle can be found using the formula
$\text{Area} = \frac{1}{2}$ base × height.

In a right triangle, the legs can be used as the base and height.

Try These A

Triangle ALC is dilated to $\triangle AL'C'$ as shown on the coordinate plane. Triangle ALC has vertices $A(0, 0)$, $L(6, 0)$, $C(0, 4\frac{1}{2})$. The length of $\overline{C'L'}$ is 5 units.

a. Substitute known values into the proportion to find the length of $\overline{CL}$.

$$\frac{LA}{L'A} = \frac{CL}{C'L'}$$

b. Determine the ratio of the perimeter of $\triangle AL'C'$ to the perimeter of $\triangle ALC$.

c. Determine the ratio of the area of $\triangle AL'C'$ to the area of $\triangle ALC$.

Check Your Understanding

5. Triangle ABC is dilated to $\triangle A'B'C'$. The ratio of the perimeter of $\triangle A'B'C'$ to the perimeter of $\triangle ABC$ is $\frac{4}{1}$. Explain how you can use this information to determine if the image has a larger or smaller perimeter than the preimage.

6. Square $TUVW$ is enlarged to form square $T'U'V'W'$. What must be true about the relationship between corresponding sides for the enlargement to be considered a dilation?

7. **Reason abstractly.** Bradley states that in theory circles with different diameters are all dilations of each other. Susan states that in theory rectangles with different side lengths are all dilations of each other. Do you agree with either, both, or neither statement? Explain your reasoning.

LESSON 21-1 PRACTICE

8. Rectangle *ABCD* is dilated to the rectangle *EFGH*. It is given that *AB* = 48 ft, *BC* = 24 ft, and *FG* = 10 ft.

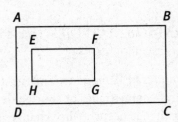

   a. Determine the ratio between corresponding side lengths.
   b. Explain how knowing the ratio of corresponding side lengths helps you to determine the length of $\overline{EF}$.
   c. Find the length of $\overline{EF}$.

9. A right triangle has vertices *A*(0, 0), *B*(10, 0), and *C*(10, 24). The triangle is dilated so that the ratio between corresponding side lengths of the preimage to the image is $\frac{3}{1}$. Explain the effect on the area and perimeter of the dilated triangle.

10. **Reason quantitatively.** Figure *ABCD* is shown on the coordinate plane. Suppose a graphic designer wants to dilate the figure so that the resulting image has a smaller area than figure *ABCD*. Describe a way the designer can achieve this type of dilation.

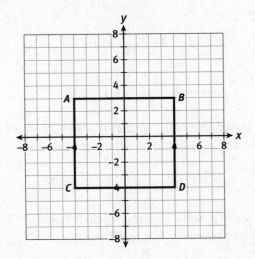

11. **Construct viable arguments.** Alice's teacher explains that all circles are similar and asks the class to investigate relationships between a circle with radius 4 cm and a circle with radius 6 cm. Dante claims that the ratio of the areas of the circles is $\frac{4}{9}$, while Louisa claims that the ratio of the areas is 2.25 to 1. Who is correct? Give evidence to support the claim.

My Notes

Learning Targets:

- Determine the effect of the value of the scale factor on a dilation.
- Explore how scale factor affects two-dimensional figures on a coordinate plane.

> **SUGGESTED LEARNING STRATEGIES:** Look for a Pattern, Graphic Organizer, Create Representations

In the story *Alice's Adventures in Wonderland*, when Alice drinks a potion or eats a cake, she physically becomes taller or shorter, depending on a given factor. When this height change occurs, Alice changes size, but she does not change shape. Each dimension of her body is proportionally larger or smaller than her original self.

The factor by which Alice's height is changed, or dilated, is known as a **scale factor**.

The *scale factor of dilation*, typically represented by the variable k, determines the size of the image of a dilated figure.

If $0 < k < 1$, then the image will be smaller than the original figure. In this case, the dilation is called a **reduction**.

If $k > 1$, then the image will be larger than the original figure, and dilation is called an **enlargement**.

MATH TERMS

The **scale factor of dilation** is the factor by which each linear measure of the figure is multiplied.

1. Consider the similar triangles shown.

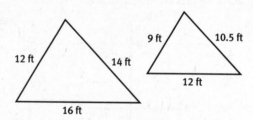

a. By what scale factor is the smaller triangle enlarged? Explain why the factor given must result in an enlargement.

b. By what scale factor is the larger triangle reduced? Explain why the factor given must result in a reduction.

c. What is the relationship between the two scale factors?

2. Suppose a point with coordinates (x, y) is a vertex of a geometric figure and that figure is dilated by a scale factor of k with the ***center of dilation*** at the origin.

   a. Create an ordered pair to represent the coordinates of the corresponding point on the image.

   b. Predict the size of the image as it compares to the preimage if k is 10.

   c. Predict the size of the image as it compares to the preimage if k is 0.5.

MATH TERMS

The **center of dilation** is a fixed point in the plane about which all points are expanded or reduced. It is the only point under a dilation that does not move. The center of dilation determines the location of the image.

Example A

Triangle $S'B'M'$ is a dilation of $\triangle SBM$ with a scale factor of 4. Using the coordinates of the vertices of $\triangle SBM$, determine the coordinates of the vertices of $\triangle S'B'M'$. Then plot $\triangle S'B'M'$ on the coordinate plane.

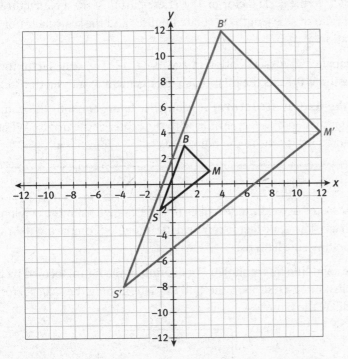

Step 1: Determine if the dilation is a reduction or enlargement.
    Since the scale factor is 4 and $4 > 1$, the dilation is an enlargement.

Step 2: Multiply the coordinates of the vertices of $\triangle SBM$ by the scale factor.
    $\triangle SBM$: $S(-1, -2), B(1, 3), M(3, 1)$
                Multiply each coordinate by 4.
    $\triangle S'B'M'$: $S'(-4, -8), B'(4, 12), M'(12, 4)$

Step 3: Plot the coordinates of the vertices of $\triangle S'B'M'$ on the coordinate plane.

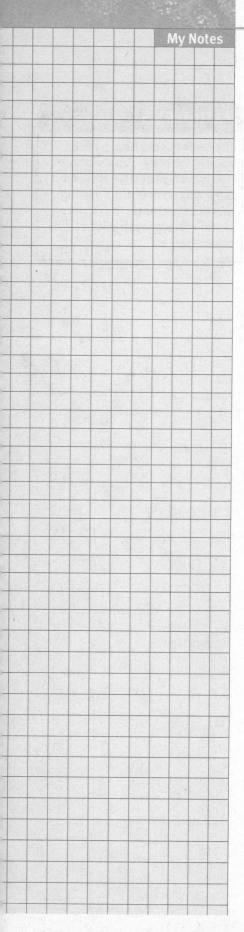

Try These A

a. Suppose the scale factor of dilation of $\triangle SBM$ in Example A is $\frac{1}{2}$. Determine if the resulting image, $\triangle S'B'M'$, will be a reduction or an enlargement of $\triangle SBM$. Then, determine the coordinates of $\triangle S'B'M'$.

b. Figure $A'B'C'D'$ is a dilation of figure $ABCD$ with a scale factor of 5. Given the coordinates of the vertices of $A(0, 0)$, $B(0, 2)$, $C(-2, -2)$, $D(-2, 0)$, determine the coordinates of the vertices of figure $A'B'C'D'$.

Check Your Understanding

3. Compare the ratio of the side lengths of figure $A'B'C'D'$ and figure $ABCD$ to the scale factor in Try These part b. Make a conjecture about the ratio of side lengths of dilated figures and the scale factor of dilation.

4. Triangle $P'Q'R'$ is a dilation image of $\triangle PQR$. The scale factor for the dilation is 0.12. Is the dilation an enlargement or a reduction? Explain.

5. **Make use of structure.** A geometric figure contains the point $(0, 0)$ and is dilated by a factor of m with the center at the origin. What changes will occur to the point $(0, 0)$?

The scale factor of dilation describes the size change from the original figure to the image. The scale factor can be determined by comparing the ratio of corresponding side lengths.

6. The solid line figure shown is a dilation of the figure formed by the dashed lines. Describe a method for determining the scale factor used to dilate the figure.

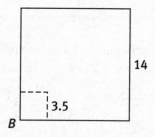

7. **Critique the reasoning of others.** Josie found the scale factor in Item 6 to be $\frac{1}{4}$. Explain why Josie got the wrong scale factor.

There exists a relationship between the area of dilated figures and the perimeter of dilated figures.

8. Make a prediction about the effect of the scale of dilation on the area and perimeter of two figures.

9. Trapezoid *TRAP*, shown on the coordinate plane, has vertices $(-2, 8)$, $(2, 8)$, $(8, -6)$, $(-8, -6)$. Suppose trapezoid TRAP is dilated by a scale factor of $\frac{1}{4}$.

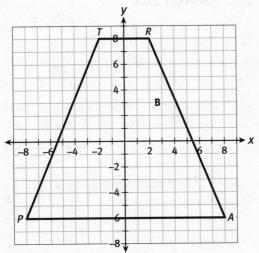

MATH TIP

The area of a trapezoid can be found using the formula Area $= \frac{1}{2} h(b_1 + b_2)$, where h is the height and b_1 and b_2 are the bases.

a. Plot and label the vertices of the image $T'R'A'P'$.

b. Determine the area of trapezoids $TRAP$ and $T'R'A'P'$.

c. What is the ratio of the area of $TRAP$ to the area of $T'R'A'P'$?

d. **Reason quantitatively.** Make a conjecture about the relationship between scale factor of dilation and the area of dilated figures.

My Notes

Check Your Understanding

10. Suppose a polygon is dilated by a scale factor of *k*. Write an expression for the ratio of the perimeters. Then, write an expression to represent the ratio of the areas.

11. A triangle is dilated by a scale factor of $\frac{2}{5}$.
    a. What is the ratio of the perimeters?
    b. What is the ratio of the areas?

12. **Construct viable arguments.** Suppose that a dilation is executed with a scale factor of 1. How would the preimage relate to the image? Using an example, justify your answer.

LESSON 21-2 PRACTICE

13. A rectangle has a perimeter of 24 ft. Following a dilation, the new perimeter of the rectangle is 36 ft.
    a. Determine the scale factor of dilation.
    b. What is the ratio of the areas?

14. A triangle has an area of 40 cm². Following a dilation, the new area of the triangle is 360 cm². What is the scale factor of dilation?

15. The vertices of trapezoid *ABCD* are *A*(−1, −1), *B*(−1, 1), *C*(2, 2), and *D*(2, −1).
    a. Draw the trapezoid and its dilation image for a dilation with center (0, 0) and scale factor 3.
    b. Determine the ratio of the perimeter.
    c. Determine the ratio of the areas.

16. **Make sense of problems.** Eye doctors dilate patients' pupils to get a better view inside the eye. If a patient's pupil had a 3.6-mm diameter before dilation and 8.4-mm diameter after dilation, determine the scale factor used to dilate the pupil. Explain why this created an enlargement.

MATH TIP

The area of a circle can be found using the formula Area $= \pi r^2$, where *r* is the radius of the circle.

ACTIVITY 21 PRACTICE
Write your answers on notebook paper.
Show your work.

Lesson 21-1

1. **Use appropriate tools strategically.** Sketch the dilation of the image of the figure below using a scale factor of $\frac{2}{3}$.

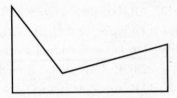

2. Does the size of a preimage increase or decrease when
   a. dilated by a factor greater than 1?
   b. dilated by a factor between 0 and 1?

3. The ratio of the area of $\triangle X'Y'Z'$ to the area of $\triangle XYZ$ is $\frac{2}{9}$. Explain how you can use this information to determine if the image is greater or smaller in area than the preimage.

4. The solid line figure is a dilation of the dashed line figure. Tell whether the dilation is an enlargement or a reduction. Then find the scale factor of the dilation.

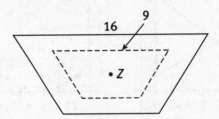

5. Explain how dilations are different from other types of transformations you have studied.

6. If the radius of a circle is 24 ft, how many circles can be the dilations of this circle? Why?

Lesson 21-2

7. A dilation has a center $(0, 0)$ and scale factor 1.5. What is the image of the point $(-3, 2)$?

8. A triangle has vertices $(-1, 1)$, $(6, -2)$, and $(3, 5)$. If the triangle is dilated with a scale factor of 3, which of the following are the vertices of the image?
   A. $(-3, 3)$, $(18, -6)$, $(9, 15)$
   B. $(3, 3)$, $(18, 6)$, $(9, 15)$
   C. $(-3, 3)$, $(18, 6)$, $(9, 15)$
   D. $(3, 3)$, $(18, -6)$, $(9, 15)$

9. Figure *B* is the result of a dilation of Figure *A*.

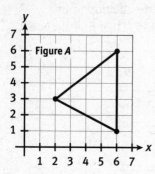 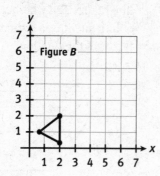

What is the scale factor of dilation?

A. 3

B. 2

C. $\frac{1}{3}$

D. $\frac{1}{2}$

10. Rhombus *RHMB* has vertices (2, 5), (5, 1), (2, −3), and (−1, 1). This figure has been dilated to rhombus *R′H′M′B′*, as shown on the coordinate plane.

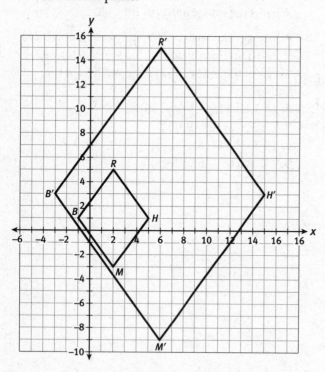

The area of rhombus *RHMB* is 24 square units. Which of the following is the area of rhombus *R′H′M′B′*?

A. 216 square units

B. 72 square units

C. 8 square units

D. 2.7 square units

11. The diagonals of rhombus *ABCD* are 6 ft and 8 ft. Rhombus *ABCD* is dilated to rhombus *RSTU* with the scale factor 8. What is the perimeter of rhombus *RSTU*?

MATHEMATICAL PRACTICES
Reason Abstractly and Quantitatively

12. The endpoints of $\overline{AB}$ are *A*(78, 52) and *B*(26, −52). $\overline{AB}$ is dilated to $\overline{GH}$ with endpoints at *G*(30, 20) and *H*(10, −20). Then, $\overline{GH}$ is dilated to $\overline{PQ}$ with endpoints at *P*(42, 28) and *Q*(14, −28). If $\overline{AB}$ is dilated directly to $\overline{PQ}$, what will be the scale factor?

z is a commercial artist working for Business as Usual. The company
ecializes in small-business public relations. Liz creates appealing logos
r client companies. In fact, she helped create the logo for her company.
usiness As Usual will use its logo in different sizes, with each design
cluding a triangle similar to the one shown.

1. The advertisement and stationery letterhead–size logos are shown
   below with the measurements of some of the side lengths. Determine
   the missing measures of the sides.

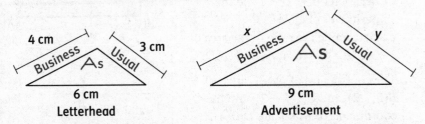

Letterhead

Advertisement

2. To create the triangles in the design, Liz wants to determine the measure
   of each angle in the designs. The advertisement logo is shown below
   including the measures of two of its angles. The business card logo will
   be similar to the advertisement so that $\triangle BAU \sim \triangle CRD$. Determine the
   measure of each angle.
   a. $m\angle C = $ _____
   b. $m\angle R = $ _____
   c. $m\angle D = $ _____

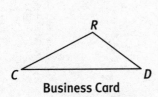

Business Card

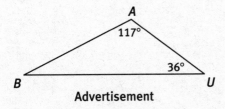

Advertisement

Liz tries to incorporate triangles and quadrilaterals into many of the logos she designs for her clients. She begins her layout by laying it out on a coordinate plane.

3. Quadrilateral *QUAD* is shown.
   a. Quadrilateral $Q'U'A'D'$ is a dilation of *QUAD* with scale factor $\frac{1}{2}$. List the coordinates of $Q'U'A'D'$ and sketch the graph on a coordinate plane.
   b. Determine the ratio of the perimeter of $Q'U'A'D'$ to the perimeter of *QUAD*.
   c. Determine the ratio of the area of $Q'U'A'D'$ to the area of *QUAD*.

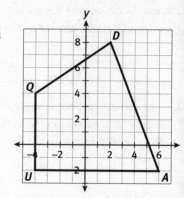

4. The coordinates of △*ABC* are *A*(0, 8), *B*(5, −2), and *C*(−4, −2), and the coordinates of △*DEF* are *D*(0, 4), *E*(3, −1), and *F*(−2, −1). Determine whether or not △*ABC* is similar to △*DEF*. Defend your answer.

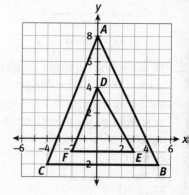

5. You have been chosen to work with Liz on a logo for a new client, Mountain Sky, a company that provides camping equipment and guides. Using either the logo design shown or a design of your own, recreate the design in sizes appropriate for a business card, business stationery letterhead, and an advertisement. Use properties of similar triangles to explain to Liz how you know the designs are dilations of the original. Include scale factors for each design.

Scoring Guide	Exemplary	Proficient	Emerging	Incomplete
	The solution demonstrates these characteristics:			
Mathematics Knowledge and Thinking (Items 1, 2a-c, 3a-c, 4, 5)	• Accurately finding side lengths and angle measures in similar triangles. • Accurately using dilations and scale factors.	• Finding side lengths and angle measures in similar triangles. • Using dilations and scale factors with few errors.	• Difficulty finding side lengths and angle measures in similar triangles. • Difficulty using dilations and scale factors.	• Little or no understanding of finding side lengths in similar triangles. • Little or no understanding of dilations.
Problem Solving (Items 3b-c, 4, 5)	• An appropriate and efficient strategy that results in a correct answer.	• A strategy that may include unnecessary steps but is correct.	• A strategy that results in some incorrect answers.	• No clear strategy when solving problems.
Mathematical Modeling / Representations (Items 3a, 5)	• Modeling dilations accurately and clearly.	• Drawing similar figures correctly.	• Difficulty drawing similar figures accurately.	• Incorrectly transforming pre-images and drawing the images.
Reasoning and Communication (Items 4, 5)	• Using precise language to justify that two triangles are similar.	• Explaining why two triangles are similar.	• A confusing explanation of triangle similarity.	• An inaccurate explanation of triangle similarity.

The Pythagorean Theorem

Stop the Presses

Lesson 22-1 Pythagorean Theorem: Squares of Lengths

Learning Targets:

● Investigate the Pythagorean Theorem.

● Understand and apply the Pythagorean Theorem.

SUGGESTED LEARNING STRATEGIES: Predict and Confirm, Marking the Text, Look for a Pattern, Interactive Word Wall, Create Representations

Jayla and Sidney are co-editors-in-chief of the school yearbook. They have just finished the final layouts of this year's edition. It is due at the print shop before it closes at 4 o'clock. The print shop is on her way home, so Jayla agrees to drop off the layouts at the print shop on the corner of 7th Avenue and Main Street. Sidney has a copy of the layouts with him to check one more time.

Jayla and Sidney part company at the front door of their school, which is located on the corner of 7th Avenue and D Street. Jayla walks toward the print shop on 7th Avenue and Sidney bikes toward his home on D Street.

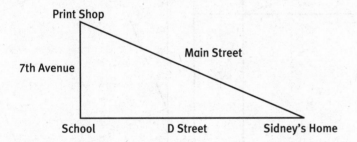

When Jayla gets to the print shop, she notices that the set of layouts is missing the last three pages. She calls Sidney at home to see whether he can quickly bring his copy of the layouts to the print shop.

Sidney leaves his house at 3:45 P.M. and starts biking along Main Street to the print shop. As he is pedaling, he wonders how far it is to the print shop. His house is 12 blocks away from the school and the print shop is five blocks away from the school. He can travel, at the most, one block per minute on his bike.

1. Read the scenario carefully and discuss with a partner or in your group the key information provided and how you might use it. Then predict whether Sidney makes it to the print shop before it closes.

The lengths of the three sides of any right triangle have a relationship that you could use to answer Item 1. It is one of the most useful properties you will use as you study mathematics.

MATH TIP

It does not matter which leg is labeled Leg 1 and which is labeled Leg 2.

MATH TERMS

The **hypotenuse** is the longest side of a right triangle. It is the side that is opposite the right angle.

The **legs** of a right triangle are the two sides that create the right angle.

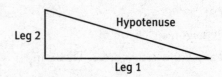

2. The *hypotenuse* of a right triangle is the side that is opposite the right angle. It is always the longest side of the triangle. The *legs* of a right triangle are the sides that form the right angle. Both Figures 1 and 2 have been formed using four congruent right triangles like the one above.

   a. Use grid paper to cut out four congruent right triangles with Leg 1 equal to seven units and Leg 2 equal to two units. Recreate Figures 1 and 2 on another piece of graph paper by tracing your four congruent triangles and adding line segments to complete L and M. Then complete Case 1 in Table A at the bottom of this page.

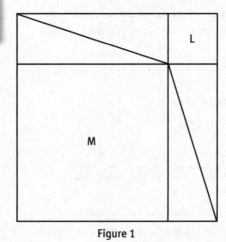

Figure 1

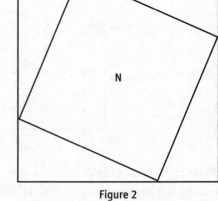

Figure 2

Table A

Case	Length Leg 1	Length Leg 2	Width Figure 1	Length Figure 1	Area Figure 1	Width Figure 2	Length Figure 2	Area Figure 2
1	7	2						
2	6	3						
3	4	3						
4								

   b. Complete Cases 2 and 3 in Table A by cutting out triangles to recreate Figures 1 and 2 using the lengths given in the table.

   c. Complete Case 4 in Table A by choosing your own leg lengths for a right triangle.

   d. What do you notice about Figure 1 and Figure 2 in each case?

3. Now use the figures you drew for Cases 1 through 4 to complete the first seven columns (Case through Area of Shape M) in Table B. For Case 5, use the variables *a* and *b* as the lengths of Leg 1 and Leg 2.

Table B

Case	Length Leg 1	Length Leg 2	Dimensions Shape L	Area Shape L	Dimensions Shape M	Area Shape M	Area Shape N
1	7	2					
2	6	3					
3	4	3					
4							
5	*a*	*b*					

4. Describe the relationship between the areas of shapes L, M, and N and complete the Area of Shape N column of Table B.

5. Describe the lengths of the sides of shapes L, M, and N in terms of the sides of the right triangles.

6. Find the area of shapes L, M, and N in terms of the lengths of the sides of the right triangles.

7. Make use of structure. Use *a* for the length of Leg 1, *b* for the length of Leg 2, and *c* for the length of the hypotenuse to write an equation that relates the areas of shapes L, M, and N.

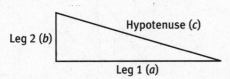

Leg 2 (*b*) — Hypotenuse (*c*) — Leg 1 (*a*)

The relationship that you have just explored is called the ***Pythagorean Theorem***.

MATH TERMS

The **Pythagorean Theorem** states that the sum of the squares of the lengths of the legs of a right triangle equals the square of the length of the hypotenuse.

CONNECT TO HISTORY

Although the Pythagorean Theorem is named for Pythagoras, a Greek mathematician who lived about 500 B.C.E., the ancient Babylonians, Chinese, and Egyptians understood and used this relationship even earlier.

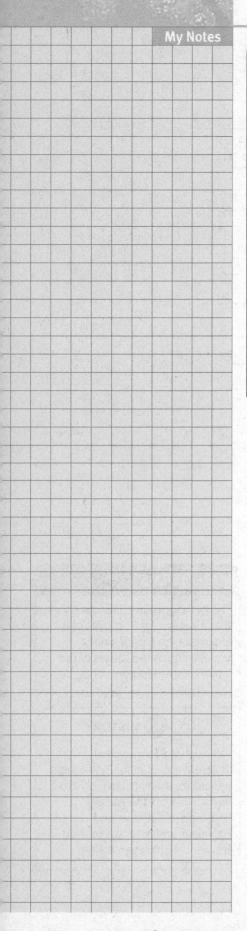

Check Your Understanding

8. Label this triangle using a for leg 1, b for leg 2, and c for the hypotenuse:

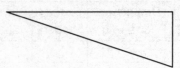

Use the figure to answer Items 9–10.

9. If the right triangle used to make the figure has leg lengths of 6 units and 8 units, what is the area of the inner square, S?

10. Write an equation in the form $a^2 + b^2 = c^2$ for the figure.

LESSON 22-1 PRACTICE

Find c^2 for the following right triangles.

11.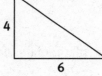

12.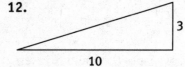

13.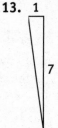

14. What does the Pythagorean Theorem state? Explain in your own words.

15. Construct viable arguments. Riley drew a triangle with the following dimensions:

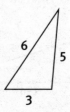

Is this triangle a right triangle? Explain your reasoning.

Learning Targets:
- Investigate the Pythagorean Theorem.
- Find missing side lengths of right triangles using the Pythagorean Theorem.

SUGGESTED LEARNING STRATEGIES: Predict and Confirm, Visualization, Look for a Pattern, Critique Reasoning, Sharing and Responding

The Pythagorean Theorem states that the sum of the squares of the lengths of the legs of a right triangle equals the square of the length of the hypotenuse. This relationship can be used to determine the missing length of a side of a right triangle when you are given two lengths.

Example A

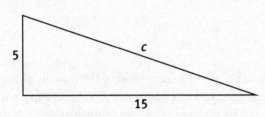

Find the length of the hypotenuse, c.

Step 1: Substitute the given lengths into the equation: $a^2 + b^2 = c^2$.
$$5^2 + 15^2 = c^2$$

Step 2: Square the lengths and add.
$$25 + 225 = c^2$$
$$250 = c^2$$

Step 3: Find the square root to solve for c. Since 250 is not a perfect square, round to the nearest tenth when finding the square root.
$$250 = c^2$$
$$15.8 = c$$

Solution: The length of the hypotenuse, c, is 15.8.

Try These A

Use the Pythagorean Theorem to find the unknown length to the nearest tenth.

a.
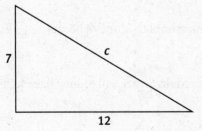

b.
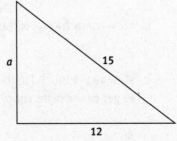

My Notes

c.

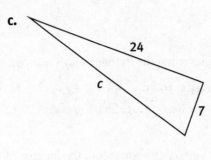

24

c

7

d.

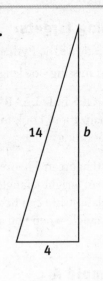

14

b

4

e. Leg 1 = 6
   Leg 2 = 10

1. Now that you know the relationship of the lengths of the three sides of any right triangle, you can figure out whether Sidney will make it to the print shop before it closes using the Pythagorean Theorem. Recall that Sidney leaves his house at 3:45 P.M. to try to make it to the print shop before 4:00 P.M. He starts biking down Main Street to the print shop. As he is pedaling, he wonders how far it is to the print shop. His house is 12 blocks away from the school and the print shop is five blocks away from the school. He can travel, at the most, one block per minute on his bike.

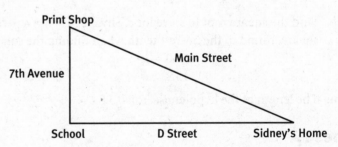

   a. How many blocks is it from the school to the print shop?

   b. How many blocks is it from the school to Sidney's home?

   c. How many block lengths down Main Street will Sidney have to bike to get to the print shop?

d. **Model with mathematics.** Can Sidney make it to the print shop on time? Explain your reasoning.

2. When you used the Pythagorean Theorem to find the distance from Sidney's house to the print shop, the formula gave you the square of the distance. What did you have to do to get the actual distance?

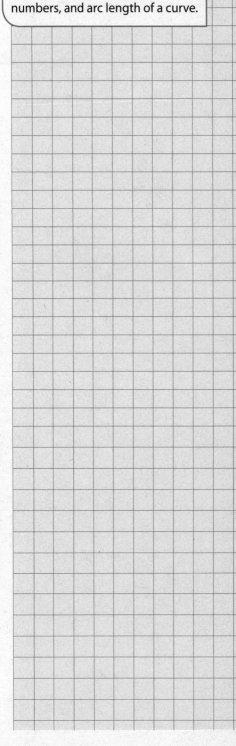

CONNECT TO AP

The Pythagorean Theorem is fundamental to the development of many more advanced mathematical topics such as the distance formula, complex numbers, and arc length of a curve.

Check Your Understanding

Use the Pythagorean Theorem to find the unknown length to the nearest tenth.

3.

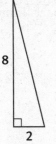

4.

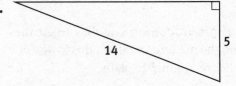

5.

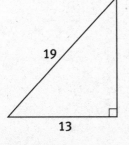

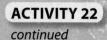

My Notes

LESSON 22-2 PRACTICE

6. Explain in your own words how the Pythagorean Theorem can be used to find a missing length of a right triangle.

7. Find the length of the hypotenuse in this right triangle:

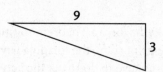

8. Walter is riding his bike across a park as shown. How far does he travel?

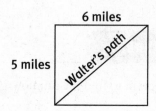

9. A playground slide measures 8 feet long. The slide ends 6 feet from the ladder. What is the length of the ladder?

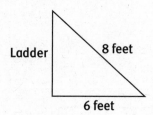

10. **Critique the reasoning of others.** Shanti says she can use the Pythagorean Theorem to find the missing length on this isosceles triangle. Do you agree with her reasoning? Explain.

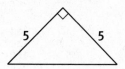

ACTIVITY 22 PRACTICE

Write your answers on notebook paper.
Show your work.

Lesson 22-1

1. This diagram shows the squares of the lengths of the sides of a right triangle. Copy the table and refer to the diagram to complete.

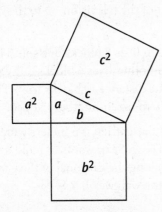

Case	a	b	c	a^2	b^2	c^2
1	3	4	5			
2				81	144	225
3				36	64	100
4	8	15	17			

2. Find c^2 given a triangle whose legs measure 5 units and 8 units.

3. Write the Pythagorean Theorem equation for this right triangle.

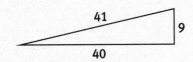

4. If you know the lengths of the sides of a triangle, how might you use the Pythagorean Theorem to tell if the triangle is or is not a right triangle?

5. Which of the following is a right triangle?

A.

B.
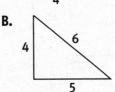

C.
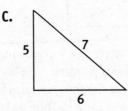

D.
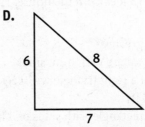

6. Roman says the Pythagorean Theorem applies to all triangles. Do you agree with his statement? Explain your reasoning.

Lesson 22-2

7. Find x in the triangle below.

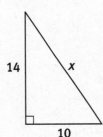

8. Find x in the triangle below.

9. Find x in the triangle below.

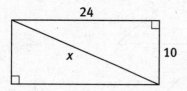

10. A painter uses a ladder to reach a second-story window on the house she is painting. The bottom of the window is 20 feet above the ground. The foot of the ladder is 15 feet from the house. How long is the ladder?

11. Which length is the greatest?
   A. the diagonal of a square with 4-in. sides
   B. the hypotenuse of a right triangle with legs of length 3 in. and 4 in.
   C. the diagonal of a rectangle with sides of 5 in. and 12 in.
   D. the perimeter of a square with side lengths of 1 in.

12. A hiker leaves her camp in the morning. How far is she from camp after walking 9 miles west and then 10 miles north?
   A. 19 miles
   B. 4.4 miles
   C. 181 miles
   D. 13.5 miles

13. A brick walkway forms the diagonal of a square playground. The walkway is 20 m long. To the nearest tenth of a meter, how long is one side of the playground?

14. The screen size of a television is measured along the diagonal of the screen from one corner to another. If a television has a length of 28 inches and a diagonal that measures 32 inches, what is the height of the television set to the nearest tenth?

15. Tim's cousin lives 8 blocks due south of his house. His grandmother lives 6 blocks due east of him. What is the distance in blocks from Tim's cousin's house to Tim's grandmother's house?

16. A rectangular garden is 6 meters wide and 12 meters long. Sean wants to build a walkway that goes along the diagonal of the garden. How long will the walkway be?

MATHEMATICAL PRACTICES
Attend to Precision

17. Use grid paper to draw a right triangle. Count the units for the legs. Calculate the length of the hypotenuse using the Pythagorean Theorem.

Applying the Pythagorean Theorem

Diamond in the Rough
Lesson 23-1 The Pythagorean Theorem in Two and Three Dimensions

Learning Targets:

- Apply the Pythagorean Theorem to solve problems in two dimensions.
- Apply the Pythagorean Theorem to solve problems in three dimensions.

> **SUGGESTED LEARNING STRATEGIES:** Marking the Text, Close Reading, Paraphrasing, Identify a Subtask, Think-Pair-Share

Cameron is a catcher trying out for the school baseball team. He has played baseball in the community and is able to easily throw the ball from home plate to second base to throw out a runner trying to steal second base. However, the school baseball diamond is a regulation-size field and larger than the field he is accustomed to.

The distance between each consecutive base on a regulation baseball diamond is 90 feet and the baselines are perpendicular. The imaginary line from home plate to second base divides the baseball diamond into two right triangles. There is a relationship between the lengths of the three sides of any right triangle that might be helpful for determining if Cameron can throw across a regulation baseball diamond.

> **DISCUSSION GROUP TIPS**
>
> In discussion groups, read the text carefully to clarify the meaning of math terms and other vocabulary.

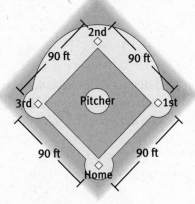

1. Sketch a diagram of a regulation baseball diamond showing the baselines and the imaginary line from home plate to second base. Identify and label the hypotenuse and legs of any right triangles. What are the lengths of the legs of the triangles?

My Notes

MATH TIP

The Pythagorean Theorem states that the square of the length of the hypotenuse of a right triangle is equal to the sum of the squares of the lengths of the legs of the triangle.

MATH TIP

If you take the square root of a number that is not a perfect square, the result is a decimal number that does not terminate or repeat and is therefore an irrational number.

2. Write an equation that can be used to find the distance from home plate to second base.

3. **Use appropriate tools strategically.** Can the distance from home plate to second base be found without a calculator? Why or why not?

4. Is this value from Item 3 a rational or irrational number? Using a calculator, give the approximate length of the distance from home plate to second base.

5. If Cameron can throw the baseball 130 feet, will he be able to consistently throw out a runner trying to steal second base? Explain your reasoning.

6. On a regulation softball diamond, the distance between consecutive bases is 60 feet and the baselines are perpendicular.
   a. Sketch and label a scale drawing of a softball diamond.

   b. Use your sketch to approximate the distance from home plate to second base on a softball field. Show all your work.

Check Your Understanding

7. A rectangular garden is 6 meters wide and 12 meters long. Sean wants to build a walkway that goes through the diagonal of the garden. How long will the walkway be? Round to the nearest hundredth.

8. A rectangular computer screen has a diagonal length of 21 inches. The screen is 11 inches wide. To the nearest tenth of an inch, what is the length of the screen?

During summer vacation, Cameron's parents take him to see his favorite baseball team play. On their last day of vacation, he discovers that he will not be able to carry the autographed bat that he won home on the plane. His dad suggests that he speak to the concierge at the hotel about options for shipping the bat home.

The concierge has only one box that he thinks might be long enough. After measuring the dimensions of the box to be 16 in. × 16 in. × 27 in., the concierge apologizes for not having a box long enough for the 34 inch bat. Cameron thinks he might still be able to use the box. His idea is to put the bat in the box at an angle as shown in the diagram below. He wonders if the bat will fit in the box.

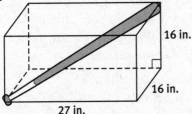

16 in.

16 in.

27 in.

9. The diagonal of the box is the hypotenuse of a right triangle. Outline this triangle in the diagram above.

10. What are the lengths of the legs of this right triangle? Show any work needed to find these lengths.

11. Find the length of the diagonal of the box. Show any necessary calculations.

12. Will Cameron be able to use the box to ship his bat? Justify your response.

> **CONNECT TO TRAVEL**
>
> In a hotel, a concierge is a person who helps guests with various tasks ranging from restaurant reservations to travel plans.

My Notes

Check Your Understanding

Cameron brought some collapsible fishing rods on his vacation. Find the length of the longest fishing rod that he can fit in each of the boxes shown below. Round to the nearest tenth.

13.

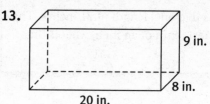

9 in.
8 in.
20 in.

14.

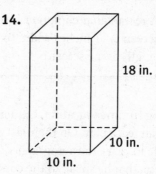

18 in.
10 in.
10 in.

LESSON 23-1 PRACTICE

15. A rectangular photograph has a diagonal length of 18 centimeters. The photograph is 10 centimeters wide. What is the length of the photograph to the nearest hundredth of a centimeter?

16. A square window is 2 meters long on each side. To protect the window during a storm, Marisol plans to put a strip of duct tape along each diagonal of the window. To the nearest tenth of a meter, what is the total length of duct tape Marisol will need?

17. The figure shows the dimensions of a classroom. What is the distance that a moth travels if it flies in a straight line from point *A* to point *B*? Round to the nearest tenth.

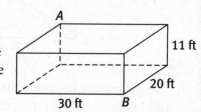

A
11 ft
20 ft
30 ft
B

18. **Make sense of problems.** A city employee is organizing a race down Broadway, from Beale Street to Grand Avenue. There will be a water station at the beginning and end of the race. There will also be water stations along the route, with no more than one mile between stations. What is the minimum number of water stations for this race?

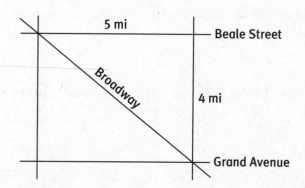

5 mi
Beale Street
Broadway
4 mi
Grand Avenue

Learning Targets:

- Apply the Pythagorean Theorem to right triangles on the coordinate plane.
- Find the distance between points on the coordinate plane.

> **SUGGESTED LEARNING STRATEGIES:** Create Representations, Think-Pair-Share, Identify a Subtask, Group Presentation

Effective baserunning is one of the essential skills that every baseball player must master. Cameron's coach spends a lot of time working with his players to help them be successful when running bases.

Part of the coach's baserunning training involves drills. A drill is an exercise for teaching a particular skill. To teach baserunning, the coach sets up a coordinate plane on the field, as shown below. Each unit of the coordinate plane represents 10 feet. The coach places bases on the coordinate plane and has players sprint or slide between the bases in various patterns.

For the first drill, the coach places bases at $A(-3, -3)$, $B(-3, 1)$, and $C(3, 1)$. The coach has the players run from A to B to C and then run and slide back to A as quickly as possible.

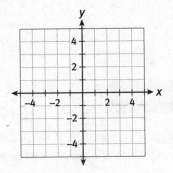

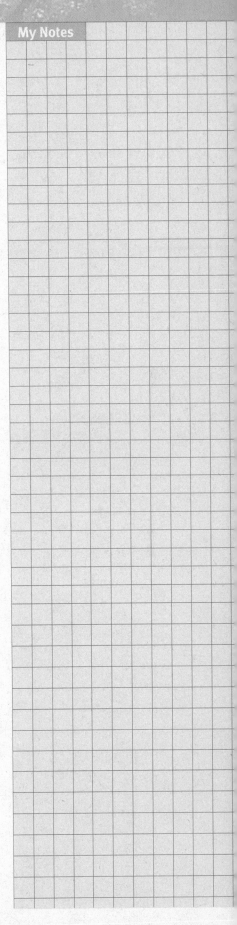

My Notes

Cameron's coach wants to know approximately how far the players will run and slide as they go from base *C* back to base *A*.

1. Plot and label the bases on the coordinate plane on the previous page.

2. What is the distance between bases *A* and *B*? What is the distance between the bases *B* and *C*?

3. Can you use the same method that you used in Item 2 to find the distance between bases *C* and *A*? Why or why not?

4. **Make use of structure.** Calculate the shortest distance between bases *C* and *A*. Explain and justify your method.

Check Your Understanding

Use the My Notes column on this page to plot the points to find the length of the hypotenuse in each right triangle. Round to the nearest tenth, if necessary.

5. $D(-3, 0)$, $E(0, 0)$, $F(0, 4)$

6. $G(-4, 2)$, $H(3, 2)$, $J(3, -2)$

Example A

Find the distance between $R(-2, 4)$ and $S(3, -3)$.

Step 1: Plot the points.

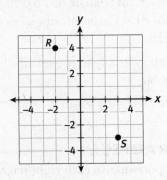

Step 2: Draw a right triangle. Find the length of the legs.

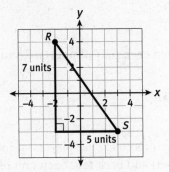

Step 3: Use the Pythagorean Theorem to find the length of the hypotenuse.

$$RS^2 = 7^2 + 5^2$$
$$RS^2 = 74$$
$$RS \approx 8.6 \text{ units}$$

Solution: The distance between the points is approximately 8.6 units.

Try These A

Find the distance between each pair of points. Round to the nearest tenth, if necessary.

a. $(-1, 3)$ and $(2, 1)$

b. $(6, 2)$ and $(-4, -2)$

WRITING MATH

Write $\overline{RS}$ to represent the line segment with endpoints R and S. Write RS to represent the length of the line segment or the distance between R and S.

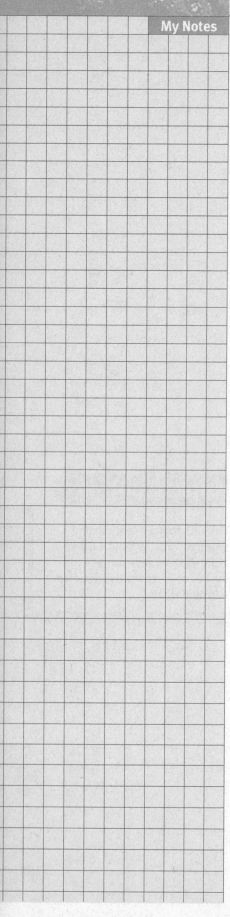

My Notes

Check Your Understanding

7. Carlos looked at the figure in Example A and said that there is a different way to draw a right triangle that has $\overline{RS}$ as its hypotenuse. Draw a figure to show what Carlos means. Does this right triangle give the same result? Explain.

8. Use what you know about triangles to explain why the answer to Example A is reasonable.

LESSON 23-2 PRACTICE

Find the length of the hypotenuse in each right triangle. Round to the nearest tenth, if necessary.

9. $P(1, 3)$, $Q(5, 3)$, $R(5, -1)$

10. $L(-3, 2)$, $M(-3, -3)$, $N(4, -3)$

Find the distance between each pair of points. Round to the nearest tenth, if necessary.

11. $(-2, -2)$ and $(-1, 3)$

12. $(1, -3)$ and $(6, 5)$

13. During a drill, Cameron's coach has players sprint from $J(3, 2)$ to $K(-4, 2)$ to $L(-4, -3)$ and back to J. Each unit of the coordinate plane represents 10 feet. To the nearest foot, what is the total distance players sprint during this drill?

14. **Attend to precision.** On a map of Ayana's town, the library is located at $(-5, -3)$ and the middle school is located at $(0, 2)$. Each unit of the map represents one mile. Ayana wants to bike from the middle school to the library. She knows that it takes her about 5 minutes to bike one mile. Will she be able to make the trip in less than half an hour? Explain.

ACTIVITY 23 PRACTICE

Write your answers on notebook paper.
Show your work.

Lesson 23-1

Find x in each of the following figures. Round to the nearest tenth, if necessary.

1.

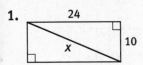

2.

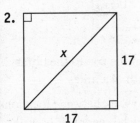

3.

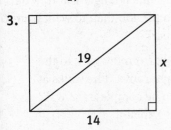

4. Riyo wants to place a string of lights across the ceiling of her bedroom. The room is a rectangle that is 18 feet long and 15 feet wide. Her string of lights is 20 feet long. Will the string of lights be long enough to hang diagonally from one corner of the ceiling to the other? Explain.

5. Which of the following lengths is the greatest?
  A. the diagonal of a square with 4-in. sides
  B. the hypotenuse of a right triangle with legs of length 3 in. and 4 in.
  C. the diagonal of a rectangle with sides of length 5 in. and 12 in.
  D. the perimeter of a square with side lengths of 1 in.

6. Gary has a rectangular painting that is 21 inches wide and 36 inches long. He wants to place wire in the shape of an X on the back of the painting along its diagonals so that he can hang the painting on the wall. Which is the best estimate of the total amount of wire Gary will need?
  A. 42 inches   **B.** 57 inches
  C. 84 inches   **D.** 114 inches

7. What is the length of the longest fishing pole that will fit in a box with dimensions 18 in., 24 in., and 16 in.?

8. The box below has dimensions 25 cm, 36 cm, and x cm. The diagonal shown has a length of 65 cm. Find the value of x. Round to the nearest tenth, if necessary.

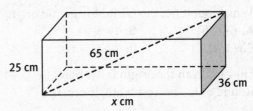

9. A brick walkway forms the diagonal of a square playground. The walkway is 20 m long. To the nearest tenth of a meter, how long is one side of the playground?

10. A television set's screen size is measured along the diagonal of the screen from one corner to another. If a television screen has a length of 28 inches and a diagonal that measures 32 inches, what is the height of the screen to the nearest tenth?

11. A rectangle has sides of length p and q. Which expression represents the length of the diagonal of the rectangle?
  A. $2(p+q)$ **B.** $p^2 + q^2$
  C. $\sqrt{p+q}$ **D.** $\sqrt{p^2 + q^2}$

Lesson 23-2

For Items 12–17, find the distance between each pair of points. Round to the nearest tenth, if necessary.

12. $(0, 0)$ and $(3, 2)$

13. $(-3, -1)$ and $(0, 2)$

14. $(-1, 1)$ and $(3, -2)$

15. $(2, -1)$ and $(2, 5)$

16. $(6, -2)$ and $(-2, 4)$

17. $(-3, -5)$ and $(5, 5)$

18. Which is the best estimate of the distance between the points $A(4, -5)$ and $B(-2, 1)$?
    A. 7 units
    B. 7.5 units
    C. 8 units
    D. 8.5 units

19. Which point lies the farthest from the origin?
    A. $(-6, 0)$
    B. $(-3, 8)$
    C. $(5, 1)$
    D. $(-4, -3)$

20. How far from the origin is the point $(-2, -4)$? Round to the nearest tenth, if necessary.

21. For a baserunning drill, a coach places bases at $A(1, 1)$ and $B(4, 1)$, where each unit of the coordinate plane represents 10 feet. The coach wants to locate base C so that the distance from B to C is 40 feet and so that the three bases form a right triangle.
    a. What is a possible location for base C?
    b. Is there more than one possibility for the location of base C? Explain.
    c. What is the distance from base A to base C? Does this distance depend upon which of the possible locations for base C the coach chooses? Justify your response.

The coordinate plane shows a map of Elmville. Each unit of the coordinate plane represents one mile. Use the map for Items 22–24.

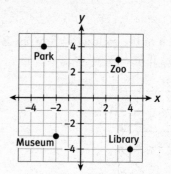

22. What is the distance from the zoo to the library? Round to the nearest tenth of a mile.

23. Assuming it is possible to walk between locations in a straight line, how much longer is it to walk from the museum to the zoo than to walk from the museum to the park?

24. Donnell plans to walk from the park to the library along a straight route. If he walks at 4 miles per hour, can he complete the walk in less than 2 hours? Explain.

MATHEMATICAL PRACTICES
Reason Abstractly and Quantitatively

25. Consider the points $A(5, 0)$, $B(-3, 4)$, and $C(-4, 3)$.
    a. Find the distance of each point from the origin.
    b. Give the coordinates of four additional points that are this same distance from the origin.
    c. Plot the given points and the points you named in part b.
    d. Suppose you continued to plot points that are this same distance from the origin. What geometric figure would the points begin to form?

The Converse of the Pythagorean Theorem

Paper Clip Chains

Lesson 24-1 The Converse of the Pythagorean Theorem

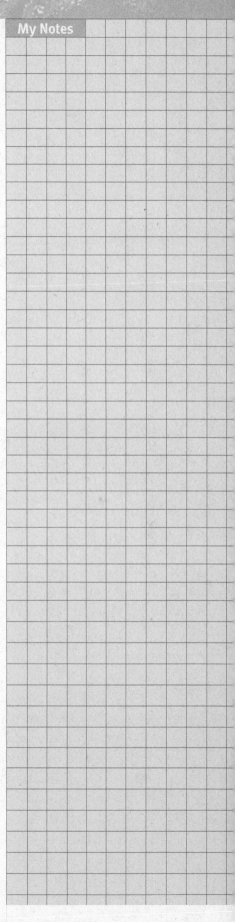

Learning Targets:

- Explain the converse of the Pythagorean Theorem.
- Verify whether a triangle with given side lengths is a right triangle.

> SUGGESTED LEARNING STRATEGIES: Graphic Organizer, Visualization, Discussion Group, Create Representations, Note Taking

It is believed that the Pythagorean Theorem was applied in the building of the pyramids and the establishment of land boundaries in ancient Egypt. Egyptian surveyors, known as rope stretchers, applied the theorem to reestablish property lines after the annual flooding of the Nile. They created right angles by forming right triangles using long ropes with 13 equally spaced knots tied in them to create 12 equal sections of rope.

To understand how the Egyptian rope stretchers made their right triangles, complete the following items.

1. Use 12 paper clips to create a right triangle like the ones the Egyptians made from rope. Draw a sketch of the triangle you created. Label the number of paper clips on each side and the location of what you believe is the right angle.

2. Give reasons to support your belief that your triangle is a right triangle.

3. Form another triangle with the 12 paper clips, with side lengths different from your original triangle. What are the lengths of the sides? What is the best name for the triangle you made?

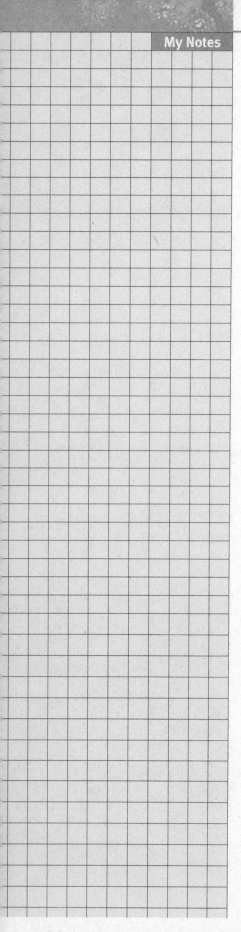

My Notes

4. Use paper clips to create triangles having the given side lengths. Use a corner of an index card to test the largest angle of each triangle for a right angle and predict whether or not the given triangles are right triangles. Draw and label a sketch of each triangle formed.

Triangle Side Lengths	Right Triangle?	Pictorial Representation
6, 8, 10		
5, 9, 10		
5, 12, 13		

Triangle Side Lengths	Right Triangle?	Pictorial Representation
4, 12, 14		
9, 15, 16		
8, 15, 17		

My Notes

5. Using $c^2 = a^2 + b^2$, where c is the longest side, support your predictions for each triangle in Item 4. Use the chart below to show your work.

Triangle Side Lengths	c^2	(?) = or ≠	$a^2 + b^2$	Prediction Correct?
6, 8, 10				
5, 9, 10				
5, 12, 13				
4, 12, 14				
9, 15, 16				
8, 15, 17				

READING MATH

The symbol = is read "is equal to" and the symbol ≠ is read "is not equal to."

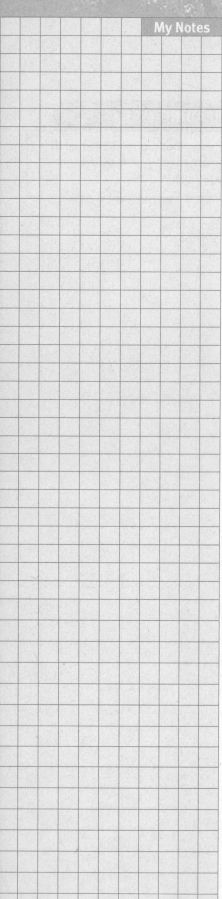

6. **Express regularity in repeated reasoning.** If the sides of a triangle satisfy the equation $c^2 = a^2 + b^2$, what can be said about the triangle? What must be true about c?

The relationship that you have just explored is called the Converse of the Pythagorean Theorem. It states that if the sum of the squares of the two shorter sides of a triangle equal the square of the longest side, then the triangle is a right triangle.

Check Your Understanding

Tell whether each set of side lengths forms a right triangle. Justify your response.

7. 7, 24, 25

8. 6, 12, 13

LESSON 24-1 PRACTICE

Tell whether each set of side lengths forms a right triangle. Justify your response.

9. 8, 12, 16

10. 10, 24, 26

11. Isabella has sticks that are 10 cm, 11 cm, and 13 cm long. Can she place the sticks together to form a right triangle? Justify your answer.

12. The triangular sail of a toy sailboat is supposed to be a right triangle. The manufacturer says the sides of the sail have lengths of 4.5 inches, 6 inches, and 7 inches. Is the sail a right triangle? If not, how could you change one of the lengths to make it a right triangle?

13. Model with mathematics. Alan made a small four-sided table for his office. The opposite sides of the table are 27 inches long and 36 inches long. If the diagonal of the table measures 40 inches, does the table have right angles at the corners? Why or why not?

Learning Targets:

- Verify whether a set of whole numbers is a Pythagorean triple.
- Use a Pythagorean triple to generate a new Pythagorean triple.

> **SUGGESTED LEARNING STRATEGIES:** Graphic Organizer, Visualization, Discussion Group, Create Representations, Note Taking

A **Pythagorean triple** is a set of three whole numbers that satisfies the equation $c^2 = a^2 + b^2$.

1. **Make use of structure.** Choose 3 Pythagorean triples from Lesson 24-1 and list them in the first column of the table below. Multiply each Pythagorean triple by 2. Is the new set of numbers a Pythagorean triple? Repeat by multiplying each original set of numbers by 3.

Pythagorean Triple	Multiply by 2	Pythagorean Triple?	Multiply by 3	Pythagorean Triple?

2. What do you notice when you multiply each value in a Pythagorean triple by a whole-number constant? Make a conjecture based on your results in the table.

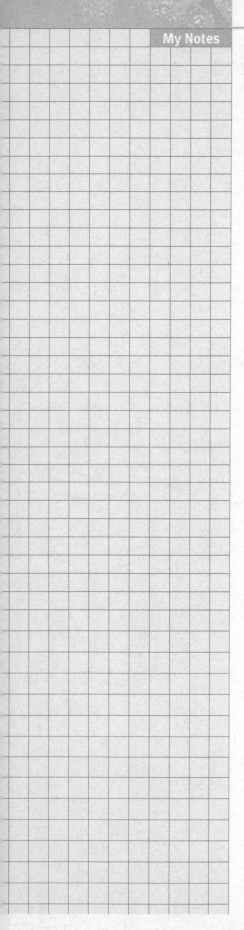

My Notes

Check Your Understanding

3. How many Pythagorean triples can be created by multiplying the side lengths in a known triple by a constant? Explain your answer.

4. Do the numbers 65, 156, and 169 form a Pythagorean triple? Why or why not?

LESSON 24-2 PRACTICE

5. Below are sets of triangle side lengths. Sort the sets of lengths into two groups. Explain how you grouped the sets.

3, 4, 5	6, 8, 10	5, 12, 13	14, 48, 50
10, 24, 26	8, 15, 17	9, 12, 15	16, 30, 34
7, 24, 25	20, 48, 52	24, 45, 51	12, 16, 20

6. What number forms a Pythagorean triple with 14 and 48?

7. Point C is located on line m. What is the location of point C if the side lengths of $\triangle ABC$ form a Pythagorean triple? Is there more than one possibility? Explain.

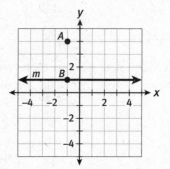

8. Lisa says that if you start with a Pythagorean triple and add the same whole number to each number in the set, then the new set of numbers will also be a Pythagorean triple. Explain why Lisa is correct or provide a counterexample to show that she is not correct.

9. Critique the reasoning of others. Devon knows that 5, 12, 13 is a Pythagorean triple. He states that he can form a new Pythagorean triple by multiplying each of these values by 1.5. Is Devon correct? Justify your answer.

ACTIVITY 24 PRACTICE
Write your answers on notebook paper.
Show your work.

Lesson 24-1

1. Is a triangle with sides measuring 9 feet, 12 feet, and 18 feet a right triangle? Justify your answer.

2. Determine whether $\frac{4}{5}$, $\frac{3}{5}$, and 1 can be the sides of a right triangle. Justify your answer.

3. The lengths of four straws are listed below. Which three of the straws can be placed together to form a right triangle? Why?

   5 cm

   6 cm

   12 cm

   13 cm

4. The lengths of the three sides of a right triangle are three consecutive even integers. What are they?

5. Which equation guarantees that $\triangle PQR$ is a right triangle?

   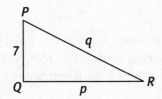

   A. $q^2 + 49 = p$
   B. $q^2 - 7 = p^2$
   C. $q^2 - 49 = p^2$
   D. $q^2 + 7 = p$

Determine whether each statement is true or false. If the statement is false, explain why.

6. If a triangle has sides of length 8 cm, 10 cm, and 12 cm, then the triangle does not contain a right angle.

7. If you have sticks that are 15 in., 36 in., and 39 in. long, you can place the sticks together to form a triangle with three acute angles.

8. A triangle that has sides of length 7.5 cm, 10 cm, and 12.5 cm must be a right triangle.

9. The converse of the Pythagorean theorem says that in a right triangle the sum of the squares of the lengths of the legs equals the square of the hypotenuse.

Lesson 24-2

10. Is 9, 40, 41 a Pythagorean triple? Explain your reasoning.

11. The numbers 3, 4, 5 form a Pythagorean triple. Give four other Pythagorean triples that can be generated from this one.

12. Keiko said that the numbers 3.6, 4.8, and 6 form a Pythagorean triple since $6^2 = 3.6^2 + 4.8^2$. Do you agree or disagree? Explain.

13. Consider the following sets of whole numbers. Which sets form Pythagorean triples?

    I.   6, 8, 10

    II. 15, 36, 39

    III. 10, 12, 14

    IV. 16, 30, 34

    A. I only
    B. II and III
    C. III and IV
    D. I, II, and IV

14. Which whole number should be included in the set {8, 15} so that the three numbers form a Pythagorean triple?
    A. 5   **B.** 12
    C. 17   **D.** 19

15. Mario said the Pythagorean triple 7, 24, 25 is the only Pythagorean triple that includes the number 24. Do you agree or disagree? Justify your response.

16. Give an example of a Pythagorean triple that includes two prime numbers.

17. Explain the connection between Pythagorean triples and right triangles.

Determine whether each statement is always, sometimes, or never true.

18. A Pythagorean triple includes an odd number.

19. Two of the numbers in a Pythagorean triple are equal.

20. A Pythagorean triple includes a number greater than 3 and less than 4.

21. The greatest number in a Pythagorean triple can be the length of the hypotenuse of a right triangle while the other two numbers can be the lengths of the legs.

22. The lengths of the sides of $\triangle PQR$ form a Pythagorean triple. Which of the following could be the coordinates of point R?

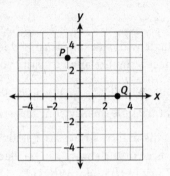

    A. $(-3, -3)$ **B.** $(3, 3)$
    C. $(3, -3)$ **D.** $(0, 3)$

MATHEMATICAL PRACTICES
Reason Abstractly and Quantitatively

23. Euclid's formula is a formula for generating Pythagorean triples. To use the formula, choose two whole numbers, m and n, with $m > n$. Then calculate the following values.

$$a = m^2 - n^2$$
$$b = 2mn$$
$$c = m^2 + n^2$$

    a. Choose values for m and n. Then generate the numbers a, b, and c according to the formula. Is the resulting set of numbers a Pythagorean triple?

    b. Does the formula work when $m = n$? Why or why not?

Sam is spending part of his summer vacation at Camp Euclid with some of his friends. On the first day of camp, they must pass an open-water swimming test to be allowed to use the canoes, kayaks, and personal watercraft. Sam and his friends must be able to swim across the river that they will be boating on.

The river is 30 meters wide. On the day of the test, Sam begins on one bank and tries to swim directly across the river to the point on the opposite bank where his counselor is waiting. Because the river has a slight current, Sam ends up 35 meters downstream from his counselor.

1. Copy and label the diagram for the problem situation.

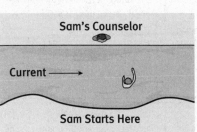

2. How far did Sam actually swim? Justify your answer.

3. Sam's friend Alex started at the same spot but swam 50 meters. How far downstream was Alex from their counselor when he arrived at the opposite bank? Justify your answer.

In a lake fed by the river, a triangular area marked with buoys is roped off for swimming during free time at camp. The distances between each pair of buoys are 40 meters, 50 meters, and 60 meters.

4. Draw and label a diagram for the problem situation.

5. Is the swimming area a right triangle? Justify your answer.

6. Find the missing side length in each of the following triangles. Show all your work.

   a.

   b.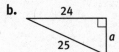

   c.

7. Determine which of the following sets of triangle side lengths form right triangles. Justify each response.

   a. 9, 40, 41

   b. 20, 21, 31

   c. $\frac{6}{7}, \frac{8}{7}, \frac{10}{7}$

8. After the swimming test, Alex makes his way back to camp. On a coordinate plane, Alex is at the point $(-4, 3)$ and camp is at the point $(3, -1)$. What is the shortest distance Alex will have to travel to get back to camp? Assume each unit of the coordinate plane represents one kilometer.

Scoring Guide	Exemplary	Proficient	Emerging	Incomplete
	The solution demonstrates these characteristics:			
Mathematics Knowledge and Thinking (Items 2, 3, 5, 6a–c, 7a–c, 8)	• Using the Pythagorean Theorem to accurately find missing triangle side lengths and distance in the coordinate plane. • Using the converse of the Pythagorean Theorem to correctly determine if a triangle is a right triangle.	• Using the Pythagorean Theorem to find missing triangle side lengths and distance in the coordinate plane with few errors. • Using the converse of the Pythagorean Theorem to decide if a triangle is a right triangle.	• Difficulty in finding missing triangle side lengths and distance in the coordinate plane. • Difficulty determining if a triangle is a right triangle.	• Little or no understanding of using the Pythagorean Theorem. • Little or no understanding of using the converse of the Pythagorean Theorem.
Problem Solving (Items 2, 3, 5, 6, 7, 8)	• An appropriate and efficient strategy that results in a correct answer.	• A strategy that may include unnecessary steps but is correct.	• A strategy that results in some incorrect answers.	• No clear strategy when solving problems.
Mathematical Modeling / Representations (Items 1, 4)	• Precisely modeling a problem situation with an accurate diagram.	• Drawing a reasonably accurate diagram to model a problem situation.	• Difficulty drawing a diagram to model a problem situation.	• Drawing an incorrect diagram to model a problem situation.
Reasoning and Communication (Items 2, 3, 5, 7)	• Correctly using the Pythagorean Theorem to justify answers to problems.	• Explaining an answer using the Pythagorean Theorem.	• Difficulty using the Pythagorean Theorem to justify answers.	• Little or no understanding of the Pythagorean Theorem.

Surface Area
Greenhouse Gardens
Lesson 25-1 Lateral and Surface Areas of Prisms

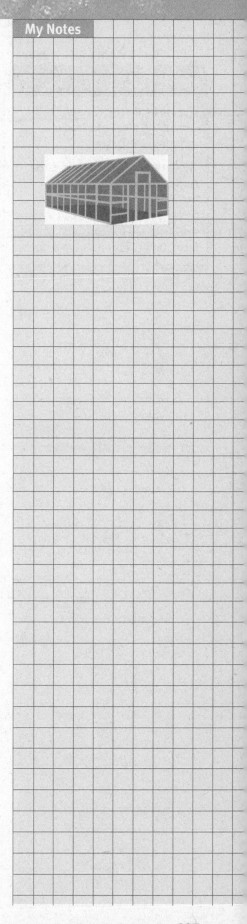

Learning Targets:

● Find the lateral and surface areas of rectangular prisms.
● Find the lateral and surface areas of triangular prisms.

> **SUGGESTED LEARNING STRATEGIES:** Create Representations, Visualization, Think-Pair-Share

A greenhouse is a building used to grow plants. These buildings can vary widely in size and shape. By using a greenhouse, a gardener is able to grow a wider range of plants. The greenhouse shelters plants from weather and insects that can cause damage.

Marie and Ashton are planning to help build a greenhouse for their middle school. The local gardening club is donating funds and materials to get the greenhouse built.

When a diagram like the one above accompanies a verbal description, use the visual along with the scenario to activate prior knowledge. For example, identify geometric shapes you see in the greenhouse and review formulas for finding perimeter and area of those figures. Review with your group any background information that will be useful in applying these concepts as you solve the item below.

1. Marie looks at the first design for the greenhouse. The design is a rectangular prism with a length of 12 feet, a width of 10 feet, and a height of 9 feet. Sketch a model of the greenhouse.

Marie and Ashton are asked to determine the cost of the glass that will be used to build the greenhouse. Glass will cover all of the walls of the greenhouse and the roof.

As you read Example A, clarify and make notes about any terms or descriptions you do not understand. Be sure to mark the text and label diagrams.

My Notes

My Notes

MATH TERMS

The **surface area** of a solid is the sum of the areas of all faces including the bases.

The **lateral area** of a solid is the sum of the areas of all faces excluding the bases. In a rectangular prism, you can assume the bases are the top and bottom faces, unless otherwise specified.

Example A

What is the surface area of the greenhouse that will be covered with glass? How would the lateral area differ from the surface area? Show all of your work.

Step 1: Identify the relevant faces. The *surface area* of a prism includes all faces. In this case, there is no glass on the bottom face, so find the area of the other five faces.

Step 2: Find the area of the front and back faces.
$2(12 \times 9) = 216 \text{ ft}^2$

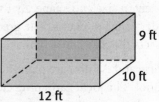

Step 3: Find the area of the left and right faces.
$2(10 \times 9) = 180 \text{ ft}^2$

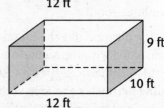

Step 4: Find the area of the top.
$1(12 \times 10) = 120 \text{ ft}^2$

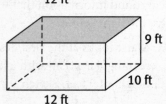

Step 5: Add the areas.
$216 + 180 + 120 = 516 \text{ ft}^2$

Solution: 516 ft^2 will be covered with glass. The *lateral area* does not include the top or bottom faces, so the lateral area is $216 + 180 = 396 \text{ ft}^2$.

Try These A

Find the surface area and lateral area of the figures below. Show all work.

a.

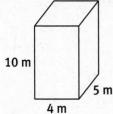

10 m
5 m
4 m

b.

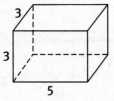

3
3
5

c.

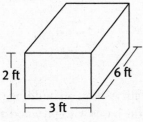

2 ft
6 ft
3 ft

2. The glass for the greenhouse costs $8 per square foot. What will be the cost of the glass if this design is used?

My Notes

3. In the right triangular prism below, mark the bases with a *B*. What two-dimensional shapes make up the lateral area of the figure?

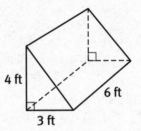

4 ft 6 ft 3 ft

4. Ashton is building containers to hold plant food in the greenhouse. The design for these containers is shown above. Ashton will use plywood to cover the lateral area of the right triangular prism. What is the lateral area of the container? Show your work.

5. **Attend to precision.** Marie is working with Ashton on building the containers. She suggests that Ashton cover the bases with plywood as well. Ashton realizes he needs to find the total surface area of the right triangular prism to determine how much plywood he needs. Calculate the surface area of the container.

My Notes

Check Your Understanding

6. Find the lateral area and surface area of the rectangular prism.

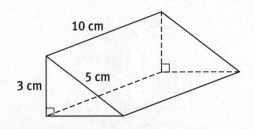

10 in.

6 in.

14 in.

7. Find the lateral area and surface area of the right triangular prism.

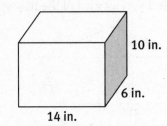

10 cm

5 cm

3 cm

8. a. Sal is painting a bedroom with the dimensions of 12 feet long by 10 feet wide by 7 feet high. If he only paints the four walls of the room, how much area will he need to paint?

b. Sal used this formula for indicating how much wall area to paint in a room. In this formula, l is the length of the room, w is the width, and h is the height, or distance from the floor to the ceiling.

$$L = 2 \cdot l \cdot h + 2 \cdot w \cdot h.$$

Explain how this formula gives the lateral area of the room.

c. Sal's sister Simone claims that the formula $L = Ph$, where P is the perimeter of the room and h is the height of the room, also works. Is Simone's claim correct? Explain.

d. If Sal decides to paint the total surface area of the room, including the floor and ceiling, what will he need to add to his formula? Explain. Then write a formula for total surface area using l for length, w for width, and h for height.

9. Make sense of problems. How many gallons of paint will Marie and Ashton need to paint five of the right triangular prisms that will hold the plant food from Item 5 if one gallon of paint covers about 200 square feet? Assume they paint all sides of the containers. Explain your answer.

My Notes

LESSON 25-1 PRACTICE

10. A cube is a rectangular prism with square faces. Suppose a cube has edges 9 cm long. What is its lateral area? What is its surface area?

11. Find the lateral area and surface area of the triangular prism.

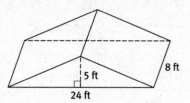

5 ft
8 ft
24 ft

12. The prism shown here is made from centimeter cubes. Find the lateral and surface area of the prism.

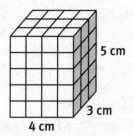

5 cm
3 cm
4 cm

13. A gift box is a cube that measures 8 inches by 8 inches on all sides. What is the lateral and surface area of the gift box without the lid?

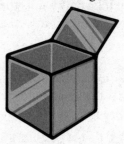

14. **Construct viable arguments.** Which cereal box requires more cardboard to manufacture? Justify your answer.

A.

depth = 3 in.
width = 9 in.
height = 12 in.

B.

depth = 2 in.
width = 7 in.
height = 14 in.

15. Use 8 cubes to create as many prisms as you can. Find and describe the prism with the least surface area and the greatest surface area.

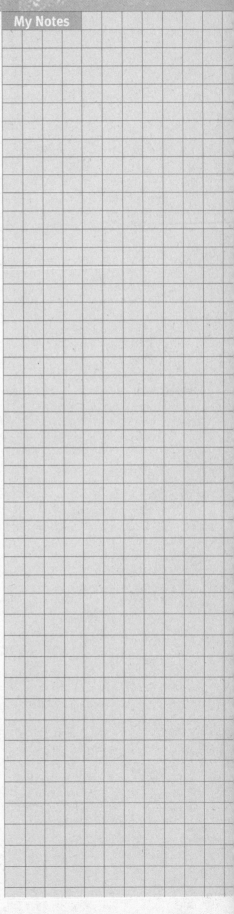

Learning Targets:
- Find the lateral area of cylinders.
- Find the surface area of cylinders.

SUGGESTED LEARNING STRATEGIES: Create Representations, Visualization, Think-Pair-Share

1. Marie looks at sketches for the containers that will hold individual plants. The plant containers are in the shape of a cylinder. Marie wants to wrap decorative paper around the curved surfaces of the containers. The circular bases on the top and bottom of the containers will not be covered with the paper. What part of each cylinder will be covered?

2. **Make use of structure.** The design for the cylindrical plant containers is shown on the left below. The rectangle shows a strip of paper that perfectly fits the lateral surface of the cylinder, without gaps or overlap. Explain how to find the dimensions of this rectangle.

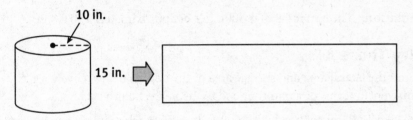

10 in.

15 in.

3. What does your answer to Item 2 tell you about how to find the lateral area of a cylinder?

Example A

Calculate the surface area of the plant container from Item 2.

Step 1: Calculate the lateral area.

The lateral area is the area of the rectangle that covers the curved surface of the cylinder.

$LA = $ (height of cylinder) $\times$ (circumference of base)

$= (15)(2\pi \cdot 10) = 300\pi$

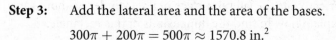

Step 2: Calculate the area of the bases.

Each base is a circle with area πr^2.
The area of each base is $\pi(10)^2 = 100\pi$.
So the total area of the two bases is $2 \cdot 100\pi = 200\pi$.

Step 3: Add the lateral area and the area of the bases.

$300\pi + 200\pi = 500\pi \approx 1570.8$ in.^{2}

Solution: The surface area is 500π in.^{2} or approximately 1,570.8 in.^{2}.

Try These A

Find the lateral area and surface area of the objects below. Give your answers in terms of π and rounded to the nearest tenth.

a. a cylindrical hat box with diameter 30 cm and height 20 cm

b. a six-pack of juice cans where each can has a radius of 2 inches and a height of 7 inches

4. What are the lateral area and surface area of the cylinder below using variables r and h?

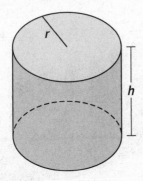

5. In the above figure, suppose $r = 5$ ft and $h = 15$ ft. What are the lateral area and surface area of the cylinder in this case? Show all work and leave your answers in terms of π.

Check Your Understanding

6. Find the lateral area and surface area of the cylinder. Leave your answers in terms of π.

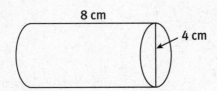

8 cm

4 cm

7. Is it ever possible for the lateral area of a cylinder to equal the surface area of the cylinder? Justify your response.

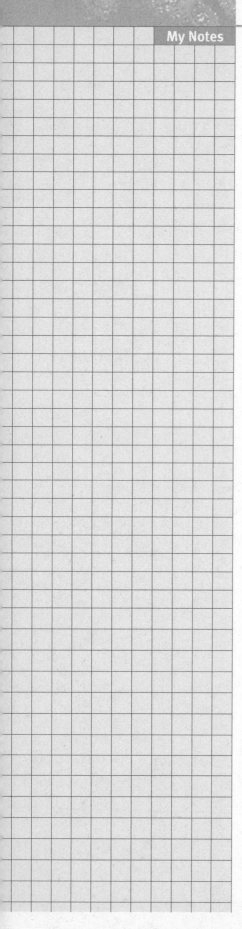

LESSON 25-2 PRACTICE

This cylinder activity is used to promote fine-motor skills and spatial learning in young children. Use the figure for Items 8–11 and leave your answers in terms of π.

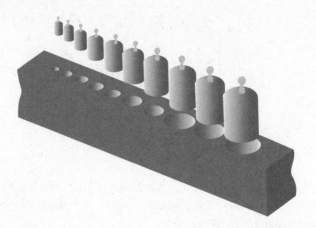

8. Calculate the lateral area of the largest peg to the far right of the diagram if its height is 2.5 inches and radius is 2 inches.

9. What is the surface area of the largest peg?

10. What is the lateral area of the smallest peg to the far left of the diagram if its height is $\frac{1}{2}$ inch and radius is $\frac{1}{4}$ inch?

11. What is the surface area of the smallest peg?

12. **Model with mathematics.** A water bottle has a label that is 3.5 inches high. If the bottle has a radius of 2 inches, how much paper would be needed to put labels on one dozen water bottles? Round to the nearest tenth.

ACTIVITY 25 PRACTICE
Write your answers on notebook paper.
Show your work.

Lesson 25-1

1. Find the surface area of the rectangular prism shown below.

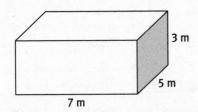

2. Find the surface area of the cube shown below.

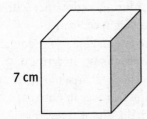

3. The dimensions of a nylon tent are shown in the figure.

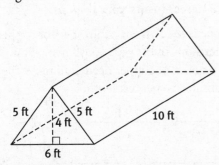

   a. How much nylon is needed to make the sides and floor of the tent?
   b. How much nylon is needed to make the triangular flaps at the front and back of the tent?
   c. What is the surface area of the triangular prism? How is this related to your responses to parts a and b?

4. A gift box is 6 inches long, 3 inches wide, and 3 inches tall.
   a. How much paper is needed to wrap the box? Assume the box is wrapped with the minimum amount of paper and no overlap.
   b. How much wrapping paper should you buy to wrap the box if you assume you will need 15% extra for waste and overlap?

5. Find the lateral area and surface area of the triangular prism.

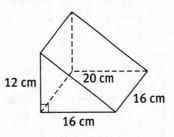

The figure below is made from one-inch cubes. Use the figure for Items 6 and 7.

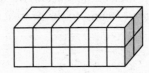

6. What are the dimensions of the figure?

7. What is the surface area of the figure?

8. A cube has a surface area of 96 m². What is the length of each edge of the cube?
   A. 2 m   **B.** 4 m
   C. 6 m   **D.** 8 m

9. A window box for flowers is a rectangular prism with an open top, as shown. Tyrell wants to coat the inside and outside of the box with a special varnish that will protect it from the effects of water, cold, and harsh weather. The varnish comes in cans that can cover 500 square inches. How many cans of the varnish should Tyrell buy? Explain your answer.

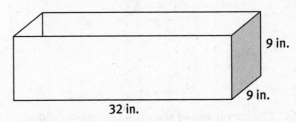

10. Which is the best estimate of the lateral area of a cube with edges that are 2.1 inches long?
    A. 9 in.²   **B.** 16 in.²
    C. 25 in.²   **D.** 36 in.²

Lesson 25-2

11. Find the lateral area and surface area of the cylinder. Leave your answers in terms of π.

6 m

5 m

12. What is the area of the label on the soup can shown below? Round to the nearest tenth.

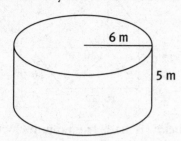

5 cm

SOUP 12 cm

13. An orange juice can has a diameter of 4 inches and a height of 7 inches. The curved surface of the can is painted orange. How much paint is needed?
A. 14π in.^{2} **B.** 16π in.^{2}
C. 28π in.^{2} **D.** 36π in.^{2}

14. The height of the cylinder shown below is twice the radius. What is the lateral area of the cylinder? Round to the nearest tenth.

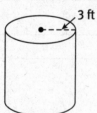

3 ft

15. The lateral area of the cylinder shown below is 12π m^2. What is the radius of the cylinder?

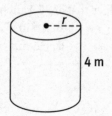

r

4 m

A. 1.5 m   **B.** 3 m
C. 6 m   **D.** 8 m

16. Which expression best represents the surface area of the cylinder shown below?

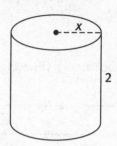

x

2

A. $2\pi x + 2\pi x^2$ **B.** $2\pi x + 4\pi x^2$
C. $4\pi x + 4\pi x^2$ **D.** $4\pi x + 2\pi x^2$

17. Mei is designing a cylindrical container for her ceramics class. The container will be open on top. She is considering a container with a radius of 5 cm and a height of 8 cm.
  a. Find the lateral area of the container. Leave your answer in terms of π.
  b. What is the total area of the container? Leave your answer in terms of π.
  c. Mei's friend Victor states that if she doubles the radius of the container she will double the total area of the container. Do you agree or disagree? Justify your response.

18. A pipe is made from a thin sheet of copper. The dimensions of the pipe are shown below. What is the amount of copper needed to make the pipe? Round to the nearest tenth.

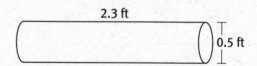

2.3 ft

0.5 ft

MATHEMATICAL PRACTICES
Look For and Express Regularity in Repeated Reasoning

19. Consider a cylinder with a height of 1 cm.
  a. Find the lateral area of the cylinder if the radius is 2 cm, 4 cm, 8 cm, and 16 cm. Leave your answers in terms of π.
  b. Use your results to make a conjecture about what happens to the lateral area of a cylinder when the radius is doubled.

Volumes of Solids

Castles in the Sand
Lesson 26-1 Volumes of Prisms and Pyramids

Learning Targets:
- Apply the formula for the volume of a prism.
- Apply the formula for the volume of a pyramid.

> SUGGESTED LEARNING STRATEGIES: Create Representations, Visualization, Think-Pair-Share, Group Presentation

The eighth-grade class at LWH Middle School in Montana hosted a spring festival to raise money for their end-of-year trip to the beach. They decided to sponsor a sand castle–building contest as part of the festivities. Because the sand for the sand castles had to be trucked in to the school, students who wanted to participate in the castle-building contest were required to submit a proposal to Archie Medes, the geometry teacher. The proposals had to contain a sketch of the castle the student or group of students wanted to build, a list of the solids used and their dimensions, and the volume of sand required to build it.

Shayla wanted to enter the contest. She decided to research castles to help brainstorm ideas for her proposal. One of the castles she looked at was Fantasy Castle in a nearby theme park.

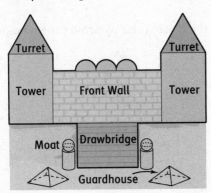

1. What solids could Shayla use to build a sand replica of Fantasy Castle?

Shayla's friend Shelly built last year's winning castle out of prisms, pyramids, cylinders, cones, and spheres. To help Shayla prepare for the contest, Shelly showed Shayla her plans from last year and explained how she determined the amount of sand she would need to build her winning castle.

My Notes

MATH TIP

The formula for the volume V of a prism is $V = Bh$, where B is the area of the base and h is the height. For a rectangular prism with length ℓ, width w, and height h, the formula may be written as $V = \ell wh$.

MATH TIP

The formula for the volume V of a pyramid with base area B and height h is $V = \frac{1}{3}Bh$.

Example A

Find the volume of the rectangular prism shown below.

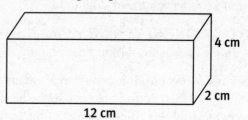

Step 1: Write the volume formula, $V = \ell wh$. Identify the values of the variables.

$$\ell = 12 \text{ cm}, \ w = 2 \text{ cm}, \text{ and } h = 4 \text{ cm}$$

Step 2: Substitute the dimensions into the formula.

$$V = \ell wh$$
$$= 12 \bullet 2 \bullet 4 = 96$$

Solution: $V = 96 \text{ cm}^3$

Example B

Find the volume of the rectangular pyramid shown below.

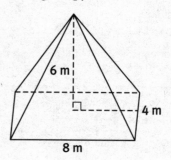

Step 1: Write the volume formula, $V = \frac{1}{3}Bh$. Identify the known values of the variables.

$$h = 6 \text{ m}$$

Step 2: Calculate the area of the base.

$$B = 8 \times 4 = 32 \text{ m}^2$$

Step 3: Substitute the dimensions into the formula.

$$V = \frac{1}{3}Bh$$

$$= \frac{1}{3}(32)(6) = 64$$

Solution: $V = 64 \text{ m}^3$

My Notes

Try These A–B

Find the volume of each solid.

a.

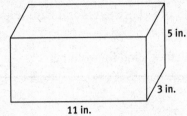

5 in.
3 in.
11 in.

b.

5 cm
3 cm
10 cm

2. Shayla begins to plan the front wall of the castle.
   a. Draw and label a sketch of the prism used for the front wall of the castle if the wall is 36 inches long, 24 inches high, and 4 inches wide.

   b. Use the volume formula for a prism to find the number of cubic inches of sand needed to build the front wall.

3. **Make sense of problems.** Next, Shayla plans the guardhouses in front of the moat.
   a. Draw and label a sketch of one of the pyramids used for the guardhouses at the entrance to the drawbridge given that each pyramid has a height of 9 inches and given that the base of each pyramid is a square with side lengths of 6 inches.

   b. Use the volume formula for a pyramid to find the number of cubic inches of sand needed to build both guardhouses.

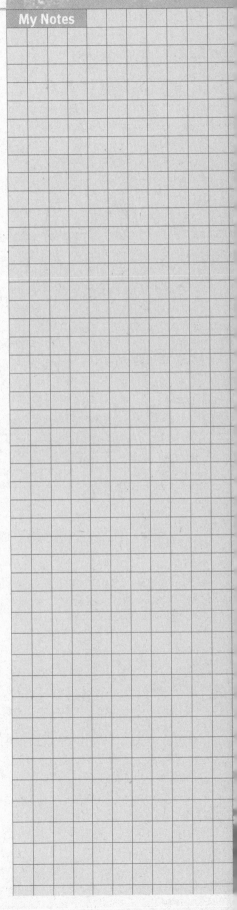

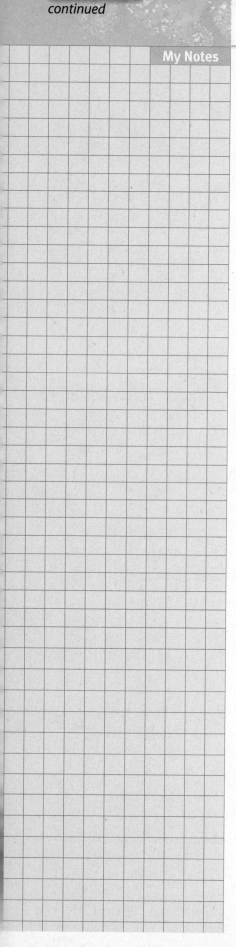

My Notes

Check Your Understanding

4. Draw a square pyramid with a height of 8 centimeters and base side lengths of 6 centimeters. Find the volume.

5. Draw a cube with side lengths of 4 inches. Find the volume.

LESSON 26-1 PRACTICE

6. Julian measures the edges of a box in millimeters. What units should he use for the surface area of the box? What units should he use for the volume of the box?

7. Find the volume of a triangular prism with a base area of 14 square centimeters and a height of 5 centimeters.

8. A triangular pyramid has a volume of 20 in.^{3}. The base area of the pyramid is 6 in.^{2}. What is the height of the pyramid?

9. Find the volume of the solid shown below.

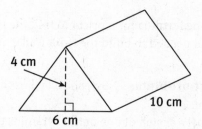

4 cm

10 cm

6 cm

10. **Reason quantitatively.** A toy manufacturer makes alphabet blocks in the shape of cubes with a side length of 1 inch.
    a. The manufacturer plans to pack the blocks in a box that is a rectangular prism. The box is 7 inches long, 4 inches wide, and 3 inches tall. What is the volume of the box?
    b. Suppose the manufacturer packs the blocks efficiently, so that as many blocks fit in the box as possible. How many blocks can fit? Describe how they would be packed.
    c. Describe the connection between your answers to parts a and b.

Learning Targets:

- Apply the formula for the volume of a cone.
- Apply the formula for the volume of a cylinder.
- Apply the formula for the volume of a sphere.

> **SUGGESTED LEARNING STRATEGIES:** Create Representations, Think-Pair-Share, Group Presentation, Quickwrite, Visualization

Shayla's friend Shelly continues to help Shayla prepare for the contest by showing her how to calculate the amount of sand needed to build various solids.

Example A

Find the volume of the cylinder.

Step 1: Write the volume formula, $V = Bh$. Identify the known values of the variables.
$$h = 11 \text{ in.}$$

Step 2: Calculate the area of the base.
$$B = \pi r^2 = \pi(3)^2 = 9\pi \text{ in.}^2$$

Step 3: Substitute the dimensions into the formula.
$$V = Bh$$
$$= 9\pi(11)$$
$$= 99\pi$$

Solution: $V = 99\pi \text{ in.}^3 \approx 311.02 \text{ in.}^3$

3 in.

11 in.

> **MATH TIP**
>
> The formula for the volume V of a cylinder is $V = Bh$, where B is the area of the base and h is the height. Since $B = \pi r^2$, the formula may be written as $V = \pi r^2 h$.

Example B

Find the volume of the cone.

Step 1: Write the volume formula, $V = \frac{1}{3} Bh$. Identify the known values of the variables.
$$h = 7 \text{ mm}$$

Step 2: Calculate the area of the base.
$$B = \pi r^2 = \pi(2)^2 = 4\pi \text{ mm}^2$$

Step 3: Substitute the dimensions into the formula.
$$V = \frac{1}{3} Bh$$
$$= \frac{1}{3}(4\pi)(7)$$
$$= \frac{28\pi}{3}$$

Solution: $V = \frac{28\pi}{3} \text{ mm}^3 \approx 29.32 \text{ mm}^3$

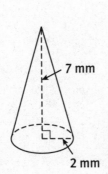

7 mm

2 mm

> **MATH TIP**
>
> The formula for the volume V of a cone is $V = \frac{1}{3} Bh$, where B is the area of the base and h is the height. Since $B = \pi r^2$, the formula may be written as $V = \frac{1}{3} \pi r^2 h$.
>
> Compare the volume formulas for a cylinder and a cone. How are they the same? How are they different?

My Notes

MATH TIP

The formula for the volume V of a sphere is $V = \frac{4}{3}\pi r^3$

Example C

Find the volume of the sphere shown below.

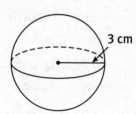

3 cm

Step 1: Write the volume formula, $V = \frac{4}{3}\pi r^3$.
Identify the values of the variables.
$$r = 3 \text{ cm}$$

Step 2: Substitute the value of r into the formula.
$$V = \frac{4}{3}\pi r^3$$
$$= \frac{4}{3}\pi(3)^3$$
$$= 36\pi$$

Solution: $V = 36\pi \text{ cm}^3 \approx 113.10 \text{ cm}^3$

Try These A–B–C

Find the volume of each solid. Leave your answers in terms of π and round to the nearest tenth.

a.

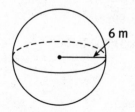

6 m

b.

⊢8 cm⊣

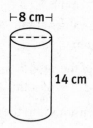

14 cm

c.

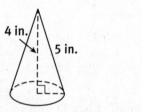

4 in.

5 in.

My Notes

1. Shayla begins work on the cylindrical towers on either side of the front wall.
   a. Draw and label a sketch of one of the cylinders used to create the two towers if the diameter of each cylinder is 10 inches and the height of each cylinder is 28 inches.

   b. Use the volume formula for a cylinder to find the number of cubic inches of sand needed to build the two congruent cylindrical towers.

2. Shelly tells Shayla that she uses the formula $V = Bh$ to find the volume of both cylinders and prisms. Why does this work?

3. Now Shayla works on the turrets.
   a. Draw and label a sketch of one of the cones used to create the turrets if the diameter of the base of each cone is 10 inches and the height of each cone is 16 inches.

   b. **Attend to precision.** Use the volume formula for a cone to find how many cubic inches of sand are needed to build the two congruent conical turrets. How many cubic feet are needed?

> **MATH TIP**
>
> $1 \text{ ft}^3 = 1{,}728 \text{ in.}^3$

My Notes

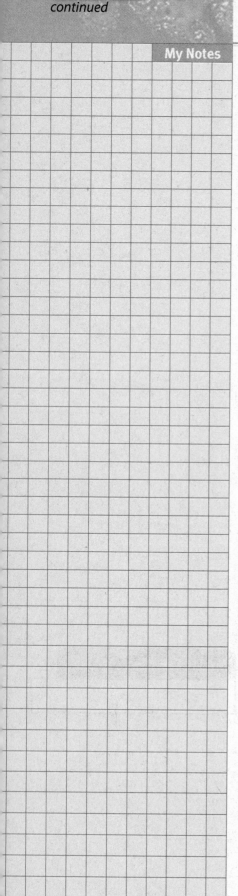

4. Use the volume formula for a sphere to find how many cubic inches of sand are needed to build the three congruent decorative hemispheres on top of the wall if the radius of each hemisphere is 2 inches.

5. Finally, Shayla considers the posts in front of the drawbridge.
   a. Draw and label a sketch of one of the posts in front of the drawbridge if the diameter of the base of the cylinder is 12 inches and the height of the cylinder is 15 inches. The sphere on top of each post has the same radius as the cylinder.

   b. Use the volume formulas for a sphere and cylinder to find how many cubic inches of sand are needed to build the two posts in front of the drawbridge. How many cubic feet are needed?

Check Your Understanding

6. Draw a cone with a height of 12 cm and a radius of 5 cm. Find the volume.

7. Draw a sphere with a radius of 10 ft. Find the volume.

8. a. Draw a cylinder with a height of 9 in. and a diameter of 4 in. Find the volume.
   b. Draw a cone with a height of 9 in. and a diameter of 4 in. Find the volume.
   c. How many times the volume of the cone is the volume of the cylinder?
   d. State a rule for the relating the volumes of a cylinder and cone that have the same height and diameter.
   e. Would your rule also apply to the volumes of a cylinder and cone that have the same height and radius?

My Notes

LESSON 26-2 PRACTICE

9. How is the relationship between the formula for the volume of a cone and the formula for the volume of a cylinder related to the relationship between the formula for the volume of a pyramid and the formula for the volume of a prism?

10. Find the volume of a beach ball with a radius of 12 inches. Round to the nearest tenth.

11. A glass jar has a height of 5 inches and a radius of 2.5 inches. Vanessa wants to fill the jar with beads that cost $0.12 per cubic inch. How much will it cost for her to fill the jar?

12. **a.** The figure shows the dimensions of a paper cone that will be filled with popcorn. The popcorn costs $0.02 per cubic inch. What is the cost of filling the cone with popcorn?

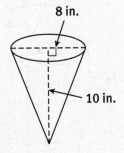

8 in.

10 in.

   b. Popcorn is also sold in cylindrical tubs that have a diameter of 8in. and a height of 10 in. What is the cost of filling the cylinder with popcorn?
   c. Explain how you could determine the answer to part b without using the formula for volume of a cylinder.

13. **Critique the reasoning of others.** Jason states that the volume of the cone shown below must be one-third of the volume of the cylinder since the two solids have the same height. Do you agree or disagree? Justify your response.

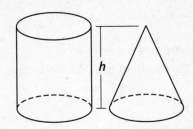

h

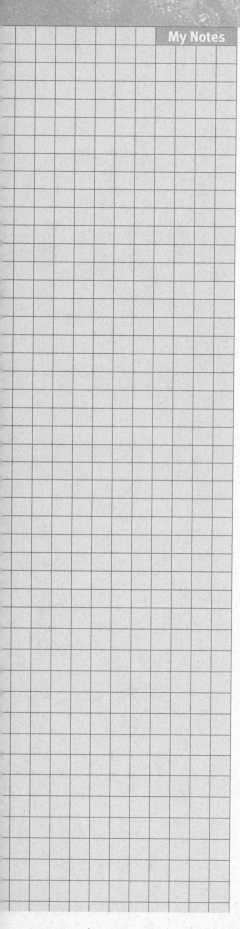

My Notes

Learning Targets:

- Decompose composite solids into simpler three-dimensional figures.
- Find the volume of composite solids.

SUGGESTED LEARNING STRATEGIES: Visualization, Identify a Subtask, Think-Pair-Share, Group Presentation

A **composite solid** is a solid that consists of two or more simpler solids, such as prisms, pyramids, cylinders, cones, or hemispheres.

Example A

Find the volume of the composite solid shown below.

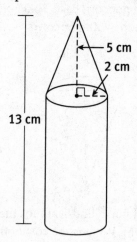

5 cm
2 cm
13 cm

Step 1: Identify the solids that make up the composite figure.
The composite figure consists of a cone and a cylinder.

Step 2: Find the volume of the cone.
$V = \frac{1}{3} Bh$
$= \frac{1}{3} \pi (2)^2 (5)$
$= \frac{20\pi}{3} \approx 20.9 \text{ cm}^3$

Step 3: Find the volume of the cylinder.
Note that the height of the cylinder is $13 - 5 = 8$ cm.
$V = Bh$
$= \pi (2)^2 (8)$
$= 32\pi \approx 100.5 \text{ cm}^3$

Step 4: Add the volume of the cone and the cylinder.
$V = 20.9 + 100.5 = 121.4 \text{ cm}^3$

Solution: $V \approx 121.4 \text{ cm}^3$

Try These A

a. Sketch a composite figure consisting of two congruent square pyramids, joined at the bases, with a base edge length of 4 cm and an overall height of 12 cm.

b. Calculate the volume of the composite figure.

1. **Model with mathematics.** Shayla realizes that many parts of her castle design could be considered composite solids. Use composite solids and the calculations you made in Lessons 26-1 and 26-2 to find the total number of cubic inches of sand Shayla needs to build her castle. Show your work.

2. How many cubic feet of sand will Shayla need?

Check Your Understanding

Find the volume of each composite solid. Round to the nearest tenth.

3.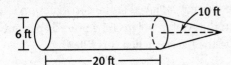

4.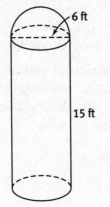

5.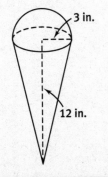

My Notes

LESSON 26-3 PRACTICE

6. Describe a composite solid you have seen in the real world. Explain how the composite figure is made up of simpler solids.

7. Find the volume of the composite solid shown below.

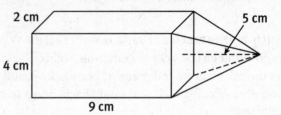

2 cm   5 cm

4 cm

9 cm

8. Find the volume of a composite figure comprised of two cones that are joined at the congruent circular bases, where one cone has a base radius of 8 inches and a height of 14 inches and the other cone has a height of 10 inches. Round to the nearest tenth.

9. A portable barrier that is used at construction sites is composed of three prisms, as shown below.

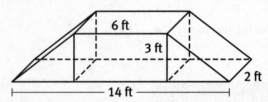

6 ft

3 ft

2 ft

14 ft

a. What is the volume of the barrier?
b. The barrier is made of hollow, lightweight plastic for easy transportation. Once the barrier is placed at the construction site, it is filled with water. Given that water weighs 62.4 pounds per cubic foot, what is the weight of the barrier when it is filled?

10. Construct viable arguments. If Shayla builds a sand castle with dimensions twice as large as the dimensions of Shelly's winning castle, will Shayla need twice as much sand? Provide an argument to justify your response.

ACTIVITY 26 PRACTICE
Write your answers on notebook paper.
Show your work.

Lesson 26-1

1. Find the volume of a rectangular prism with a length of 5 inches, width of 8 inches, and height of 6 inches.

2. Find the volume of a cube with side lengths of 7.1 millimeters.

3. Find the volume of a square pyramid with a base edge length of 12 centimeters and a height of 20 centimeters.

4. Find the volume of the solid shown below.

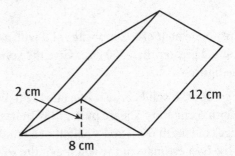

5. A rectangular prism has a volume of 80 cubic feet. The length of the prism is 8 feet and the height of the prism is 4 feet. What is the width of the prism?

6. Jayden has a planter box in the shape of a cube. Each edge is 1.5 feet long. He fills the box with sand that weighs 100 pounds per cubic foot. Which of the following is the best estimate of the weight of the sand in the box once it is filled?
   A. 150 pounds B. 230 pounds
   C. 300 pounds D. 330 pounds

7. A cube has edges of length 6 inches. Casey calculates the surface area and the volume of the cube and states that the surface area equals the volume. Do you agree or disagree? Explain.

8. A square pyramid has a volume of 60 cubic meters. The height of the pyramid is 5 meters.
   a. What is the area of the base of the pyramid?
   b. What is the length of each edge of the square base?

9. A square pyramid has edges of length p and a height of p as well. Which expression represents the volume of the pyramid?
   A. $\frac{1}{3}p^3$ B. $\frac{1}{3}p^2$
   C. $\frac{1}{3}p^2 + p$ D. $\frac{1}{3}p + p^2$

Lesson 26-2

10. Find the volume of a cone with a radius of 3 inches and a height of 12 inches. Round to the nearest tenth.

11. Find the volume of a sphere with a radius of 9 centimeters. Round to the nearest tenth.

12. Find the volume of a cone having a base circumference of 36π meters and height of 12 meters. Leave your answer in terms of π.

13. What is the formula for the volume of a cone with radius r and a height of $2r$?

14. A regulation NBA basketball has a diameter of 9.4 inches. What is the volume of one of these basketballs? Round to the nearest tenth.

15. A cylinder has a volume of 18π cubic inches. The radius of the cylinder is 3 inches. What is the height of the cylinder?

16. Which is the best estimate of the amount of soup that can fit in a soup can with the dimensions shown below?

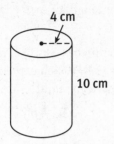

4 cm

10 cm

A. 60 cm³ **B.** 125 cm³
C. 170 cm³ **D.** 500 cm³

17. You buy two cylindrical cans of juice, as shown in the figure below. Each can holds the same amount of juice. What is the height of can B?

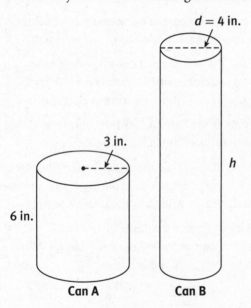

d = 4 in.

3 in.

h

6 in.

Can A   Can B

18. Which of these solids has the greatest volume?
A. a cylinder with radius 3 cm and height 3 cm
B. a cone with radius 3 cm and height 3 cm
C. a sphere with radius 3 cm
D. a cube with edges 3 cm long

19. A cylindrical glass has a radius of 3 cm and height of 14 cm. Elena pours water into the glass to a height of 8 cm.
a. What is the volume of the water in the glass?
b. What is the volume of the empty space in the glass?

Lesson 26-3

20. Find the volume of the composite solid below. Round to the nearest tenth.

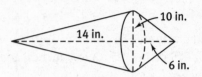

10 in.

14 in.

6 in.

21. Find the volume of the composite solid below. Round to the nearest tenth.

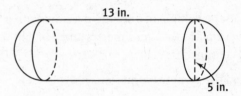

13 in.

5 in.

22. Create a sketch of a composite solid with a total volume greater than 500 cm³. Give the volume of the figure.

23. A composite solid consists of a cube with edges of length 6 cm and a square pyramid with base edges of length 6 cm and a height of 6 cm. Which is the best estimate of the volume of the solid?
A. 100 cm³ **B.** 200 cm³
C. 300 cm³ **D.** 400 cm³

MATHEMATICAL PRACTICES
Use Appropriate Tools Strategically

24. Can rounding make a difference in your results when you calculate a volume? Consider a sphere with a radius of 3.9 inches.
a. Calculate the volume of the sphere by first finding r^3. Then round to the nearest tenth. Calculate the volume using this value of r^3 and 3.14 for π.
b. Now calculate the volume without rounding the value of r^3 and by using the π key on your calculator.
c. How do the results compare? Which value do you think is more accurate? Why?

Surface Area and Volume
AIR DANCING

A group of students who will be attending the new Plato Middle School want to find a way to welcome the entire student body on the first day of school. After some investigation, the students decide an air dancer is a good idea and begin brainstorming ideas. The design they finally agree on has two cylindrical legs, a rectangular prism for a body, two right triangular prisms for arms, a cylindrical neck, a spherical head, and a cone-shaped hat.

Note: The drawing at the right does not necessarily represent the design that the students chose. To complete the items below, make your own drawing, showing the correct shape for each body part.

1. Sketch the air dancer design that the students chose.

2. The students must consider fans to keep a certain amount of air moving in the dancer. In order to determine the amount of air needed to inflate the air dancer, the students must calculate the volume.
    a. Find the volume of the cylindrical legs if each one is 10 feet tall and 2 feet in diameter.
    b. Find the volume of the rectangular prism to be used for the body. The dimensions are 6 feet long, 4 feet wide, and 8 feet high.
    c. Find the volume of the right triangular prisms used for arms. A diagram for one of the arms is shown to the right.
    d. Find the volume of the cylindrical neck if it is 2 feet tall and has a diameter of 1.5 feet.
    e. Find the volume of the spherical head if it has a radius of 3 feet.
    f. Find the volume of the cone-shaped hat if it has a radius of 3 feet and a height of 4 feet.
    g. What is the total volume of the air dancer?

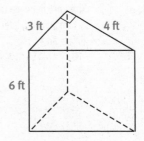

3. a. Find the lateral area of one of the cylindrical legs using the dimensions from Item 2a.
    b. Find the lateral area of each of the right triangular prisms that are used for arms using the dimensions from Item 2c.
    c. The air dancer will be placed on a box that is a rectangular prism. The dimensions of the box are 12 feet long by 6 feet wide by 4 feet high. What is the total surface area of the box?

Scoring Guide	Exemplary	Proficient	Emerging	Incomplete
	The solution demonstrates these characteristics:			
Mathematics Knowledge and Thinking (Items 1, 2a–g, 3a–c)	• Accurately and efficiently finding the surface area and volume of three-dimensional figures.	• Finding the surface area and volume of three-dimensional figures with few, if any, errors.	• Difficulty finding the surface area and volume of three-dimensional figures.	• No understanding of finding the surface area and volume of three-dimensional figures.
Problem Solving (Items 2a–g, 3a–c)	• An appropriate and efficient strategy that results in a correct answer.	• A strategy that may include unnecessary steps but results in a correct answer.	• A strategy that results in some incorrect answers.	• No clear strategy when solving problems.
Mathematical Modeling / Representations (Item 1)	• Precisely modeling a problem situation with an accurate diagram.	• Drawing a reasonably accurate diagram to model a problem situation.	• Difficulty drawing a diagram to model a problem situation.	• Drawing an incorrect diagram to model a problem situation.
Reasoning and Communication (Items 3a–c)	• Correctly understanding the difference between total surface area and lateral surface area.	• Distinguishing between total surface area and lateral surface area.	• Confusion in distinguishing between total surface area and lateral surface area.	• No understanding of the difference between total surface area and lateral surface area.

Functions

Unit Overview

In this unit you will study relations and functions. You will evaluate functions and represent them graphically, algebraically, and verbally. You you will compare and contrast linear and non-linear patterns and write expressions to represent these patterns

Key Terms

As you study this unit, add these and other terms to your math notebook. Include in your notes your prior knowledge of each word, as well as your experiences in using the word in different mathematical examples. If needed, ask for help in pronouncing new words and add information on pronunciation to your math notebook. It is important that you learn new terms and use them correctly in your class discussions and in your problem solutions.

Academic Vocabulary

- contraption

Math Terms

- relation
- set
- ordered pair
- function
- domain
- range
- discrete data
- continuous data
- rate of change
- trend line
- scatter plot

ESSENTIAL QUESTIONS

? Why is it important to consider domain, range, and intercepts in problem situations?

? Why is it important to be able represent functions as tables, graphs, algebraically, and verbally?

EMBEDDED ASSESSMENTS

These assessments, following activities 29 and 31, will give you an opportunity to demonstrate your understanding of functions.

1. On the grid below, draw a figure that illustrates the meaning of linear.

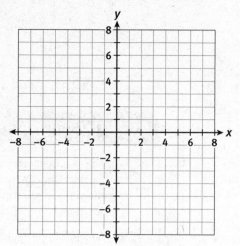

2. Name five ordered pairs that would be on a graph made from the following table.

Input	Output
5	1
10	2
15	3

3. If $x + 2y = 13$ find the value of y when x is
   a. 3   **b.** 8   **c.** 2.1

4. Name 3 ordered pairs that satisfy each of the following equations.
   a. $2y = 6$ **b.** $3x + 2y = 9$ **c.** $3x = 12$

5. Which of the following equations represents the data in the table?

x	1	3	5	7
y	1	8	14	19

   A. $y = 2x - 3$ **B.** $y = 2x + 3$
   C. $y = 3x - 2$ **D.** $y = 3x + 2$

6. Harry earns $300 a week plus $25 for each insurance policy he sells.
   a. Write an equation to determine how much Harry can earn each week.
   b. How many policies did Harry sell last week if he earned $550?

7. What is the relationship between x and y values in the following?

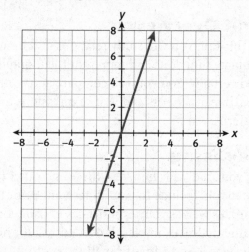

8. On the grid provided draw a representation that is not linear.

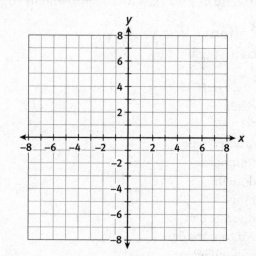

Introduction to Functions

It's All Related

Lesson 27-1 What Is a Function?

Learning Targets:

- Define relation and function.
- Evaluate functions.

SUGGESTED LEARNING STRATEGIES: Graphic Organizer, Visualization, Discussion Groups, Create Representations, Note Taking

Mathematicians study relationships in the world around us in order to learn how things work. For example, the relationship between gasoline, air, and fire is what makes a motorcycle move. Understanding the relationship between carbonation and motion allows us to know that opening a bottle of carbonated drink that has been shaken is probably not a good idea.

1. In a relationship, one item depends on another. In the example below, a car taking us home depends on there being enough gas in the car to reach the destination. List other relationships that exist in the real world.

Desired Result:	Depends On:
1. Car taking us home	Having enough gas in the car

A *relation* is a *set* of one or more *ordered pairs*. For example, the pairing of having enough gas in the car with the car taking us home is a relation. This relation can be written: {(having enough gas in the car, car takes us home)}.

2. Use the table you completed in Item 1 to write other relations.

My Notes

MATH TERMS

A **set** is a collection of objects, like points, or a type of number, like the real numbers. The symbols {} indicate a set.

An **ordered pair** is two numbers written in a certain order. Most often, the term *ordered pair* will refer to the x and y coordinates of a point on the coordinate plane, which are always written (x, y). The term can also refer to any values paired together according to a specific order.

Example A

Write a relation using the table or graph.

Input (*x*)	Output (*y*)
2	4
−3	−6
5	−1

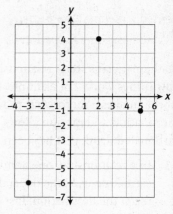

Step 1: Look at the input (*x*) and output (*y*) values.

Step 2: Create each ordered pair (*x*, *y*) by writing the input value and corresponding output value in parentheses.

Step 3: Use braces to write the ordered pairs as a set.

Solution: {(2, 4), (−3, −6), (5, −1)}

Try These A

a. Write a relation from the table of values.

x	*y*
−10	5
20	−10
−30	−15
40	20

b. Write a relation from the graph.

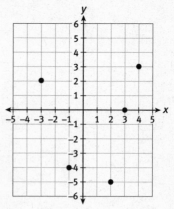

A *function* is a special kind of relation in which one input has only one output. One way to think of a function is as a machine. A machine has an input and an output and a relationship exists between the input and the output. The machine receives the input and transforms it into the output. For example, a toaster is a machine. When bread is the input, the machine toasts the bread and the output is toast.

CONNECT TO AP

Functions and relations, which describe how two varying quantities are related, form the basis of much of the work you will do in calculus.

3. With your group, list other machines along with their inputs and outputs.

Input	Machine	Output
1. Bread	Toaster	Toast

DISCUSSION GROUP TIPS

Working with a partner or in small groups provides an opportunity for you to clarify your understanding of relations and functions.

In mathematics, if x is the input and y is the output, the value of y depends on the value of x. The relationship between x and y is determined by the function, or rule (the machine). The function changes, or transforms, x into y, so y is a function of x.

4. A function represented by the equation $y = x + 5$ has inputs labeled x and outputs labeled y. The diagram below represents that function.

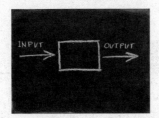

a. If $x = 5$ is used as an input in the diagram, what is the output?

b. If $x = -3$ is used as an input in the diagram, what is the output?

c. If $x = 0.03$ is used as an input in the diagram, what is the output?

d. If $x = -\frac{1}{2}$ is used as an input in the diagram, what is the output?

e. **Reason abstractly.** For this particular function, is it possible to have the same y-value when using two different x-values? Explain.

5. Complete the function table. Use the given input (*x*) values and determine the corresponding output (*y*) values based on the given function.

Input (*x*)	Function	Output (*y*)
	$y = 2x - 1$	

6. Create your own function. Choose any values for *x* and determine the corresponding values for *y* based on the function you write.

Input (*x*)	Function	Output (*y*)

7. Write the *x*- and *y*-values from the function that you created in Item 6 above as ordered pairs.

Check Your Understanding

8. Complete the function table below. Choose any values for *x* and determine the corresponding values for *y*.

Input (*x*)	Function	Output (*y*)
	$y = x - 9$	

9. Write the *x*- and *y*-values from the function in Item 8 as a set of ordered pairs.

LESSON 27-1 PRACTICE

For Items 10 and 11, write each relation as a set of ordered pairs.

10.

x	y
−15	3
2	−11
−3	−7
12	4

11.

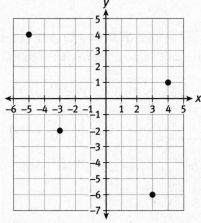

For Items 12 and 13, make a function table of values for each function with the given input values.

12. $y = 5x - 1$ for $x = -4$, $x = 12$, $x = 0$, and $x = 0.5$

13. $y = 1.7x$ for $x = 1.7$, $x = 5$, $x = -5$, and $x = 100$

14. **Critique the reasoning of others.** Josie used the function $y = 4x$ to complete the table below.

x	1	3	5	7
y	4	12	20	28

Then she wrote these ordered pairs: (4, 1), (12, 3), (20, 5), (28, 7).
Do you agree with Josie's work? Justify your reasoning.

My Notes

My Notes

Learning Targets:

● Understand that a function is a rule that assigns exactly one output to each input.

● Identify functions using ordered pairs, tables, and mappings.

SUGGESTED LEARNING STRATEGIES: Graphic Organizer, Visualization, Discussion Groups, Create Representations, Note Taking

One type of representation that helps to determine if a relation is a function is a *mapping*. The diagram in the My Notes column is a mapping. This particular mapping is a function because every input (*x*-value) is mapped to exactly one output (*y*-value).

In the mapping below, all input values are written in an oval, and all output values are written in another oval. Each input value is connected with its output value.

$$\{(1, 2), (2, 4), (3, 5), (8, 3)\}$$

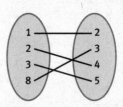

1. Is this relation a ***function***? Justify your response.

MATH TERMS

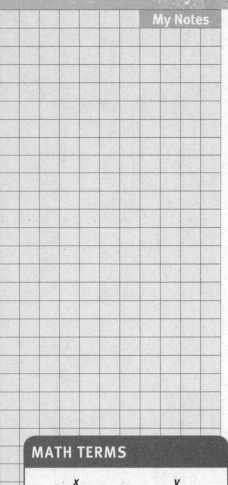

A **function** is a special kind of relation in which each input value is paired with exactly one output value.

In functions, *y*-values can be associated with more than one *x*-value. However, each input (*x*) has exactly one output (*y*).

2. Construct viable arguments. One of the relations mapped below is a function, and one is not. Determine which relation is a function and which is not. Justify your responses.

a. $\{(1, 2), (1, 4), (5, 3), (2, 5)\}$ **b.** $\{(1, 2), (3, 4), (2, 3), (4, 4)\}$

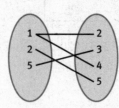   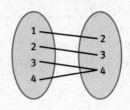

Check Your Understanding

Use mapping to determine if the following are functions. Explain.

3. {(1, 3), (1, 4), (1, 5)}

4. $y = x + 2$ for $x = \{0, 1, 2, 3, 4\}$

5.

x	1	3	5	7
y	2	5	3	2

6. Confirm that the relation you created in Item 6 in Lesson 27-1 is a function using mapping.

It is also possible to determine if a relation is a function by looking at ordered pairs. There should be only one output for each input. The ordered pairs can also be represented in a table.

7. Determine if the following relations are functions. Explain why they are or are not.

a.

x	y
−3	2
5	5
2	8
3	−3
−5	−5
6	2
−2	5
8	8

b.

x	y
−5	5
−4	4
−3	3
−2	2
−1	1
0	0
1	1
2	2

c.

x	y
2	3
4	5
6	7
8	9
3	11
4	13
5	15
6	17

8. a. Create two tables of values to represent two relations, one that is a function and one that is *not* a function.

b. Justify your answers to part a using a mapping.

9. Make use of structure. Explain how you can identify from a table a relation that does not represent a function.

Check Your Understanding

10. Which relation represents a function? Justify your choice.

A.

x	y
1	5
3	7
3	8
4	10

B.

x	y
1	5
3	7
4	8
5	8

LESSON 27-2 PRACTICE

Use mappings to determine if each relation represents a function.

11. {(7, 5), (8, 6), (9, 7), (10, 8)}

12. {(4, 24), (8, 18), (12, 2), (16, 6)}

13. {(−1, 1), (−1, 0), (−1, −1), (−1, −2)}

For Items 14–16, explain why each relation is or is not a function.

14.

x	2	4	6	8
y	14	28	42	56

15.

x	y
−1	−2
5	−6
−1	−3
5	−7

16.

x	0	10	20	30
y	5	5	5	5

17. Model with mathematics. Draw a mapping to prove the following relation is a function. Explain your reasoning.

$$\{(1, 1), (2, 8), (3, 27), (4, 64)\}$$

My Notes

Learning Targets:
● Define domain and range.
● Determine the domain and range of a relation.

> SUGGESTED LEARNING STRATEGIES: Graphic Organizer, Visualization, Discussion Groups, Create Representations, Note Taking

The set of all the input values is called the **domain**. In a relation, all domain values must be matched with an output value. The set of all output values is called the **range**.

DISCUSSION GROUP TIPS

As you read and define new terms, discuss their meanings with other group members and make connections to prior learning.

Example A
Find the domain and range of the relation:

$$\{(1, 2), (2, 4), (4, 5), (8, 3)\}$$

Step 1: Look at the *x*-coordinate in each ordered pair to identify the domain values. Write these numbers as a set.

Step 2: Look at the *y*-coordinate in each ordered pair to identify the range values. Write these numbers as a set.

Solution: The domain is {1, 2, 4, 8} and the range is {2, 3, 4, 5}.

Try These A
Determine the domain and range of each relation.
a. {(2, 4), (2, 5), (2, 6), (2, 7), (2, 8)}

b.

x	y
3	12
4	12
12	12
1	8

1. **Construct viable arguments.** Use mappings to explain why each relation in Try These A is or is not a function.

My Notes

Check Your Understanding

Determine the domain and range in each relation. Then state whether the relation is or is not a function.

2. {(3, 5), (3, 6), (3, 7), (3, 8), (3, 9)}

3.

x	y
1	10
2	11
12	12
3	9

4.

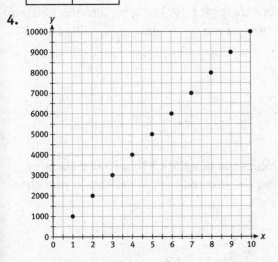

Relationships can also exist between different sets of information. For example, the pairing of the names of students in your class and their heights is one such relationship.

5. Collect the following information for 10 members of your class.

Student Number	First Name	Height (cm)	Length of Index Finger (cm)
1			
2			
3			
4			
5			
6			
7			
8			
9			
10			

CONNECT TO AP

When conducting observational studies in AP Statistics, the data collected are not always numerical. For example, a study might compare the fruit-juice flavor preferred by male students compared with the flavor preferred by female students.

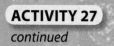

My Notes

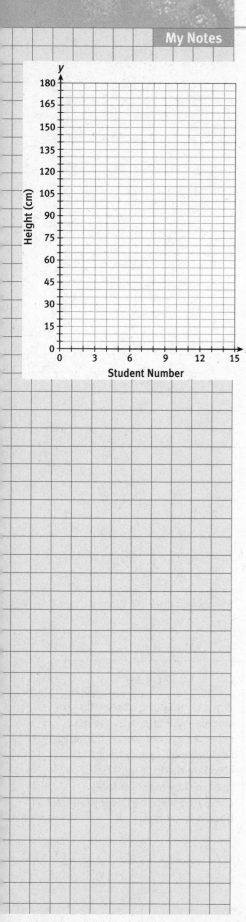

6. Write the student numbers and heights of 5 students in the class as ordered pairs (Student Number, Height).

7. Graph and label the coordinates of a point for each of the five ordered pairs you wrote in Item 6.

8. **Use appropriate tools strategically.** Using the information from the table, what relationships can you create other than student number to height?

9. Using one of the relationships you described in Item 8 that contains only numeric values, create five ordered pairs of students in your class.

10. Using the table in Item 5, what would be the domain of the relation that associates length of index finger to height?

11. What would be the range of the relation that associates length of index finger to height?

12. Is the relation that associates student numbers to their height a function? Use a mapping to justify your response.

13. In your mapping in Item 12, label the two ovals with the terms *domain* and *range*.

Check Your Understanding

The table shows the results of a survey of 5 students about the number of siblings they have and the number of pets they have. Use the table to answer Items 14 and 15.

Number of Siblings	1	0	2	4	3
Number of Pets	2	0	1	1	3

14. Use a mapping to determine if the relation that associates number of siblings to number of pets is a function. Explain your reasoning.

15. Use a mapping to determine if the relation that associates the number of pets to the number of siblings is a function. Explain your reasoning.

LESSON 27-3 PRACTICE

16. What are the domain and range of the relation in Item 14?

17. What are the domain and range of the relation in Item 15?

For Items 18 and 19, determine the domain and range of each relation.

18. $\{(3, -5), (5, 6), (-3, 7), (4, 8), (2, -8)\}$

19.

x	y
−3	8
4	12
12	12
4	8

20. Use mappings to determine which of the relations in Items 18 and 19 is a function. Justify your response.

21. **Reason abstractly.** Ryan copied the table below.

x	5	7	8	4	?
y	2	0	1	6	1

He forgot to copy one of the *x*-values into the table. If he knows the table represents a function, what are the possible values for the *x*-value that is missing in the table? Explain your reasoning.

MATH TIP

Summarize in your own words the ways to recognize a function when it is represented graphically.

Learning Targets:

● Identify functions using graphs.

● Understand the difference between discrete and continuous data.

SUGGESTED LEARNING STRATEGIES: Graphic Organizer, Visualization, Discussion Group, Create Representations, Note Taking

You can also determine if a relation is a function by looking at its graph. Knowing that in a function every x-value has only one y-value allows the vertical line test to be used to determine if a graph represents a function. If any vertical line intersects a graph at only one point, then the graph represents a function.

Example A

Determine which of the following graphs of relations represents a function.

Step 1: Apply the vertical line test.

Relation A:
$\{(-2, -1), (-1, 2), (0, 0),$
$(1, -2), (2, 2)\}$

Relation B:
$\{(-1, -1), (-1, 2), (0, 0),$
$(1, 2), (1, -2)\}$

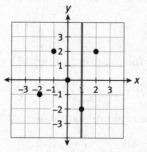
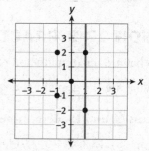

Step 2: Look at the graph to determine if any of the domain values have more than one range value.

Solution: Relation A is a function since each input has only one output. Relation B is not a function because at least one input has two different outputs.

Relation C: $y = |x|$

Relation D: $x = y^2$

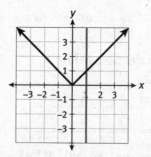
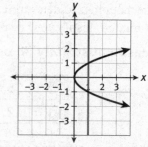

Solution: Relation C is a function since each input has only one output. Relation D is not a function because at least one input has two different outputs.

My Notes

Try These A

State whether each graph represents a function. Explain your reasoning.

a.

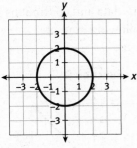

b.

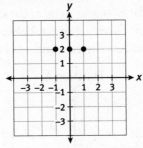

1. What does a vertical line in the vertical line test represent?

2. **Reason abstractly.** Explain how the vertical line test works. In other words, when looking at a graph of a relation, how can you determine if it is a function?

Check Your Understanding

3. Which of the following graphs represents a function? Explain your reasoning.

A.

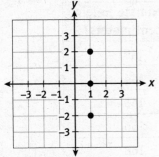

B.

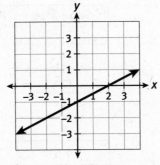

MATH TERMS

Data are **discrete** if there are only a finite number of values possible or if there is a space on the number line or on a graph between each 2 possible values.

Data are **continuous** if there are no breaks in their domain or range or if the graph has no breaks, holes or gaps.

Discrete data are data that can only have certain values such as the number of people in your class. On a graph there will be a space between every two possible values. *Continuous data* can take on any value within a certain range, for example, height. On a graph, continuous data and continuous functions have no breaks, holes, or gaps. In the following example, Function A is discrete and Function B is continuous.

Function A

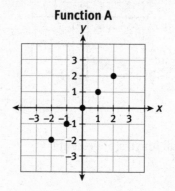

Function B

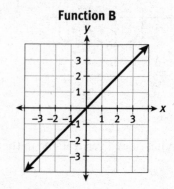

4. Functions can be represented by equations such as $y = 2x + 3$.
   a. Is there any limit to the number of input values that can be used with this equation? Explain your reasoning.

   b. Is the function discrete or continuous? Justify your response.

Mr. Walker collected the following data about shoe size and height from 5 students in his class.

Shoe Size	Approximate Height (in centimeters)
6	140
6.5	144
7	148
8	156
9.5	168

My Notes

5. a. Use a mapping of the relation above to determine if the relation is a function. Be sure to label the domain and range.

b. Create a graph and explain how it confirms your answer to part a. Use the My Notes column if needed.

c. Reason quantitatively. An equation that can be used to represent the relation is $y = 8x + 92$, where x represents a student's shoe size and y represents a student's height. Is there any reasonable limit to the domain values that can be used with this expression? Justify your response.

d. Is the relation discrete or continuous? Explain your reasoning.

My Notes

Mr. Walker also coaches the middle school track team and collected the following sample of data regarding the times that one of his athletes clocked while running certain distances.

Time	Distance (m)
8 minutes	1,500
9 minutes	1,700
10 minutes	1,900
11 minutes	2,100
12 minutes	2,300

6. a. Use a mapping of the relation above to determine if the relation is a function.

b. Create a graph and explain how it confirms your answer to part a. Use the My Notes column if needed.

c. An equation that can be used to represent the relation is $y = 200x - 100$, where x represents the athlete's time. Is there any reasonable limit to the input values that can be used with this expression? Explain your reasoning.

d. Is the relation discrete or continuous? Explain your reasoning.

Check Your Understanding

Determine if each relation shown below is discrete or continuous.

7.

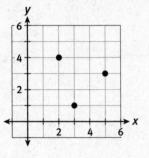

8. $y = 2x - 7$

9.

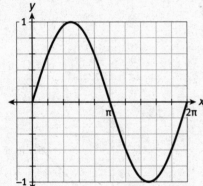

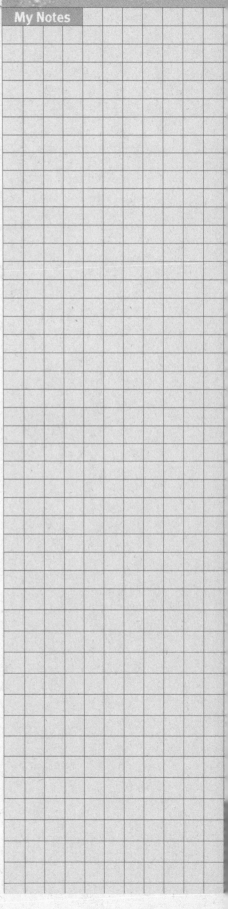

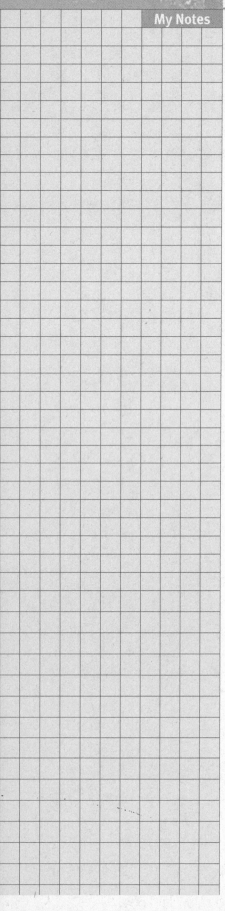

LESSON 27-4 PRACTICE

For each relation in Items 10–13:

a. Determine if it is a function.

b. Determine if it is discrete or continuous.

10.

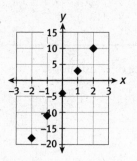

11.

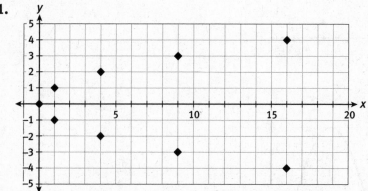

12.

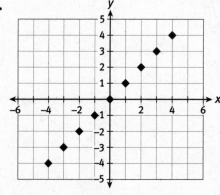

13.

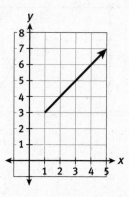

14. **Use appropriate tools strategically.** Use a graphing calculator to plot the relation {(4, −1), (1, −4), (4, −7), (7, −4)}. Determine if it is a function. Explain your reasoning.

ACTIVITY 27 PRACTICE

Write your answers on notebook paper.
Show your work.

Lesson 27-1

Evaluate each function for the given domain values.

1. $y = 2x + 4$; for $x = 3$, $x = 4$, and $x = 0.25$

2. $y = -6x + 2$; for $x = 5$, $x = \frac{1}{2}$, and $x = -7$

3. $y = 7 + (x - 9)$; for $x = 8$, $x = -1$, and $x = 10$

Write each relation as a set of ordered pairs.

4.

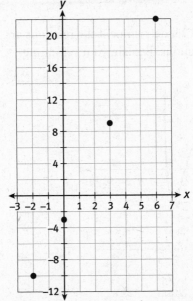

5.

x	−6	2.5	11	15
y	6	14.5	23	27

Lesson 27-2

Use mappings to determine if each relation in Items 6–11 is a function.

6. $\{(-2, 2), (-3, 4), (-4, 5), (-2, 6), (-3, 7)\}$

7. $\{(-3, 4), (-6, 1), (6, 0), (-1, 5), (-6, 4)\}$

8.

x	5	6	7	8
y	3	3	4	4

9.

x	5	6	7	8
y	3	4	5	6

10. $y = x + 5$ for $x = 3, 5, 7, 9, 11$

11. $y = x - 9$ for $x = -1, -3, -5, -7, -9$

Lesson 27-3

State the domain and range for each relation in Items 12–16.

12. $\{(-1, 7), (-2, 4), (-2, -3), (6, -3)\}$

13. $\{(11, 2), (2, -14), (-5, 13), (58, 33)\}$

14.

x	y
5	2
9	3
1	0
−2	9

15.

x	y
1	−8
3	−6
5	−4
7	−3

16.

x	y
−1	9
−5	0
9	0
−1	4

For Items 17 and 18, determine if each relation is a function. Justify your response.

17.

x	y
−2	5
−5	7
8	8
22	17
−1	32
0	76
−12	0
17	22

18.

x	y
0	7
2	5
−7	0
6	−5
0	12
5	2
−1	4
1	8

19. How do the domain and range of a relation help to determine if it is a function?

Lesson 27-4

For Items 20–23, determine if each relation is a function. Explain your reasoning.

20.

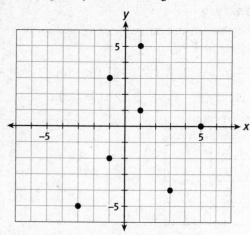

21.

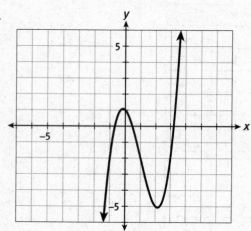

22.

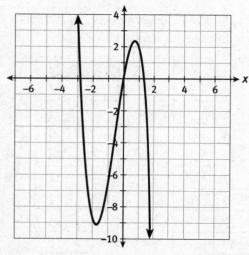

23.

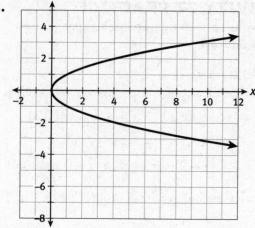

For Items 24 and 25, determine if the relations are discrete or continuous. Explain your reasoning.

24.

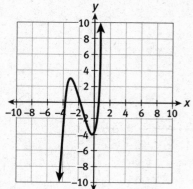

25.

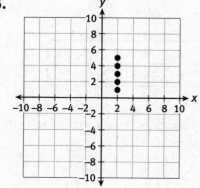

MATHEMATICAL PRACTICES
Look for and Make Use of Structure

26. Describe the various methods to determine if a relation is a function.

Comparing Functions
Which Car Wins?
Lesson 28-1 Representing Functions

Learning Targets:

- Represent functions algebraically, graphically, tabularly, or verbally.
- Compare properties of two or more functions.

SUGGESTED LEARNING STRATEGIES: Discussion Groups, Group Presentations, Graphic Organizer, Construct an Argument, Sharing and Responding, Create Representations

Functions can be represented in a variety of ways. Pages 385-388 contain graphs, equations, tables, and verbal descriptions representing a race among five model cars, each using a different type of propulsion.

1. Cut the representations apart on the dotted lines and sort the graphs, equations, verbal descriptions, and tables to create sets. The representations in each set should show the same function describing the distance and speed of one of the model cars.

2. Attach the verbal description for car #1 to the grid labeled Function 1 on the next page. Attach the graph, table, and equation that goes with car #1 as well. Repeat for the remaining sets using the grids on the following pages. Write three or four justifications for your choice in creating each set.

3. How did you make decisions about which graphs, tables, equations, and verbal descriptions to group together?

4. **Critique the reasoning of others.** In pairs or small groups, share your work with your peers.
   a. Do you agree with the work of your peers? Explain why or why not.

   b. Ask any questions you have to any of your peers about their justifications or their sets.

   c. How was your reasoning the same and different from the reasoning of the other groups in your class?

CONNECT TO PHYSICS

Propulsion is the force that propels or pushes something forward or onward.

Function 1:

Justifications:

Function 2:

Justifications:

Function 3:

<table>
<tr><td></td><td></td></tr>
<tr><td></td><td></td></tr>
</table>

Justifications:

Function 4:

Justifications:

Function 5:

Justifications:

#1 A push car travels $\frac{1}{2}$ foot per minute. It has a head start of 10 feet at the beginning of the race.

$$y = 1\frac{1}{4}x + 5$$

Time (in minutes)	Distance from starting line (in feet)
0	0
5	$6\frac{2}{3}$
7	$9\frac{1}{3}$
13	$17\frac{1}{3}$
27	36
50	$66\frac{2}{3}$
75	100
100	$133\frac{1}{3}$

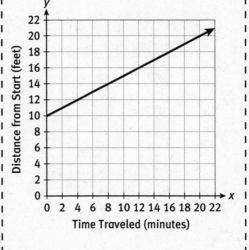

#2 A mouse trap car travels at a rate of $1\frac{1}{3}$ feet per minute and starts on the starting line at the beginning of the race.

$$y = 17$$

Time (in minutes)	Distance from starting Line (in feet)
0	5
5	$11\frac{1}{4}$
7	$13\frac{3}{4}$
13	$21\frac{1}{4}$
27	$38\frac{3}{4}$
50	$67\frac{1}{2}$
75	$98\frac{3}{4}$
100	130

This page is intentionally blank.

#3 A wind up car travels $1\frac{1}{2}$ feet per minute. It starts the race a foot behind the starting line.

$y = \frac{1}{2}x + 10$

Time (in minutes)	Distance from starting line (in feet)
0	17
5	17
7	17
13	17
27	17
50	17
75	17
100	17

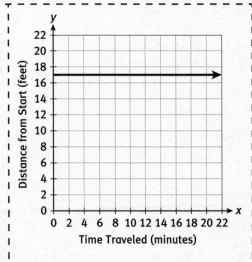

#4 A battery-powered car does not move but has a head start of 17 feet at the beginning of the race.

$y = 1\frac{1}{2}x - 1$

Time (in minutes)	Distance from starting Line (in feet)
0	10
4	12
8	14
13	$16\frac{1}{2}$
28	24
50	35
75	$47\frac{1}{2}$
100	60

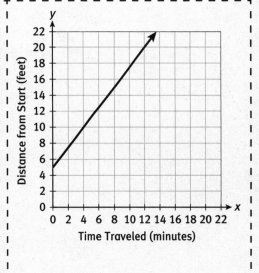

#5 A rubber band car travels at a rate of $1\frac{1}{4}$ feet per minute and has a head start of 5 feet at the beginning of the race.

$y = \frac{4}{3}x$

Time (in minutes)	Distance from starting line (in feet)
4	5
8	11
10	14
13	$18\frac{1}{2}$
24	$35\frac{3}{4}$
50	74
75	$111\frac{1}{2}$
100	149

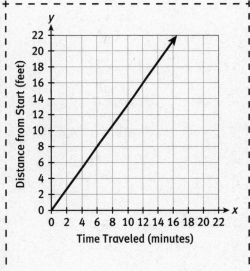

This page is intentionally blank.

Check Your Understanding

Match each verbal description with its corresponding function representation.

5. Adam is allowed 15 text messages a day on his parents' cell phone plan.

6. Ana Lucia rents a car for $20 a day.

7. Jabar starts a new job with 5 vacation days. He earns 2 additional days for every year he works.

A.

x	y
1	20
2	40
3	60
4	80
5	100

B.

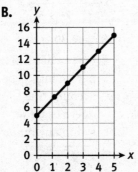

C. $y = 15x$

LESSON 28-1 PRACTICE

For Items 8–10, match each verbal description with its corresponding equation and table of values.

8. Nina starts 1.5 miles from the park path entrance and inline skates at 10 miles per hour.

9. Sasha starts 0.5 mile from the park entrance and runs at 5 miles per hour.

10. Tavon starts at the park entrance and rides his bike at 15 miles per hour.

A. $y = 5x + 0.5$ B. $y = 15x$ C. $y = 10x + 1.5$

D.

x	y
0	0
1	15
2	30
3	45
4	60

E.

x	y
0	1.5
1	11.5
2	21.5
3	31.5
4	41.5

F.

x	y
0	0.5
1	5.5
2	10.5
3	15.5
4	20.5

Model with mathematics. For Items 11-13, match each graph of a function with its corresponding equation, verbal description, and table of values.

11.

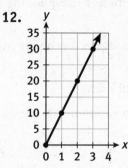

12.

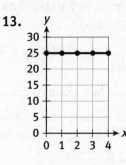

13.

A. $y = 10x$

B. $y = 30 - 4x$

C. $y = 25$

D. Javier has $30 in his savings account. He spends $4 a week.

E. Serena has $25 in her savings account. She doesn't save or spend any money.

F. Lila saves $10 a week.

G.

x	y
0	30
1	26
2	22
3	18
4	14

H.

x	y
0	0
1	10
2	20
3	30
4	40

I.

x	y
0	25
1	25
2	25
3	25
4	25

14. For Items 11–13, how did you decide which equation, verbal description, and table of values corresponds to each graph?

Learning Targets:

● Compare properties of two or more functions, each represented in a different way.

● Identify examples of proportional and nonproportional functions.

SUGGESTED LEARNING STRATEGIES: Visualization, Think-Pair-Share, Create Representations, Predict and Confirm, Marking the Text

Answer the following items regarding the five cars in the race in Lesson 28-1 and their respective functions.

1. Notice that each equation is written in the form $y = mx + b$.
   a. Which part of each equation represents the speed of the car?

   b. How is this speed represented on each graph?

   c. Where is the speed found in each table?

   d. Which car is going the fastest? Explain your reasoning.

2. In all five situations, determine how the starting place of the car is represented.
   a. Which part of the equations represent where the car started?

   b. How is this represented on each graph?

   c. Where is this information found in each table?

   d. Which car has a starting place that is farthest from the starting line? Explain your reasoning.

3. What numbers make sense for the domain and range of each of these functions?

4. Are these functions discrete or continuous? Justify your response.

My Notes

5. **Reason quantitatively.** Determine the winner of the race if the track is 60 feet long. Use multiple representations to justify your choice.

Check Your Understanding

Each pair of representations in Items 6 and 7 describes the function of a traveling vehicle. Which vehicle in each pair is traveling faster? Justify your choices. In each case, consider the time and distance units to be the same.

6. **A.**

B.

Time	Distance
5	0
10	10
15	20
20	30

7. **A.** The push car traveled at 5 mph.

B.

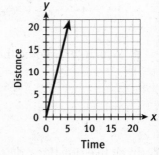

In a directly proportional function, the rate, or constant of proportionality, is steady and unchanging. Proportional functions have a distinctive equation and graph. All directly proportional functions have the form $y = kx$ and form a straight line that begins at or passes through the origin.

8. Which of the functions representing the cars in the race in Lesson 28-1 are directly proportional functions? Justify your answer using all four representations.

9. Which of the functions representing the cars in the race are not proportional functions? Justify your answer using all four representations.

Check Your Understanding

10. Determine if each function is or is not directly proportional. Justify your responses.

a. $y = -3x - 1$ b.

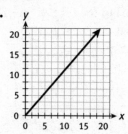

c.

Time	Distance
0	5
10	10
20	15
30	20

LESSON 28-2 PRACTICE

Each pair of representations describes the function of a traveling vehicle. Which vehicle in each pair is traveling faster? Justify your choices. In each case, consider the time and distance units to be the same.

11. A.

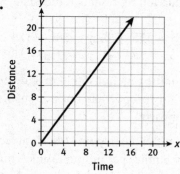

B. $y = 3x + 2$

12. A. $y = 2.5x + 10$

B.

Time	Distance
0	3
2	4.5
4	6
6	7.5

13. Determine which functions represented in Items 11 and 12 are directly proportional. Justify your response.

ACTIVITY 28 PRACTICE

Write your answers on notebook paper.
Show your work.

Lesson 28-1

Determine which graph, table, and equation match
with each of the stories. You may use square tiles or
cubes to model each situation.

1. A walkway is being laid using square tiles with no
   edges touching. Determine the total perimeter of the
   tiles in the walkway based on the number of tiles.

2. A building is being painted on all four sides as
   well as the flat square roof. Each floor is shaped
   like a cube with four square walls. In order to
   know how much paint to purchase, determine
   how many square faces need to be painted
   depending on the number of floors.

3. Another walkway is being laid, but in this case
   the square tiles each touch the one laid
   previously. Determine the total perimeter of the
   tiles in the walkway based on the number of tiles
   and not counting sides that are touching.

A.

x	y
1	5
2	9
3	13
4	17
5	21

B.

x	y
1	4
2	6
3	8
4	10
5	12

C.

x	y
1	4
2	8
3	12
4	16
5	20

D. $y = 4x$ **E.** $y = 4x + 1$ **F.** $y = 2x + 2$

G.

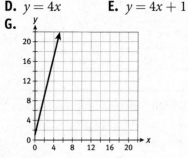

H.

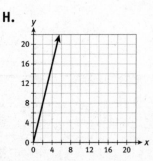

I.

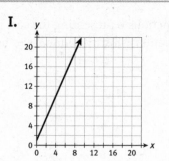

Lesson 28-2

4. Give the speed of each vehicle represented
   below as well as the vehicle's position at the
   start of the race.
   a. $y = -5x - 1$
   b.

   c.

x	y
−1	2
0	5
1	8
2	11
3	14

5. Kaneesha's new job pays her a wage of $75 each
   week plus an additional $8 for each hour worked.
   Give the rate of change for this situation and
   Kaneesha's base pay.

6. Which equation represents Kaneesha's pay rate in
   Item 5?
   A. $y = \$8x - \$75$ **B.** $y = \$8x + \$75$
   C. $y = \$75x - \$8$ **D.** $y = \$75x + \$8$

7. For each of the functions in Item 4, determine
   if it is directly proportional or not. Justify your
   answer for each.

8. A vehicle at the starting line travels at a constant
   speed of 0.5 miles per minute. Which function
   could describe this vehicle?
   A. $y = 0.5$ **B.** $y = 0.5x$
   C. $y = x + 0.5$ **D.** $y = 0.5x + 1$

MATHEMATICAL PRACTICES
Look For and Make Use of Structure

9. When comparing functions, which representation
   of a function is the easiest for you to use? Justify
   your choice using an example.

Constructing Functions

Hold On to Your Hats

Lesson 29-1 Construct a Function

Learning Targets:

- Construct a function to model a linear relationship between two quantities.
- Graph functions that model linear relationships.

SUGGESTED LEARNING STRATEGIES: Marking the Text, Sharing and Responding, Identify a Subtask, Look for a Pattern, Note Taking

Wind turbines create energy from the power of the wind. Turbines can be small and power a home or small building, or they can be large and contribute power to an entire power grid. A large group of wind turbines are run by the Tennessee Valley Authority on Buffalo Mountain near Oak Ridge, Tennessee.

Buffalo Mountain holds three older turbines that are 213 feet tall and have blades that are 75 feet in length. Each of these older turbines generates 660 kilowatts of power per hour when they are producing their maximum amount of power.

There are newer, larger turbines as well that have a height of 260 feet with blades that are 135 feet long. Each of these newer turbines creates 1,800 kilowatts of power per hour.

1. Determine how much energy, in kilowatt-hours (kWH), each of the newer turbines generates in a 24-hour day.

CONNECT TO SCIENCE

Wind power is one of many types of power currently being used. There are wind turbines in sites across the globe.

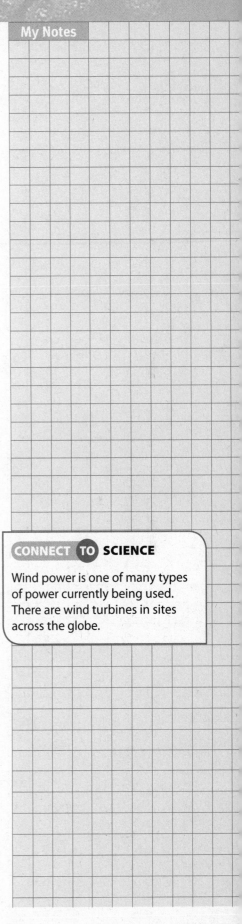

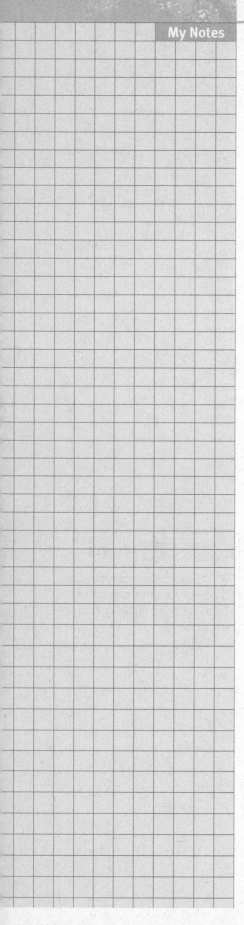

2. Write a function to represent the amount of energy generated by a newer turbine for *x* number of hours. Be sure to define the variables you use.

3. **Reason abstractly.** Explain why the function you wrote in Item 2 is directly proportional.

Unfortunately, wind turbines only produce at top capacity at a small range of wind speeds. It has been suggested that wind turbines only produce 40% of the power that they theoretically should.

4. **a.** How much energy would be generated in one 24-hour day with the turbines producing only 40% of the expected power?

   b. Rewrite your function from Item 2 to reflect that wind turbines produce only 40% of the power they are rated to produce.

5. Use the function you wrote in Item 4b to complete the table of values below.

Days	Power Generated
30	
60	
90	
120	
180	
365	

6. Graph the power generated by each of these newer turbines below.

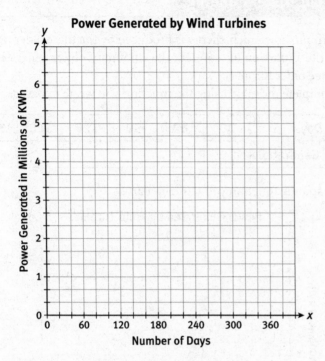

Power Generated by Wind Turbines

Power Generated in Millions of KWh (y-axis)

Number of Days (x-axis)

7. Consider the equation you wrote in Item 4b.
   a. What are the domain and range of this function?

   b. Is this function discrete or continuous?

8. **a.** How would your equation change to find the power generated by all 18 of these newer turbines on Buffalo Mountain?

   b. Rewrite your function to reflect the total number of newer turbines on the mountain.

My Notes

My Notes

Check Your Understanding

9. Determine how much energy is produced by the three older turbines.

   a. Write a function to represent the amount of power generated by the three older turbines.

   b. Complete the table using the function you wrote in part a.

Days	30	60	90	120	180	365
Power Generated						

   c. Graph the function you wrote in part a.

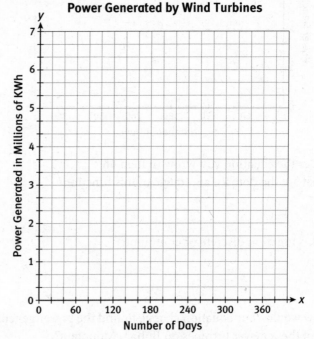

Power Generated by Wind Turbines

   d. What are the domain and range of this function?

10. How much energy is generated by all the turbines on Buffalo Mountain in one year? Show your work.

11. An average home in Oak Ridge, Tennessee, uses approximately 11,496 kilowatt-hours of electricity per year. For about how many homes could the Buffalo Mountain turbines provide energy per year?

Check Your Understanding

12. How much more energy per year does one newer turbine generate than one older turbine? Justify your response.

13. If the cost of electricity is $.09 per kilowatt-hour, what is the value in dollars of the additional electricity generated using the newer turbine over one year?

LESSON 29-1 PRACTICE

Water flows from the faucet at a rate of 2.5 gallons per minute (gpm). Use this information to answer Items 14–17.

14. Write a function to represent the problem context. Be sure to define the variables you use.

15. Use the function you wrote in Item 14 to complete the table.

Minutes	0	5	10	15	18
Gallons					

16. Use the completed table in Item 15 to graph the function you wrote in Item 14. Be sure to title the graph and write the scale on the axes.

17. Suppose that low water pressure causes the flow rate to run at 80% of the normal flow. Rewrite your function from Item 14 to reflect that the water flow is only 80% of the normal flow rate.

Connie babysits afterschool and on weekends to earn extra money. She charges $5 per hour and works 6 hours every week. Use this information to answer Items 18 and 19.

18. a. Write a function to represent Connie's situation. Be sure to define the variables you use.
    b. What are the domain and range of the function?
    c. Is the function directly proportional? Explain why or why not.

19. **Reason quantitatively.** Connie is saving her babysitting money to buy a new tablet that costs $250. How many weeks does Connie need to work to earn enough money to buy the tablet?

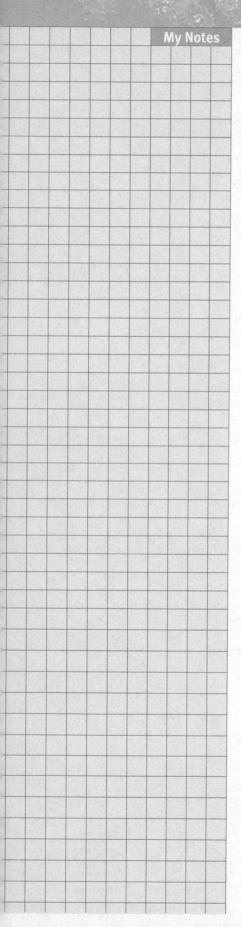

My Notes

Learning Targets:

- Determine the rate of change and initial value of a function.
- Interpret the rate of change and initial value of a linear function in terms of the situation it models.
- Identify examples of proportional and nonproportional functions that arise from mathematical and real-world problems.

SUGGESTED LEARNING STRATEGIES: Marking the Text, Create Representations, Think-Pair-Share, Visualization

Nikita is adding a small wind turbine to her home. She wants to fence off the area around the wind turbine so that children do not get hurt. She has 60 feet of fencing and wants to use it to create a rectangular border around the wind turbine. Nikita is considering various combinations of length and width for her rectangular fence.

1. Complete the table below with the possible lengths and widths of the rectangular fence Nikita plans to put around the wind turbine.

Width of Fence	Length of Fence
5	
10	
15	
	10
	5

2. Plot the data from the table on the grid provided.

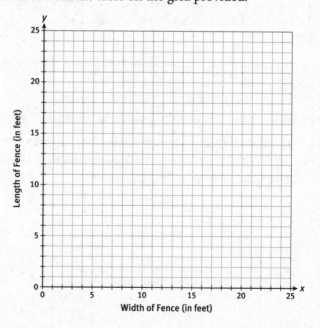

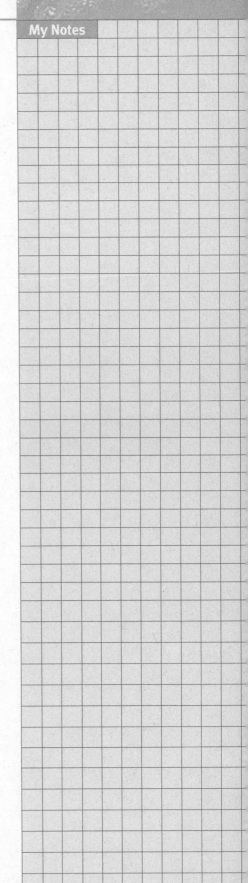

3. Examine the graph you have plotted. How are the length and width of the fence related to each other?

Example A

When she is not at home working on her wind turbine, Nikita works part-time as a salesperson.

The graph below shows the relationship between the number of sales Nikita makes and the wages she earns. Determine and explain the meaning of the rate of change and the initial value in terms of Nikita's situation. Then determine whether the function is proportional or nonproportional.

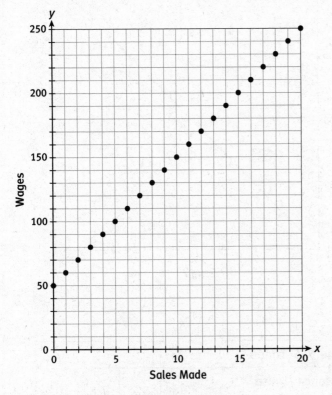

Step 1: Find the slope to find the rate of change:

$$\text{Slope} = \frac{y_2 - y_1}{x_2 - x_1} = \frac{70 - 60}{2 - 1} = \frac{10}{1}$$

Nikita earns $10 for each sale she makes.

Step 2: The initial value is found by finding the y-value when the x-value is 0. Looking at the graph, when $x = 0$, $y = \$50$. The initial value is (0, 50). This is her base salary, which she earns regardless of how many sales she makes.

My Notes

Step 3: Determine if the function is proportional or nonproportional. The graph shows a straight line that does not go through the origin, and the initial value is not (0, 0). So the function is nonproportional.

Solution: Nikita earns $10 per sale and starts with a base salary of $50 in wages, and her function of wages earned per sale is nonproportional.

Try These A

Determine and explain the meaning of the rate of change and the initial value for each of the functions represented below. State whether each function is proportional or nonproportional.

a.

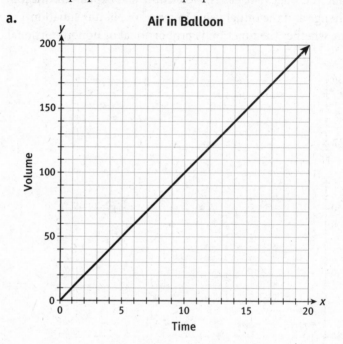

Air in Balloon

b.

Time in Seconds	0	1	2	3	4
Distance Mouse Runs in Meters	0	2.6	5.2	7.8	10.4

c. In 1 yard there are 3 feet, in 2 yards there are 6 feet, and so on.

4. **Make sense of problems.** The graph below shows the times and speeds for a commuter train with many morning stops. Determine between which two times the train displayed the greatest rate of change and explain how you know.

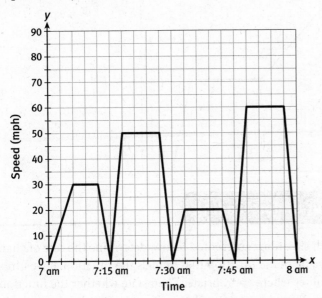

5. Describe a situation for each graph given. Share your descriptions with your group. Compare and contrast your situation choices with those of other group members.

a.

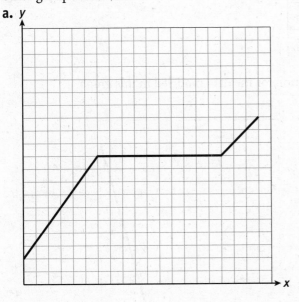

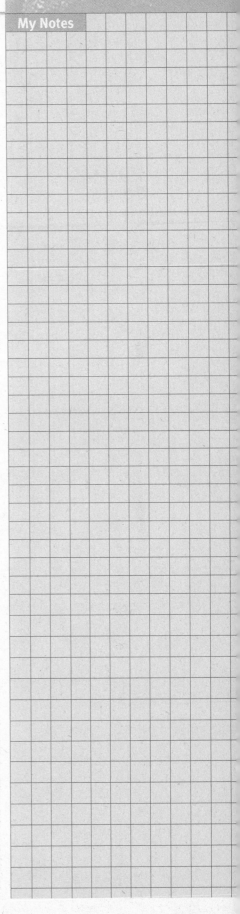

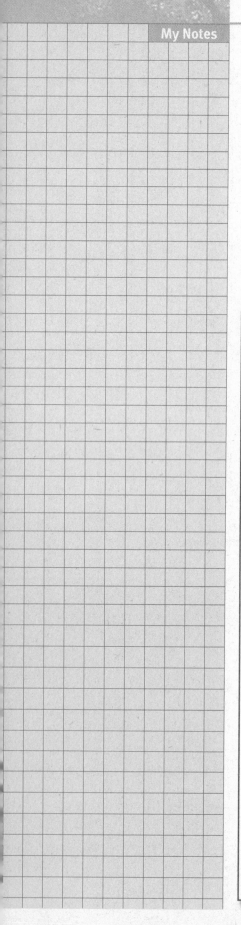

b.

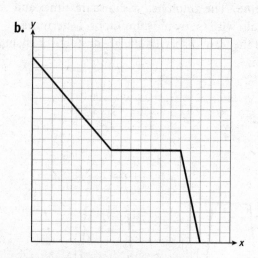

Check Your Understanding

6. For each situation represented below, determine the rate of change and initial value of the function that models the situation. Give units for these values where appropriate. Then state whether the function in each situation is proportional or nonproportional:

   a. Tommy Lee runs in marathons. When he practices, he tries to pace himself so that he runs 10 miles in 90 minutes.

   b.

x	y
0	12.5
2	37.5
4	62.5
6	87.5

7. Describe a situation for the data modeled in this graph.

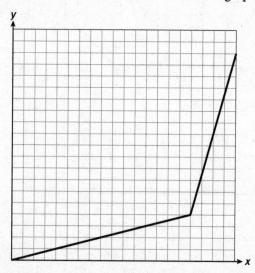

LESSON 29-2 PRACTICE

The table below shows common text messaging charges that Mrs. Troy pays.

Number of Texts	0	100	500	1,000	1,500
Charge	$20	$22	$30	$40	$50

8. Determine the rate of change of the function represented in the table. Explain the meaning of the rate of change in terms of Mrs. Troy's situation.

9. Determine the initial value of the function represented in the table. Explain the meaning of the initial value in terms of Mrs. Troy's situation.

10. Is Mrs. Troy's function for text messaging charges proportional or nonproportional? Justify your response.

Caden is saving up his money to buy a set of classic comic books. He started with $50 he got for his birthday, and now he is putting away $20 a week that he receives for doing his chores.

11. What is the rate of change of the function that models Caden's savings?

12. What is the initial value of the function?

13. Is the function proportional or nonproportional?

14. **Critique the reasoning of others.** Darren looked at the graph below and determined that the function is proportional. Do you agree with Darren? Explain your reasoning.

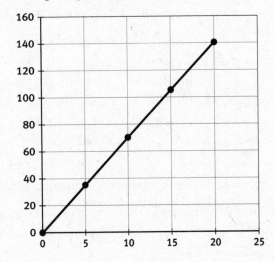

ACTIVITY 29 PRACTICE

Write your answers on notebook paper.
Show your work.

Lesson 29-1

A plant grows at a constant rate of 12 mm each day. Use this information to answer Items 1–4.

1. Make a table of the plant's height over an 8-day period.

2. Graph the plant's growth over time in days.

3. Write a function to model the plant's growth.

4. Determine the plant's height on the 80th day.

Another plant has a height of 20 millimeters when it is first measured and grows at a constant rate of 6 mm per day. Use this information to answer Items 5–8.

5. Make a table of the plant's height over an 8-day period.

6. Graph the plant's height over an 8-day period.

7. Write a function to model the plant's growth.

8. Determine the plant's height on the 80th day.

9. Compare and contrast the two functions you wrote in Items 3 and 7. Which function is directly proportional? Explain your reasoning.

For Items 10–12, use pattern blocks to create trains of polygons. Determine the perimeter of each train assuming that each side not touching another polygon is part of the perimeter and has a length of 1 unit.

10. Using squares:
    a. Sketch the pattern.
    b. Complete a table.
    c. Sketch a graph of the relation.
    d. Write an equation for the linear relation.

11. Using triangles:
    a. Sketch the pattern.
    b. Complete a table.
    c. Sketch a graph of the relation.
    d. Write an equation for the linear relation.

12. Using hexagons:
    a. Sketch the pattern.
    b. Complete a table.
    c. Sketch a graph of the relation.
    d. Write an equation for the linear relation.

Lesson 29-2

13. Consider the equations you wrote in Items 10d, 11d, and 12d. Compare and contrast these equations in terms of rate of change and initial value.

Use the equation below to answer Items 14–16.

$$y = 10 + 2x$$

14. What is the initial value?
    A. $(0, 0)$ **B.** $(0, 2)$
    C. $(0, 10)$ **D.** $(0, 12)$

15. What is the rate of change?
    A. 0   **B.** 2
    C. 10   **D.** 12

16. Is this function proportional or nonproportional? Explain your reasoning.

Use the graph below to answer Items 17–19.

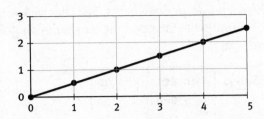

17. What is the initial value?

18. What is the rate of change?

19. Is this function proportional or nonproportional? Explain your reasoning.

Use the table below to answer Items 20–22.

Distance (miles)	Time (min)
0	0
1	6
2	12
3	18
4	24

20. What is the initial value?

21. What is the rate of change?

22. Is this function proportional or nonproportional? Explain your reasoning.

23. Describe a situation for the data modeled in the graph below:

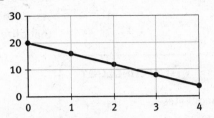

MATHEMATICAL PRACTICES
Model with Mathematics

24.

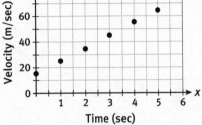

The graph above shows a skydiver's falling speed in meters per second.

a. Is this relationship proportional? Approximately what is the initial value here, and what does it represent in this situation?

b. Approximately what is the rate of change here, and what does it represent in this situation?

c. Consider what you think will happen to this graph after $x = 5$ seconds. Will the graph continue to look the same, or will it change at 6 or 7 or 8 seconds or some point after that? What is happening at that point in this situation?

Memory cards are used in many devices. You probably own several devices that use these cards to hold photos, music, or documents. The table below shows the number of songs, the minutes of video, and the number of photos that different-size memory cards can hold.

CONNECT TO TECHNOLOGY

MB = megabytes
GB = gigabytes
1,024 MB = 1 GB

Size of Memory Card	Songs	Minutes of Video	Photos
32 MB	6	2	26
64 MB	12	4	52
128 MB	24	8	104
256 MB	48	16	208
512 MB	96	32	416
1 GB	192	64	832
2 GB	384	128	1,664

1. The data in the table relating memory card size to the number of songs the card can hold represent a function. Explain why this is true.

2. The data in the table relating memory card size to the number of photos the card holds represent a function. Is this function proportional? Explain your reasoning.

3. Graph the relationship between the size of the memory card and the minutes of video the card holds.

4. How would your graph change if you were graphing the number of photos rather than the minutes of video?

5. State whether each of the following represents a function. Explain your reasoning.

a. {(1, 2), (2, 4), (4, 2), (8, 4)}

b.

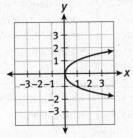

c.

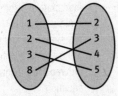

6. Two functions are shown below.

Function 1

$y = 2x + 4$

Function 2

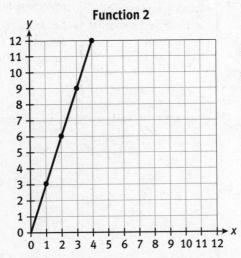

a. Use a representation different from the one given to describe each of the functions.

b. Evaluate each function for $x = 5$.

c. Compare and contrast the two functions. Use appropriate math terminology from this unit in your answer.

Scoring Guide	Exemplary	Proficient	Emerging	Incomplete
	The solution demonstrates these characteristics:			
Mathematics Knowledge and Thinking (Items 1, 2, 3, 4, 5a-c, 6a-c)	• Clear and accurate understanding of functions, proportional functions, and evaluating functions.	• Correct understanding of functions, proportional functions, and evaluating functions.	• Partial understanding of functions, proportional functions, and evaluating functions.	• Inaccurate or incomplete understanding of functions, proportional functions, and evaluating functions.
Problem Solving (Item 4)	• An appropriate and efficient strategy that results in a correct answer.	• A strategy that may include unnecessary steps but results in a correct answer.	• A strategy that results in some incorrect answers.	• No clear strategy when solving problems.
Mathematical Modeling / Representations (Items 1, 2, 3, 4, 5a-c, 6a)	• Clear and accurate understanding of representing a function using a table, a graph, a list of ordered pairs, a diagram, or an equation.	• An understanding of representing a function using a table, graph, list of ordered pairs, diagram, or equation.	• Partial understanding of representing a function using a table, graph, list of ordered pairs, diagram, or equation.	• Inaccurate or incomplete understanding of representing a function using a table, graph, list of ordered pairs, diagram, or equation.
Reasoning and Communication (Items 1, 2, 4, 5a-c, 6a, 6c)	• Precise use of appropriate math terms and language to explain why a relation is a function or a proportional function. • Precise use of appropriate math terms and language to describe a function or to compare and contrast two functions.	• An adequate explanation of why a relation is a function or a proportional function. • An adequate description of a function or comparison of two functions.	• A misleading or confusing explanation of why a relation is a function or a proportional function. • A misleading or confusing description of a function or comparison of two functions.	• An incomplete or inaccurate explanation of why a relation is a function or a proportional function. • An incomplete or inaccurate description of a function, or comparison of two functions.

Linear Functions
Get in Line
Lesson 30-1 Rate of Change

Learning Targets:

- Model linear relationships between quantities using functions.
- Identify and represent linear functions with tables, graphs, and equations.

SUGGESTED LEARNING STRATEGIES: Marking the Text, Note Taking, Sharing and Responding, Interactive Word Wall, Create Representations, Look for Patterns

The *rate of change* in a relationship represents the ratio of the vertical change in *y* (output) to the horizontal change in *x* (input).

1. The height of water in a pool is shown in the graph below.

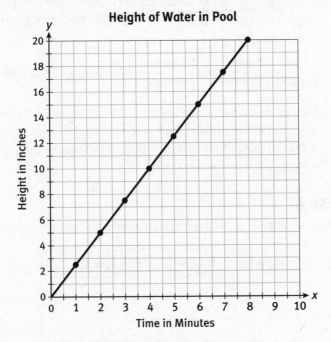

Height of Water in Pool

a. Determine the rate of change of the height of water in a pool.

b. Describe the rate of change in the graph.

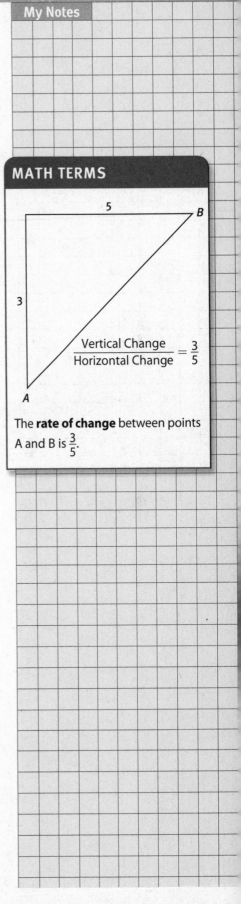

MATH TERMS

The **rate of change** between points A and B is $\frac{3}{5}$.

$$\frac{\text{Vertical Change}}{\text{Horizontal Change}} = \frac{3}{5}$$

My Notes

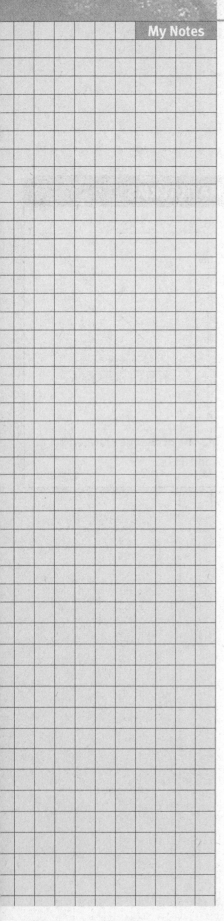

My Notes

You can also see rate of change from a table of values.

Example A

The table shows the data from the graph above. How is the rate of change from the graph above represented in this table?

Time (minutes)	0	1	2	3	4	5	6	7	8
Height (inches)	0	2.5	5	7.5	10	12.5	15	17.5	20

Step 1: Look at the change in time between consecutive minutes.

Step 2: Look at the change in height between consecutive heights.

Step 3: Write the rate of change as a ratio of the vertical change to the horizontal change.

$$\frac{\text{vertical change}}{\text{horizontal change}} = \frac{2.5 \text{ inches}}{1 \text{ minute}} = 2.5 \text{ inches for each minute}$$

Solution: The rate of change is represented in the table as 2.5 inches in height for every minute. This is represented by a constant ratio of the difference between each pair of y-values to the difference between each pair of x-values.

Try These A

The table below represents the fare schedule for a taxi cab driver's fares.

Number of Miles	Cab Fee ($)
0	5
1	8
2	11
3	14
4	17
5	20

a. Determine the rate of change.

b. Interpret the meaning of the rate of change in this context.

You can also see rate of change by looking at equations.

2. The equation for the data represented in Item 1 and Example A is $y = 2.5x$. How is the rate of change you determined in Item 1 and Example A represented in this equation?

My Notes

Check Your Understanding

3. Each representation describes the cost for beach bike rental from a different shop. Find the rate of change for each representation.

   a. $y = 20x + 2$

   b.

Number days	Cost ($)
0	15
1	18
2	21
3	24
4	27
5	30

   c.

   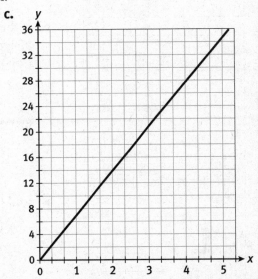

Data points are linear if they show a constant rate of change. When you plot the points of linear data on a coordinate plane, they lie on a straight line. The data points represented in Item 1 and in Example A are linear.

Jamila is using a straw to drink water from a cylindrical cup. The height of the water remaining in the cup is a function of the time the person has been drinking. The following graph gives the height of the water at different time intervals.

4. Using the data from the graph, complete the table.

Time (sec)	Height (cm)
0	
10	
20	
30	
40	
50	

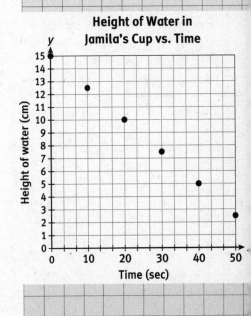

Height of Water in Jamila's Cup vs. Time

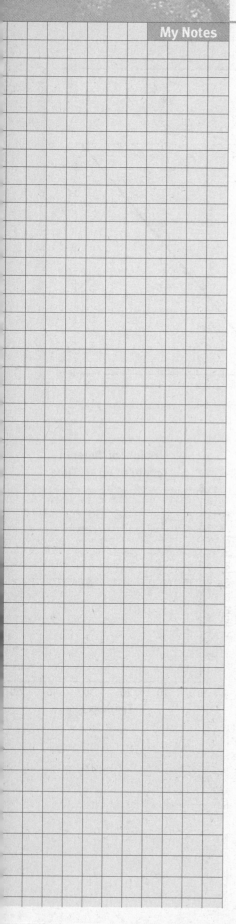

5. **Express regularity in repeated reasoning.** Describe any patterns you observe in the table about the height of the water over time.

6. Is the relationship between time and the height of the water linear?
   a. Explain using the graph.

   b. Explain using the table.

7. What is the change in the water level from 20 seconds to 30 seconds?

8. Determine the rate of change of the water level over time.

9. **Reason quantitatively.** Predict the height of the water at 52 seconds. How did you make your prediction? If you wanted to look at many different times, would your method still be effective?

10. Write a function that gives the height of the water, **h,** in terms of the time, **t.**

11. How long will it take for Jamila to drink all her water and completely empty out her cup? Use multiple representations to justify your response.

Check Your Understanding

CONNECT TO FARMING

A **silo** holds grain in storage until it is moved to a final destination to be used.

A **bushel** is a unit of dry volume, equivalent to 8 gallons. It is used most often in agriculture. It is abbreviated as bsh. or bu.

A farmer is filling a cylindrical silo with grain. The amount of grain in the silo is a function of the time the grain has been pouring into the silo.

Time (minutes)	0	20	40	60	80	100	120	140	160
Bushels	0	500	1,000	1,500	2,000	2,500	3,000	3,500	4,000

12. Complete the graph below to represent this data.

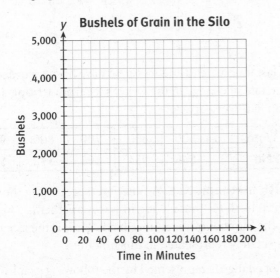

Bushels of Grain in the Silo

13. What is the rate of change shown in the table and graph above?

14. Is this function linear? Justify your response.

15. Write a function for this situation using t for the time and b for the number of bushels of grain.

16. If the silo holds 7,000 bushels, how many hours will it take to fill the silo?

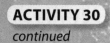

My Notes

LESSON 30-1 PRACTICE

17. Sam reads the following number of pages per week for his science class.

Week	1	2	3	4
Number of Pages Read	75	150	225	300

    a. What is Sam's rate of change in the number of pages he reads each week?

    b. At this rate, how many pages will Sam have read at the end of the class, 8 weeks?

18. Why is the data represented in this graph linear?

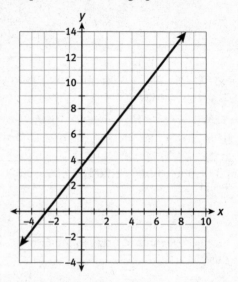

19. A writer's last four articles and fees paid have been recorded below. What is the rate of change in the writer's fee from writing a 700-word article to an 800-word article?

Total Words	500	600	700	800	900
Fees Paid	$45	$54	$63	$72	$81

20. Model with mathematics. A function representing the life expectancy at birth for those living in warm weather is $y = 0.32x - 0.03$, where x is the number of years since birth. How is the rate of change of the life expectancy represented in this function?

21. What rate of change is represented by the following graph?

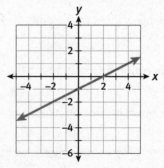

Learning Targets:

● Identify linear and non-linear functions from tables, graphs, and equations.

● Graph a linear function from a verbal description.

● Understand that $y = mx + b$ defines a linear equation.

SUGGESTED LEARNING STRATEGIES: Summarizing, Visualization, Create Representations, Think/Pair/Share

A linear relationship has a constant rate of change.

1. **Make use of structure.** In each pair below, determine which representation describes a *linear* relationship. Justify your choice.

   a. Graph 1 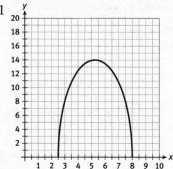   Graph 2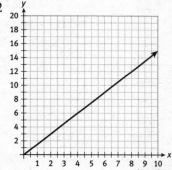

   b.

   Table 1

x	0	1	2	3	4	5
y	0	3.25	6.5	9.75	13	16.25

   Table 2

x	0	1	2	3	4	5
y	0	3.5	6.5	10	13	16.5

   c. Equation 1: $y = 3x + 2$ Equation 2: $y = x^2$

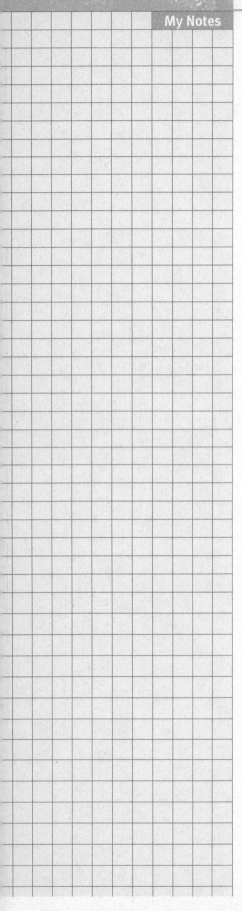

My Notes

2. **Model with mathematics.** Sketch a graph for the functions described below.

   a. At Sundae King, the price of a sundae is a function of the weight of the sundae. The king charges the same amount for each ounce of weight.

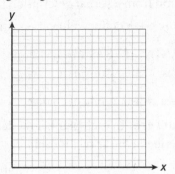

   b. The cost to join an online gaming site is $12. The player is then charged 1.75 for each hour played.

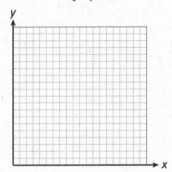

   c. $y = 3x$

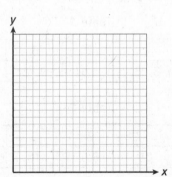

   d. A cell phone bill is a flat monthly rate of $50.

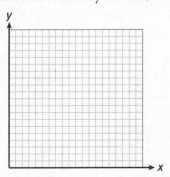

Check Your Understanding

Sketch a graph for the functions described in Items 3 and 4.

3. A fighter jet appears to be descending at a steady rate. The altitude of the jet is a function of time.

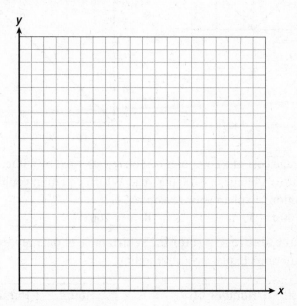

4. The value of *y* decreases as the value of *x* increases.

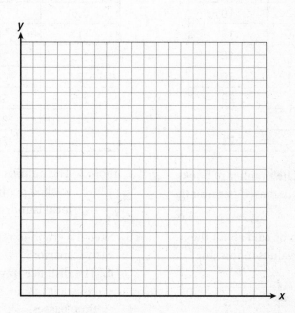

5. Sketch a pair of graphs, one representing a linear function and one representing a non-linear function.

LESSON 30-2 PRACTICE

6. Which graph is linear? Explain your reasoning.

   A.

   B.

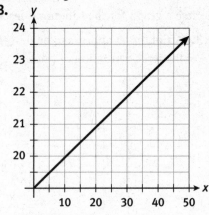

7. The average cost of a computer can be represented by a linear function with a rate of change of $700 per year. Which equation could represent this function? Explain your reasoning.

   A. $y = 700x - 30$ **B.** $y = 700x^2$

8. **Construct viable arguments.** Which table of data represents a linear function? Explain your reasoning.

Months	Number of Books purchased
1	10
2	15
3	18
4	28
5	29
6	17
7	21

Table 1. The number of books purchased per month.

Hours	Number of Shirts Washed
0.5	2
1	6
1.5	10
2	14
2.5	18
3	22
3.5	26

Table 2. The number of shirts washed per hour at a local laundry.

9. What can be said about the x- and y-values in this line?

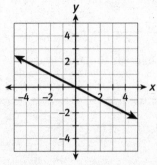

10. Sketch a graph to represent each scenario:

    a. The distance traveled at a constant rate increases as time passes.

    b. As the x-values increase the y-value stays the same.

    c. $y = -3x + 2$

ACTIVITY 30 PRACTICE

Write your answers on notebook paper.
Show your work.

Lesson 30-1

Examine the graphs in Items 1 and 2. Describe the
relationship between *x* and *y*.

1.

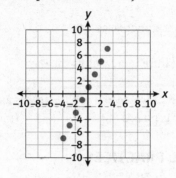

2.

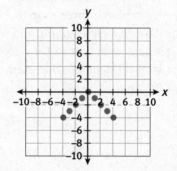

Graph the following data sets and identify each as
linear or non-linear.

3. $\{(2, -3), (4, -2), (-2, -5), (0, 4)\}$

4. $\{(3, 0), (2, 4), (-1, -4), (-2, 1)\}$

5. $\{(0, 5), (4, -3), (3, -1), (2, 1)\}$

6. $\{(5, -3), (7, -1), (9, 1), (11, 3)\}$

7. Which of the following tables display linear data?
Explain your reasoning.

A.

x	y
0	45
10	40
20	35
30	30
40	35
50	40
60	45
70	50

B.

x	y
-5	-2.5
-3	-5.5
-1	-8.5
1	-11.5
3	14.5
5	17.5
7	20.5
9	23.5

8. Identify the rate of change in each equation:
   a. $y = 8.3x - 1$
   b. $y = 5 - 0.5x$

9. Find the rate of change in the table below:

x	y
0	0
3	90
6	180
9	270
12	360

10. The rate of change for a linear equation must
be _____.
   A. constant
   B. negative
   C. positive
   D. varying

Lesson 30-2

11. Determine which of the following expressions displays a linear relationship. Use multiple representations to explain your reasoning.
A. $2x$
B. $-2x + 2$
C. $x(4x)$
D. $4 - 3x$

12. Explain how you can determine if an equation represents a linear relationship.

13. Find the rate of change for the data in each table.

a.

x	y
0	5
1	9
2	13
3	17
4	21
5	25
6	29
7	33

b.

x	y
−2	6
−1	4
0	2
1	0
2	−2
3	−4
4	−6
5	−8

14. Which equation shows a linear relationship with a rate of change of 8?
A. $y = x - 8$
B. $y = 8x - 12$
C. $y = 8 + 4x$
D. $y = \frac{1}{8}x + 16$

15. Sketch a graph for the following situations:
a. y increases as x increases
b. $y = 5x$
c. The temperature increases as the day progresses.
d. The amount of water in a tub decreases after the stopper is pulled out.

MATHEMATICAL PRACTICES
Construct Viable Arguments

16. In this activity, you explored three ways to represent linear data: in a table, graph, and with an equation. Compare and contrast the different representations of linear data. Provide examples to support your claims.

Linear and Non-Linear Functions

Measure Up
Lesson 31-1 Bean Experiment

Learning Targets:

- Determine if a function is linear or non-linear.
- Represent functions with tables, graphs, and equations.
- Find a trend line to represent data.

> **SUGGESTED LEARNING STRATEGIES:** Predict and Confirm, Use Manipulatives, Create Representations, Look for a Pattern, Visualization, Sharing and Responding, Interactive Word Wall

Using the template provided by your teacher, create the cube and cone. You will use them in an experiment to determine the volume of several solids. Before you begin the experiment, make the following predictions.

1. Predict how many groups of 20 beans you can add to the cube until it is full.

2. Predict how many groups of 20 beans you can add to the cone until it is full.

3. Explain how the shape of the figure affected your predictions.

Perform the following experiment using the cube. Each stage of the experiment consists of three steps. Each time you complete the three steps you complete a stage. Repeat the steps to complete another stage.

Step 1: Add 20 beans to the cube.

Step 2: Shake the cube gently to allow the beans to settle.

Step 3: Measure the height of the beans in centimeters.

4. **Model with mathematics.** Complete the experiment for the cube.
   a. Enter the data in the table.

   b. Describe patterns you notice in the data in the table.

Stage #	Height of Beans (cm)
1	
2	
3	
4	
5	
6	
7	

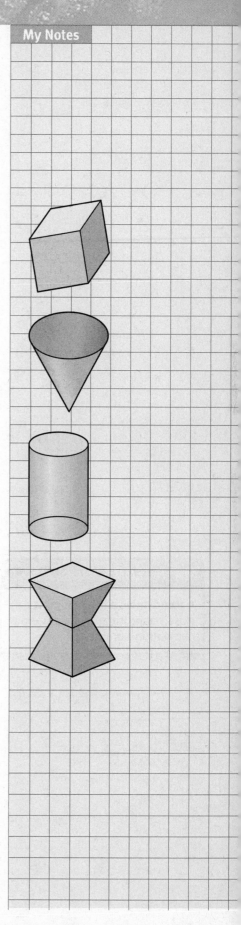

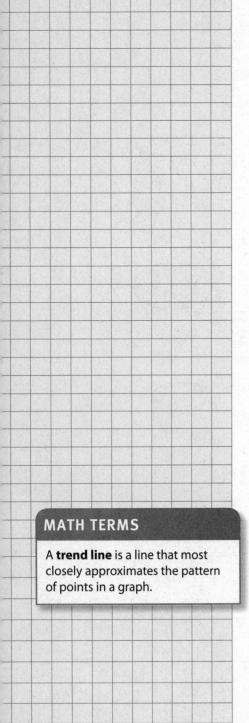

c. Plot the ordered pairs from the table onto the graph below.

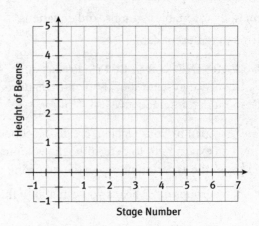

d. Looking at the graph, what do you notice about the relationship between the stage number and the height of the beans?

e. Is this data linear? Explain why or why not.

f. Does this data represent a function? Justify your answer.

MATH TERMS

A **trend line** is a line that most closely approximates the pattern of points in a graph.

When data points are not completely linear, a ***trend line*** is used to allow us to make predictions from the data. A trend line indicates the general course, or tendency, of data.

5. Which trend line is placed correctly below? Justify your choice.

6. a. **Use appropriate tools strategically.** Use a straightedge and place it on the *scatter plot* in Item 4c in a position that has about the same number of points above and below the line. On the coordinate grid, mark two points that the line passes through. They do not have to be data points.

b. Draw a line that passes through the two points. Does this line confirm the relationship that you noticed between the stage number and the height of the beans in Item 4d?

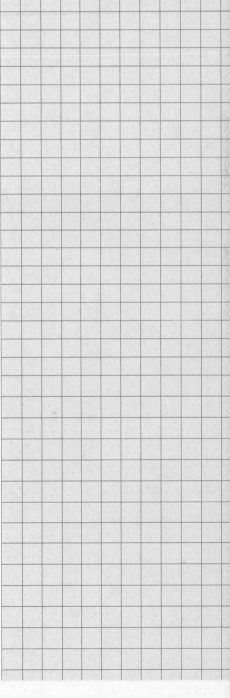

MATH TERMS

A **scatter plot** is a graph that displays bivariate data on a coordinate plane and may be used to show a relationship between two variables.

7. Complete the experiment for the cone.

a. Complete the table for each stage and plot the data on the grid.

Stage #	Height of Beans (cm)
1	
2	
3	
4	
5	
6	
7	

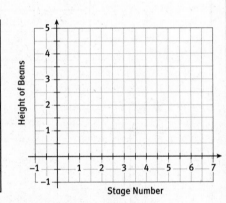

b. Look at the data in the table and the graph. What patterns do you notice about the relationship between the stage number and the height of the beans?

c. Does the data for the cone represent a function? Explain why or why not.

d. **Construct viable arguments.** Explain why a trend line cannot be drawn for this data.

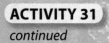

My Notes

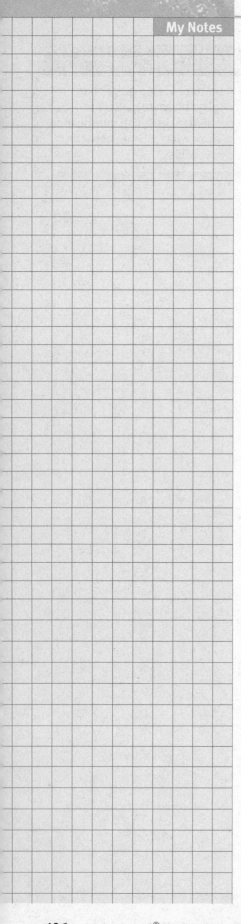

Check Your Understanding

The following data was collected as beans were added to a cylinder.

8. Plot the points on the grid for the cylinder.

Stage #	Height of Beans (cm)
1	3
2	6
3	9
4	12
5	15
6	18
7	21

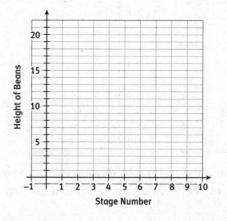

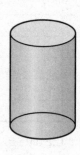

9. Describe the patterns you observe in the data in the table.

10. Looking at the graph, what patterns do you notice about the relationship between the stage number and the height of the beans?

11. Is this data linear? Justify your response using ideas from your answer to Item 9.

12. Can a trend line be drawn for this data? If so, draw one. If not, explain why not.

13. Make a conjecture about the rate of change of the height of the beans in the cylinder as the number of stages increases?

My Notes

Check Your Understanding

The following data was collected as beans were added to a pyramid.

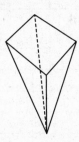

Stage #	Height of Beans (cm)
1	1.5
2	2.4
3	3.1
4	3.6
5	3.9
6	4.1
7	4.2

14. What patterns do you notice about the relationship between the stage number and the height of beans?

15. Can a trend line be drawn for this data? Explain your reasoning.

16. What conjecture can you make about the rate of change of the height of beans in the pyramid as the stages increase?

LESSON 31-1 PRACTICE

Marisol fills bags of popcorn at the local movie theater. She counted the number of scoops it takes to fill each size of bag and recorded the data in the table below.

Size of Bag	Number of Scoops
Snack	0.75
Small	2
Medium	4
Large	8
Extra Large	12

17. Draw a scatter plot to represent the popcorn data.

18. Does this data represent a function? Explain your reasoning.

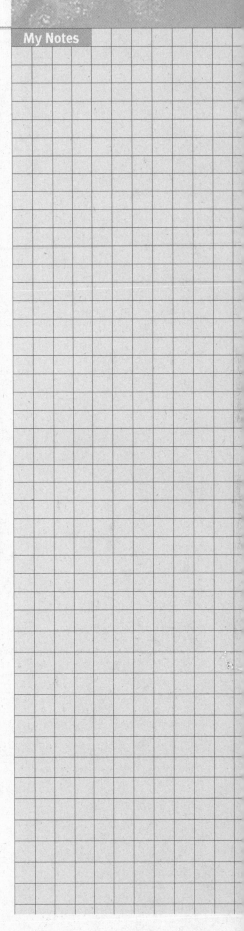

My Notes

19. Is this data linear? Explain your reasoning.

Marisol also fills drinks at the movie theater. The table shows the amount of time it takes to fill each size of drink.

Size of Drink (in oz.)	Time to Fill (in seconds)
8	2.5
16	5
24	7.5
32	10
40	12.5

20. Model with mathematics. Draw a scatter plot to represent the drink data.

21. Is this data linear? Explain your reasoning.

22. What patterns do you notice about the relationship between the time it takes to fill a drink and the drink size?

23. What conjecture can you make about the rate of change of the time to fill each drink as the drink size increases?

Learning Targets:

- Define, evaluate, and compare functions.
- Recognize patterns in non-linear functions.
- Represent functions with tables, graphs, and equations.

SUGGESTED LEARNING STRATEGIES: Summarizing, Use Manipulatives, Create Representations, Look for Patterns, Sharing and Responding, Note Taking, Think-Pair-Share

The following data was collected as beans were added to an irregular polyhedron.

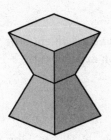

Stage #	Height of Beans (cm)
1	1
2	2
3	5
4	10
5	15
6	18
7	19

1. a. Plot the points on the grid for the irregular polyhedron.

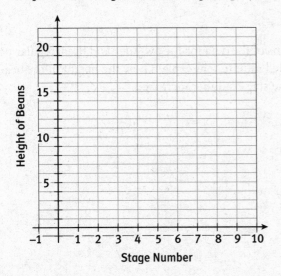

b. Make use of structure. Describe the patterns you observe in the data in the table.

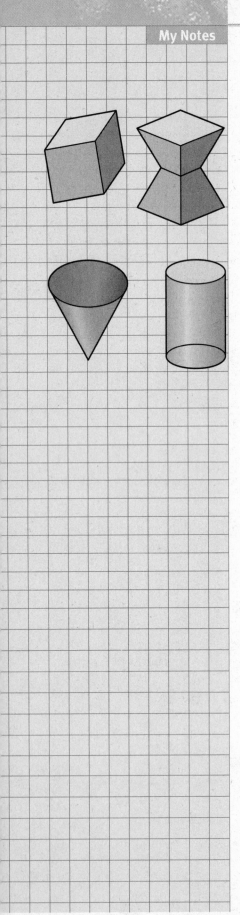

My Notes

c. Looking at the graph, what patterns do you notice about the relationship between the stage number and the height of the beans?

d. What conjecture can you make about the *rate of change* of the height of the beans as the stage numbers increase?

e. Can a trend line be drawn for this data? Why or why not?

2. How does the rate of change from the cylinder experiment differ from the rate of change for the irregular polyhedron experiment?

3. **Construct viable arguments.** Explain how the shape of the object affects the rate of change of the height of the beans for each stage of the experiment.

4. If the patterns of the data for the cylinder and the irregular polyhedron were extended indefinitely, explain how the height of the beans would change as the stage number increased.

My Notes

5. **Reason abstractly and quantitatively.** The graphs and tables below show what happened when the bean experiment was performed with each of the vases shown. Match each vase to a graph and table. Explain the reasoning behind your choices.

a.  b.  c.

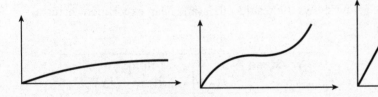

I	x	y
	0	0
	1	1
	2	2
	3	2.5
	4	3
	5	3.25
	6	4
	7	6

II	x	y
	0	0
	1	2
	2	4
	3	6
	4	7
	5	8
	6	8.5
	7	8.75

III	x	y
	0	0
	1	4
	2	8
	3	12
	4	16
	5	20
	6	24
	7	28

Check Your Understanding

6. Sketch and describe a graph that might result from performing the bean experiment with each of the containers below.

a. 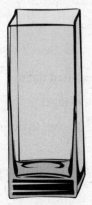 b.  c.

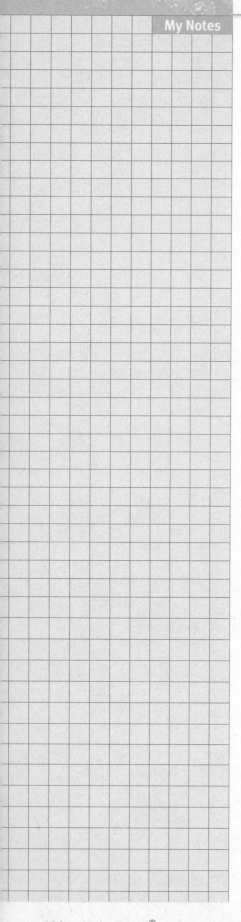

My Notes

LESSON 31-2 PRACTICE

7. Which container would have a constant rate of change in the bean experiment: a triangular pyramid or a triangular prism? Explain your reasoning.

8. Sketch a graph that might result from doing the bean experiment with this container.

The table below shows the results of Hasan's bean experiment using a large can.

Stage #	Height of Beans (cm)
1	2
2	4
3	6
4	8
5	10
6	12
7	14

Use the table to answer Items 9–12.

9. Draw a scatter plot to represent Hasan's bean experiment data.

10. What is the rate of change of the height of beans per stage?

11. Write a function to represent the data in the table. Be sure to define the variables you use.

12. **Reason quantitatively.** Use your equation to predict the height of beans at the twentieth stage.

Learning Targets:

- Recognize the relationship between verbal descriptions and graphs of linear and non-linear functions.
- Use a trend line to make predictions.

> **SUGGESTED LEARNING STRATEGIES:** Predict and Confirm, Create Representations, Look for Patterns, Visualization, Note Taking, Think-Pair-Share

The astronauts who walked on the moon thirty years ago actually *weighed less* on the moon than they did on Earth. They did not diet or exercise to lose weight. So why did they weigh less on the moon?

Another experiment you can do involves weight. Begin by finding out how a scale works. Create a scale using the following supplies: a small paper cup, a ruler, string, tape, and part of a spring.

1. Set up the scale by doing the following:
   a. Poke three holes around the top of the cup.
   b. Tie the string through the three holes in the cup.
   c. Tie the ends of the string to one end of the spring.
   d. Tape the other end of the spring to the bottom of a desk or table so that the entire device hangs freely.
   e. **Attend to precision.** Measure the distance from the floor to the bottom of the cup and put it in the table below. This is the starting weight for the empty cup.
   f. Place the weights provided from your teacher into the cup one at a time. After each cube is placed into the cup, measure the distance from the floor to the cup again and record these distances in the table below.

Number of Cubes	0	1	2	3	4	5
Distance from Floor (cm)						

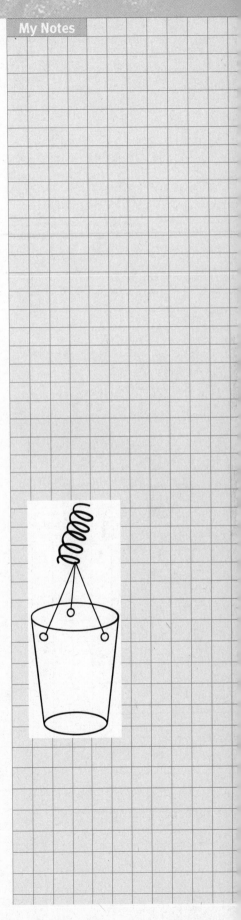

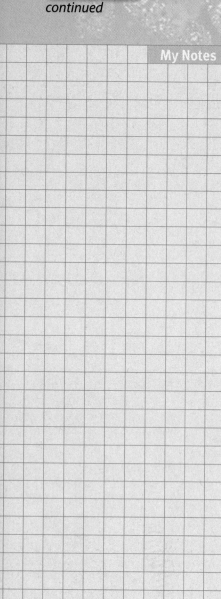

2. a. Graph the data as a scatter plot. Be sure to label the axes and title your graph.

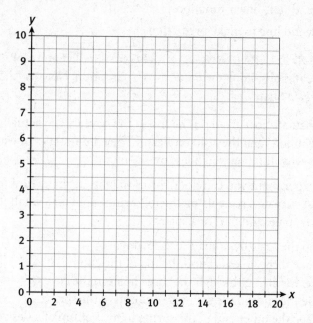

b. Draw a trend line for the data in the graph.

3. a. Write the equation for the trend line describing the function between the number of cubes in the cup and the cup's distance from the floor. Define the variables you use.

b. What is the *y*-intercept in your equation, and what is its meaning in this situation?

c. What is the rate of change in your equation, and what is its meaning in this situation?

4. a. Use your equation to predict the cup's distance to the floor when 12 cubes are in the cup.

b. Use your equation to predict how many cubes it would take for your cup to reach the floor.

5. Use your trend line to confirm your answers to Item 4. Explain why the trend line could be used to confirm these values.

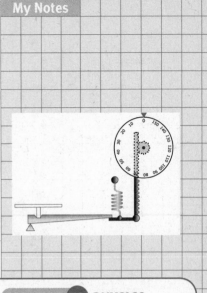

The scale you made works because it uses the same principle as a bathroom spring scale. This principle is known as Hooke's Law. Hooke's law says that the opposing force of a spring is **directly proportional** to the amount by which the spring is stretched.

In the illustration at the right, you can see the parts of a bathroom spring scale. Your weight pushes down on the lever, the lever pushes down on the spring contraption, and the spring contraption makes the gear turn which in turn makes the dial turn to show your correct weight.

6. Consider what you know about the moon and its gravity and how a scale works. Why might the astronauts have weighed less on the moon than they do on Earth?

> **CONNECT TO PHYSICS**
>
> A *contraption* is a mechanical device or gadget.
> Hooke's Law is named after the seventeenth century British physicist Robert Hooke. The law states that applied force, F, equals a constant, k, times the change in length, x: $F = kx$.

Here are the graphs for some other contraptions.

7. Reason abstractly. Add a trend line and describe in words the relationship between the two quantities in the scatter plots represented below.

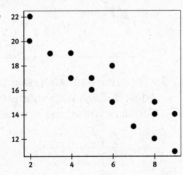

a.

b.

My Notes

Some graphs do not represent linear data; however, the relationship between the quantities can still be described.

8. **Make sense of problems.** Match each scatter plot below with the situation that best describes it.

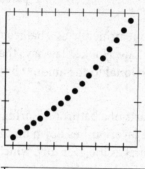

The weight of the cup increases as the amount of liquid poured into it increases.

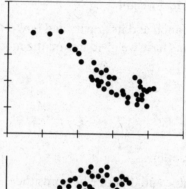

The weight of the liquid decreases at very high or very low temperatures.

The weight of the cup decreases as the amount of liquid taken out of it increases.

9. Describe a situation that these graphs could represent. Share your descriptions with your group. Compare and contrast your situation choices with those of other group members.

a.

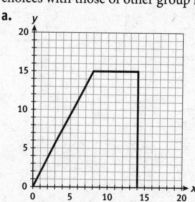

b.

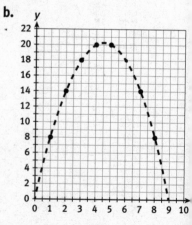

My Notes

Check Your Understanding

Sketch a graph that could represent each situation.

10. **a.** The amount of liquid a container will hold increases as the volume increases until it reaches the limit the container will hold.

  b. The number of times a frog croaks increases as the temperature rises until it reaches 96°F, and then the temperature stays constant.

11. Describe a situation that each graph could represent.

a.

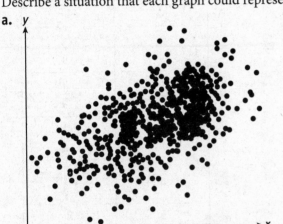

b.

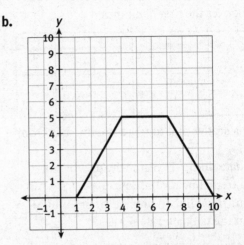

LESSON 31-3 PRACTICE

Stella measured how high a tennis ball bounced after dropping it from different heights. The data she collected is shown in the scatter plot below.

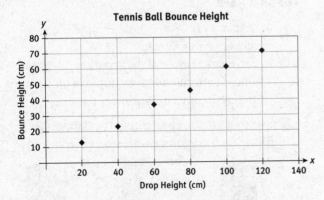

Use the scatter plot to answer Items 12–15.

12. Draw a trend line for the data in the scatter plot.

13. Write an equation for the trend line to describe the function between the drop height and the bounce height of the tennis ball. Be sure to define the variables.

14. **Critique the reasoning of others.** Stella says that the relationship between drop height and bounce height is directly proportional. Do you agree with her? Explain your reasoning.

15. Use your equation to predict the bounce height at a drop height of 200 cm.

16. Describe a situation that each graph could represent:

a.

b.

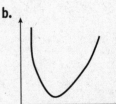

ACTIVITY 31 PRACTICE
Write your answers on notebook paper.
Show your work.

Lesson 31-1
Shaina is filling a water tank for her horse, Buddy. She knows that the hose leading to the tank has an output of 2.25 gallons per minute.

1. Complete the table showing the amount of water in the tank over the first 6 minutes.

Time (minutes)	1	2	3	4	5	6
Water (gallons)						

2. **a.** Create a scatter plot to represent the data from Item 1.
   b. Is this data linear? Explain why or why not.
   c. Draw a trend line for the data.
   d. Use your trend line to predict the amount of water in the tank after 8 minutes.

3. **a.** Write a function to represent this situation. Be sure to define the variables.
   b. Use your function to determine the amount of water in the tank after 8 minutes.
   c. Does your answer to part b confirm your prediction in Item 2d?

Shaina's friend Brittany has a puppy. Brittany buys dog food in large bags and empties them into smaller containers to store the food in her house. The table below shows the level of the dog food in a smaller container as she pours the dog food into it. Use this table to answer Items 4 and 5.

Time (seconds)	Food Level (inches)
0	0
1	$1\frac{3}{4}$
2	$3\frac{1}{4}$
3	$4\frac{1}{2}$
4	$6\frac{1}{2}$
5	8

4. Is this data linear? Explain why or why not.

5. **a.** Create a scatter plot to represent the data in the table.
   b. Draw a trend line for the data.
   c. Use your trend line to predict the amount of food in the container after 8 seconds.

Lesson 31-2
6. **a.** Explain how you can determine if data is linear or non-linear.
   b. Give an example of data that represents a linear pattern and an example of an equation that represents a non-linear pattern.

7. Sketch a graph representing the data gathered by filling each container with small marbles.
   a.   **b.**    **c.**

A chef uses rice as an ingredient in many of his dishes. The graph below shows the amount of rice left in the container after he prepares each dish.

Dishes Prepared	1	2	3	4	5
Rice Remaining in Container (cups)	21.5	18	15	11.75	8.5

8. a. Create a scatter plot to represent the data in the table.

b. Draw a trend line for the data.

c. Use your trend line to predict the amount of rice in the container after seven dishes were prepared.

Lesson 31-3

9. Sketch a graph for the following situations.

a. A family left from their home to go on vacation. After several miles, they realized that they had forgotten their camera. They drove back to their home, and then drove away again.

b. As x increases, y increases and then decreases.

c. As x increases, y decreases and then increases.

d. As the temperature of the water increases, the steam it produces increases.

10. Create a situation for each graph below.

a.

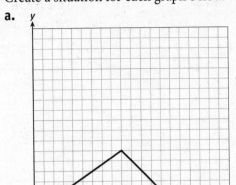

b.

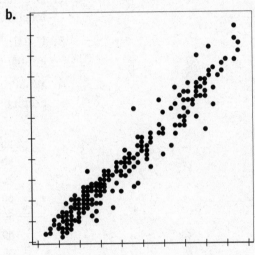

c.

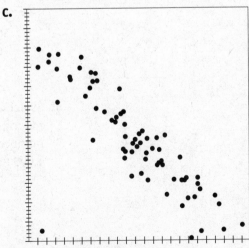

11. Reason abstractly. Explain what you can tell about a situation by looking at the graph that represents it. Use appropriate mathematical vocabulary to communicate your ideas precisely.

This graph shows the relationship between the elevation of a location and its mean annual temperature.

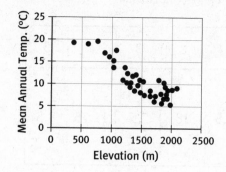

1. Draw a trend line for the graph above.

2. Use the trend line to determine the mean annual temperature for a location that has an elevation of 1,000 meters.

3. Use the trend line to predict the elevation of a location with a mean annual temperature of 10°C.

4. What relationship between latitude and temperature is suggested by the graph below?

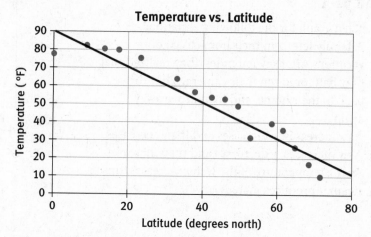

5. Sketch a graph showing the relationship between the height of a mountain and annual number of days of snow on the ground if the number of days of snow on the ground increases by 10 days for every 1,000 feet of elevation.

6. Which scatter plot below suggests a linear relationship? Explain your choice.

A.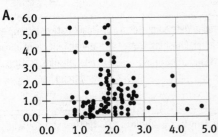

B.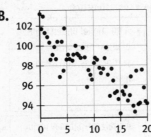

7. Which equation below will produce a linear graph? Justify your choice.

A. $a = s^2$ **B.** $y = 2.3x + 10$

The data in the table below shows the latitudes of several locations and the number of daylight hours recorded for each location on December 21, 2004.

City	Latitude	Number of Daylight Hours
Portland, OR	45°N	7
San Francisco, CA	37°N	8
Anchorage, AK	61°N	0
Jacksonville, FL	30°N	9
Santo Domingo, Dominican Rep.	18°N	11
Charlotte, NC	35°N	10
Sioux Falls, SD	43°N	9
Calgary, Alberta, Canada	51°N	8
Mexico City, Mexico	19°N	11
Quito, Ecuador	0°	12

8. a. Create a scatter plot to represent the data.

   b. Draw a trend line for the data.

   c. Use the trend line to predict the number of hours of daylight at a location with latitude of 9°N.

   d. Write an equation for this situation, and use the equation to confirm the prediction made in part c.

Scoring Guide	Exemplary	Proficient	Emerging	Incomplete
	The solution demonstrates these characteristics:			
Mathematics Knowledge and Thinking (Items 2, 3, 4, 5, 6, 7, 8c-d)	• Clear and accurate understanding of linear relationships, scatter plots, and trend lines.	• A functional understanding of linear relationships, scatter plots, and trend lines.	• Partial understanding of linear relationships, scatter plots, and trend lines..	• Inaccurate or incomplete understanding of linear relationships, scatter plots, and trend lines.
Problem Solving (Items 8c-d)	• An appropriate and efficient strategy that results in a correct answer. • Correct checking of a prediction.	• A strategy that may include unnecessary steps but results in a correct answer.	• A strategy that results in some incorrect answers. • Partial checking of a prediction.	• No clear strategy when solving problems. • No understanding of checking a prediction.
Mathematical Modeling / Representations (Items 1, 2, 3, 4, 5, 6, 7, 8a-d)	• Clear and accurate understanding of plotting data, drawing a trend line, and writing an equation from a trend line.	• Largely correct plotting of data, drawing a trend line, and writing an equation from a trend line.	• Partial understanding of plotting data, drawing a trend line, and writing an equation from a trend line.	• Inaccurate or incomplete understanding of plotting data, drawing a trend line, or writing an equation.
Reasoning and Communication (Items 4, 5a-c, 6a, 6c)	• Precise use of appropriate math terms and language to characterize a relationship from a scatter plot or trend line. • Making clear and accurate predictions from a graph.	• Correct characterization of a relationship from a scatter plot or trend line. • Making reasonable predictions from a graph.	• Misleading or confusing characterization of a relationship from a scatter plot or trend line. • Making partially correct predictions from a graph.	• Incomplete or inaccurate characterization of a relationship from a scatter plot or trend line. • Making incomplete or inaccurate predictions from a graph.

Probability and Statistics

5

Unit Overview

In this unit, you will investigate relationships between two variables, and you will practice displaying, summarizing, and analyzing bivariate (two-variable) data. Using two numerical variables, you will investigate the *strength*, *form*, and *direction* of association between the two variables. Where appropriate, you will practice developing linear equations that model some of these relationships. For the case of two categorical variables, you will develop two-way tables that summarize the data in a way that allows for easy comparison between different categories. You will also develop graphical representations that can assist in the comparison of the data between different categories.

Key Terms

As you study this unit, add these and other terms to your math notebook. Include in your notes your prior knowledge of each word, as well as your experiences in using the word in different mathematical examples. If needed, ask for help in pronouncing new words and add information on pronunciation to your math notebook. It is important that you learn new terms and use them correctly in your class discussions and in your problem solutions.

Academic Vocabulary
- association
- deviate
- cluster

Math Terms
- association
- positive association
- negative association
- linear association
- non-linear association
- linear model
- bivariate data
- mean absolute deviation
- trend line
- two-way table
- categorical variables
- segmented bar graph
- row percentages

5

5

ESSENTIAL QUESTIONS

? How does a scatter plot help you to investigate and interpret associations between two numerical variables?

? How can the slope and *y*-intercept components of a linear model be interpreted in context when used to describe a linear association between two numerical variables?

? How can a two-way table be used to assess an association between two categorical variables?

EMBEDDED ASSESSMENTS

These assessments, following activities 33 and 35, will give you an opportunity to demonstrate your understanding of bivariate association.

Embedded Assessment 1:

Scatter Plots, Associations, and Trends — p. 465

Embedded Assessment 2:

Median-Median Line and Two-Way Tables — p. 485

443

Write your answers on notebook paper.
Show your work.

1. A line contains the points (2, 5) and (4, 6).
   a. Where does it cross the *x*-axis?
   b. Where does it cross the *y*-axis?

2. Use the graph below to
   a. Plot and label the points *R*(3, 5) and *S*(6, 0).
   b. Give the coordinates of point *T*.

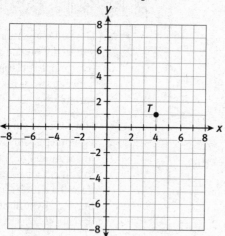

3. Write the equation of the line graphed below.

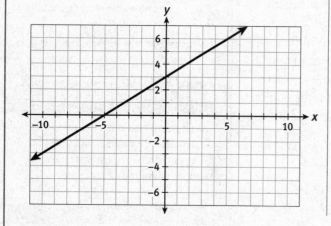

4. Find the slope of the line containing these three points.

x	y
0	11
2	7.5
4	4

5. Write the equation of the line that contains the three points listed in Item 4. Write the equation in slope-intercept form.

6. State whether each of the following is an example of a numerical or categorical variable.
   a. eye color
   b. type of fruit
   c. student height
   d. textbook weight
   e. favorite sport

7. Express the following fractions as percentages:
   a. $\dfrac{15}{60}$

   b. $\dfrac{42}{105}$

   c. $\dfrac{146}{200}$

8. Convert the following two fractions to percentages (to the nearest percent) and determine which fraction is larger:
$$\frac{45}{92}, \ \frac{34}{65}$$

Analyzing Data

Cracker Snacker

Lesson 32-1 Scatter Plots

Learning Targets:

- Make a scatter plot.
- Recognize patterns in scatter plots.

> **SUGGESTED LEARNING STRATEGIES:** Activate Prior Knowledge, Create Representations, Look for a Pattern, Think-Pair-Share

At a recent lunch, Mary was looking at the nutritional information printed on the packaging of some of the crackers she and her friends were eating. She noticed that some brands of crackers had much higher sodium than other brands, and that there was considerable variability in some of the other nutritional measurements (such as total fat). She also noticed that some of the brands that were high in one nutritional measurement were quite high or quite low in another. For example, one brand of crackers was quite high in both total carbohydrates and sodium, but it was fairly low in total fat. Mary wondered if some of the nutritional measurements for these crackers might be related.

Mary went to a large grocery that carries many brands of crackers and chose a random sample for which to record data. In a ***random sample***, each member of the population (in this case, all the brands of crackers) has an equal chance of being chosen. Mary put all the different brands of crackers in a grocery cart and then closed her eyes and pulled nine packages from the cart. She recorded the following data for the nine brands of crackers, each based on a 30-gram serving.

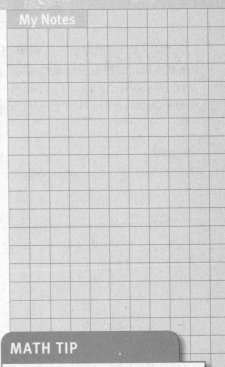

MATH TIP

Since it is often impossible to sample an entire population (think about the millions of people in a large city), a random sample can be used to estimate the traits of the entire population.

Cracker (Serving = 30 g)	Total Fat (g)	Sodium (mg)	Fiber (g)	Total Carbohydrates (g)	Whole Wheat?
Fun Crisps	6	300	0	20	No
Fun Crisps—MultiGrain	7	250	1	18	No
Snax—Cheddar	5	350	1	20	No
Snax—Pretzel	3	450	1	24	No
Super Grain	3	250	4	23	Yes
Table Thin Crisps	3	300	1	22	No
Waves of Wheat	4	200	4	21	Yes
Zaps	8	250	0	19	No
Zaps—Low Salt	8	200	5	18	Yes

1. Describe any observations you have about the table.

ACADEMIC VOCABULARY

Association is the degree to which two variables are related, generally described in terms of the association's direction, form, and strength.

2. Examine the *association* between two numerical variables by creating scatter plots.

   a. **Model with mathematics.** Make a scatter plot for the nine brands of crackers, recording total fat on the horizontal axis and total carbohydrates on the vertical axis. Place a circle around any point on the graph that represents a whole-wheat brand of cracker.

   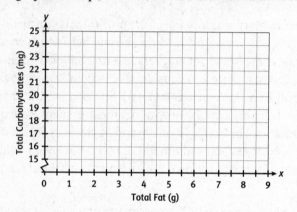

   b. Describe any patterns you observe from the scatter plot.

3. Look at the association between total carbohydrates and sodium.

   a. Construct a scatter plot for the nine brands of crackers, recording total carbohydrates on the horizontal axis and sodium on the vertical axis. As before, place a circle around any point on the graph that represents a whole-wheat brand of cracker.

   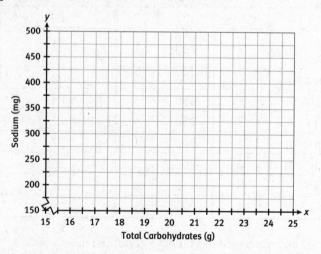

   b. Do the whole-wheat crackers generally have higher or lower sodium than the other crackers?

My Notes

4. Make a scatter plot to compare fiber and sodium for the nine brands of crackers.

   a. Record fiber on the horizontal axis and sodium on the vertical axis. Again, place a circle around any point on the graph that represents a whole-wheat brand of cracker.

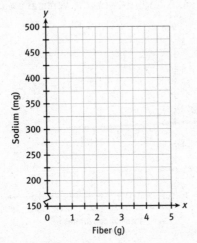

   b. Are the fiber amounts in the whole-wheat crackers very different from the fiber amounts in other crackers? How can you tell from the graph?

Check Your Understanding

5. When collecting statistical data, what is the value of using a random sample versus a sample of an entire population?

6. **Critique the reasoning of others.** Compare your three scatter plots with a classmate's, and if you want to make any changes or improvements to your graphs, do so now. Keep in mind that relationships and patterns in scatter plots need not always be lines.

7. Consider the scatter plot you constructed in Item 3. Which of the following statements (*A* or *B*) describes the pattern in this scatter plot?

   Statement A: Crackers that have more grams of total carbohydrates tend to have less sodium than crackers with less total carbohydrates.

   Statement B: Crackers that have more grams of total carbohydrates tend to have more sodium than crackers with less total carbohydrates.

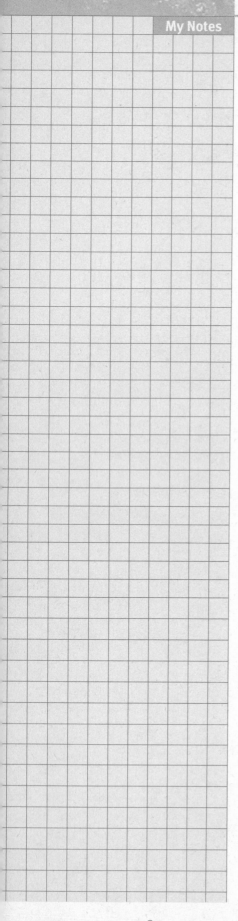

My Notes

LESSON 32-1 PRACTICE

8. Explain how you would generate a random sample, and give an example.

9. Use the cracker data to construct a scatter plot with total carbohydrates on the horizontal axis and fiber on the vertical axis.

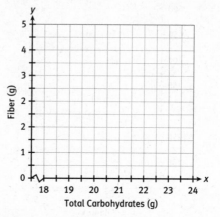

10. Notice that in the scatter plot from Item 7, three points stand out as different from the others. What do the crackers that correspond to these three points have in common?

11. Use the data for the six crackers that are not whole-wheat to construct a scatter plot that uses sodium on the vertical axis and total fat on the horizontal axis.

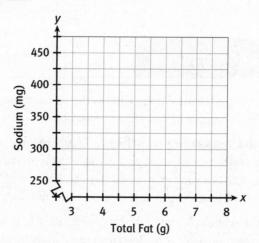

12. **Construct viable arguments.** Based on the scatter plot in Item 9, describe the relationship between total fat and sodium content for these crackers.

Learning Targets:

- Recognize patterns in scatter plots.
- Describe association between two numerical variables in terms of direction, form and strength.

SUGGESTED LEARNING STRATEGIES: Marking the Text, Close Reading, Look for a Pattern, Visualization, Summarizing, Paraphrasing

Direction, form, strength, and any other special characteristics are considered when describing the association of data in a scatter plot. As you continue reading, be sure to mark or highlight the text to identify words and phrases that help you understand the context and key terms.

Direction: Two variables have a ***positive association*** if *y* tends to increase as *x* increases. They have a ***negative association*** if *y* tends to decrease as *x* increases. If the data have no clear relationship, they have **no association.**

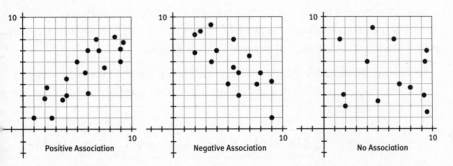

Positive Association   Negative Association   No Association

Form: If the data points in a scatter plot generally follow a linear pattern, the relationship is described as a ***linear association.*** If the collection of data points follows any type of noticeably curved pattern, the relationship is described as a ***non-linear association.*** It is also possible that there is no clear relationship at all.

Strength: When points fall close to an imaginary line or a curve, the association is considered to be *strong.* The more closely the points tend to follow the path of a line or curve, the stronger the association is. On the other hand, if the points are somewhat widely scattered around an imaginary line or curve, the association is considered to be *weak.* A *moderate* association is one that is neither strong nor week, but "in between."

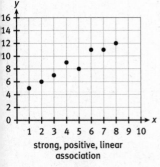

strong, positive, linear association

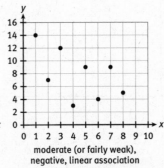

moderate (or fairly weak), negative, linear association

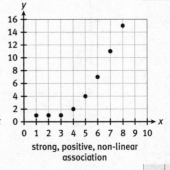

strong, positive, non-linear association

My Notes

MATH TERMS

Two variables are related in a **positive association** when values for one variable tend to increase as values for the other variable also increase; an increase in *x* corresponds with an increase in *y*.

Two variables are related in a **negative association** when values for one variable tend to decrease as values for the other variable increase; an increase in *x* corresponds with a decrease in *y*.

When a linear pattern (such as one of the form $y = mx + b$) describes the essential nature of the relationship between two variables, they have a **linear association.**

When a non-linear pattern (such as a curve) describes the essential nature of the relationship between two variables, they have a **non-linear association.**

CONNECT TO AP

In AP Statistics, you will use a statistic called the **correlation coefficient** to describe the strength and direction of a linear association.

ACADEMIC VOCABULARY

To *deviate* means "to stray or depart from an established course" or "to digress from a line of thought or reasoning."

A *cluster* is a small group or bunch of something, like points in this case.

Other Special Characteristics: Any points that substantially *deviate* from the overall pattern, called *outliers*, are worth noting. Also, anytime a noticeable concentration of points is present, that *cluster* should be noted.

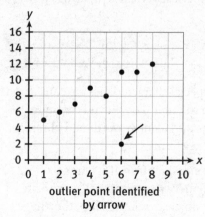

outlier point identified
by arrow

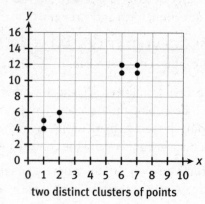

two distinct clusters of points

If more data were added to the second graph above for values of *x* from 3 to 5, they might reveal a strong linear relationship, but they might also reveal some other kind of relationship. Always be careful about inferring too much about data that are not present in your graph!

1. Complete the table below for each of the cracker data scatter plots you constructed in Items 2–4 in Lesson 32-1. State *none* for any table entry that is not applicable.

Graph	Direction	Form	Strength	Special/Other
Total Carbohydrates vs. Total Fat				
Sodium vs. Total Carbohydrates				
Sodium vs. Fiber				

2. **Reason abstractly.** Which of the three relationships above would be *best* suited for creating a *linear model* to describe the relationship? Explain your reasoning.

3. Which of the following linear models appears reasonable for describing the relationship between Total Carbohydrates (y) and Total Fat (x) based on your scatter plot?
   a. $y = 25 - x$
   b. $y = 25 + x$
   c. $y = 50 - 2x$

My Notes

MATH TERMS

A **linear model** of the form $y = mx + b$ describes the essential nature of the relationship between y and x.

Check Your Understanding

4. Compare your descriptions from your table in Item 1 with a classmate. Describe any changes you would make.

5. **Reason quantitatively.** How did you choose your answer in Item 3? How did you determine which y-intercept and slope values would be the best choices?

LESSON 32-2 PRACTICE

6. Below is a data table showing the weights of seven newborn horses and the weights of the mother horses. Use the data to construct a scatter plot with mother's weight on the horizontal axis and newborn's weight on the vertical axis.

Newborn Weight (kg)	Mother Weight (kg)
130	550
120	650
130	600
120	550
125	625
125	650
115	575
120	600

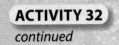

ACTIVITY 32
continued

My Notes

7. Based on the scatter plot you constructed in Item 6, is there a relationship between newborn weight and mother weight? Justify your response.

8. To make chips, tortillas are fried in oil. Below is a data table on frying time (in seconds) and moisture content (percent) for eight chips. Construct a scatter plot with frying time on the horizontal axis and moisture content on the vertical axis.

Frying Time (seconds)	Moisture Content (%)
5	14
10	10
15	8
20	9
25	3
30	6
45	2
60	1

9. Does the relationship between frying time and moisture content look linear or non-linear?

10. **Construct viable arguments.** If moisture content is high, the chip can be soggy. Based on what you see in the scatter plot you constructed in Item 8, do you think it would be better to fry chips for 10 seconds or for 50 seconds? Justify your response.

11. Would you describe the relationship between frying time and moisture content as positive or negative?

12. Would you describe the relationship between frying time and moisture content as strong or weak?

13. Which of the following two lines would be better for describing the relationship between frying time and moisture content: $y = 8 + 0.5x$ or $y = 12 - 0.2x$? Justify your choice.

ACTIVITY 32 PRACTICE

Lesson 32-1

The following data were collected for a group of students.

Hours of TV per Week	Percent of Homework Completed	Test Score
32	58	66
13	82	85
28	65	75
19	87	85
11	98	100
21	78	88
15	75	85
11	92	90
15	75	90
12	91	95
17	90	85
20	81	85

1. Construct a scatter plot that uses Hours of TV per Week on the horizontal axis and Percent of Homework Completed on the vertical axis.

2. Construct a scatter plot that uses Percent of Homework Completed on the horizontal axis and Test Score on the vertical axis.

3. Construct a scatter plot that uses Hours of TV per Week on the horizontal axis and Test Score on the vertical axis.

4. A consumer group rated the quality of nine brands of bicycle helmets. The quality ratings and the prices for these nine brands are shown below. Construct a scatter plot that uses Price on the horizontal axis and Quality Rating on the vertical axis.

Quality Rating	Price
65	35
60	30
55	40
47	23
47	30
43	18
41	28
40	20
32	25

Lesson 32-2

5. Which of the two scatter plots (from Items 1 and 2) has a positive association? How would you describe the strength and form of this association?

6. In the scatter plot of Test Score vs. Percent of Homework Completed, are there any interesting or unusual characteristics of the scatter plot or any unusual points?

7. In the scatter plot you constructed in Item 3, would you describe the relationship between Test Score and number of Hours of TV per Week as positive or negative?

8. Are there any interesting or unusual points or characteristics in the scatter plot you constructed in Item 3?

Use the scatter plot you constructed in Item 4 to answer Items 9–13.

9. Does the relationship between Price and Quality Rating look linear or non-linear?

10. Do bike helmets that cost more tend to have a higher quality rating?

11. Would you describe the relationship between Price and Quality Rating as positive or negative?

12. Would you describe the relationship between Price and Quality Rating strong, moderate or weak?

13. Which of the following two lines would be better for describing the relationship between Price and Quality Rating: $y = 7 + 1x$ or $y = 5 + \frac{1}{2}x$? Justify your choice.

14. For each of the scatter plots shown, answer the following questions.

Does there appear to be a relationship between *x* and *y*? If so, does the relationship appear to be linear? If so, would you describe the linear relationship as positive or negative?

Scatter Plot 1

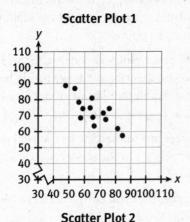

Scatter Plot 2

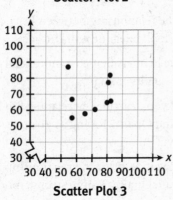

Scatter Plot 3

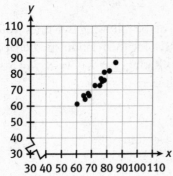

15. For each of the following pairs of variables, indicate whether you think there would be a relationship between these variables, and if so, whether it would be positive or negative.

a. time spent studying for a test and score on the test

b. a person's weight and the time it takes the person to run one mile

For each of the scatter plots in Items 16–19 below, indicate whether the graph displays a strong positive moderate positive, strong negative, or moderate negative association, or no association at all.

16.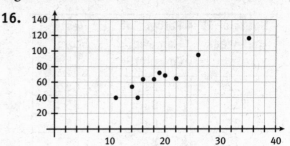

17.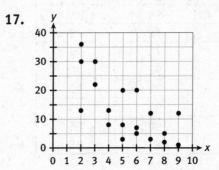

18. Graph 1
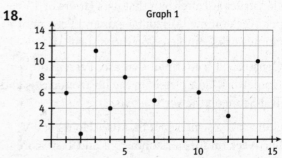

19.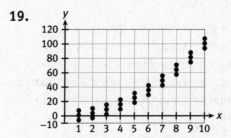

20. Which of the graphs in Items 16–19 demonstrate a linear association?

21. Describe the association between sodium and fiber in the crackers in Lesson 32-1, Item 4.

MATHEMATICAL PRACTICES
Use Appropriate Tools Strategically

22. Explain how a scatter plot can be used to describe the relationship between two variables.

Bivariate Data

Sue Swandive
Lesson 33-1 Collecting Data

Learning Targets:

- Collect bivariate data from an experiment.
- Summarize bivariate data in a scatter plot.

> **SUGGESTED LEARNING STRATEGIES:** Activating Prior Knowledge, Think-Pair-Share, Self Revision/Peer Revision, Visualization

The famous bungee jumper, Sue Swandive, is promoting her new doll line. There will be a bungee competition with the new doll. The winner gets a special prize.

The competition rules are as follows:

a. Attach a rock (or other weighted item) using tape to the back of a Sue Swandive doll.

b. Make a bungee cord by connecting rubber bands and attach it to the doll. (See diagrams at right. Secure the doll's feet together using one rubber band around the ankles. This will be used to attach the first rubber band with a slipknot.)

c. Prepare to drop the doll from an appropriate height with the bungee cord attached. Before dropping the doll, predict how far the doll will drop.

d. The winner(s) will be determined according to whose *prediction* for how far the Sue doll will drop is closest to the *actual* distance the Sue doll drops.

To help you make a prediction for the competition, you will collect data in your classroom first.

Begin the classroom part of your experiment as follows:

- Attach the bungee to the Sue doll. Hold the end of the bungee cord *and* the Sue doll's feet at the 0 position on the tape measure with the doll's head pointing straight down.
- Let go of the doll's feet *but* hold onto the bungee cord.
- Record the height of the doll's head at its lowest position. (It may be helpful to tie the doll's hair back.)
- Be prepared to repeat each jump a few times to get a representative measurement. (You might want to try each jump at least three times and record the *median* measurement from your multiple attempts using a bungee cord that has a given number of rubber bands.)
- Add rubber bands to extend the length of the bungee cord and continue to take readings. Use slipknots to attach the rubber bands.

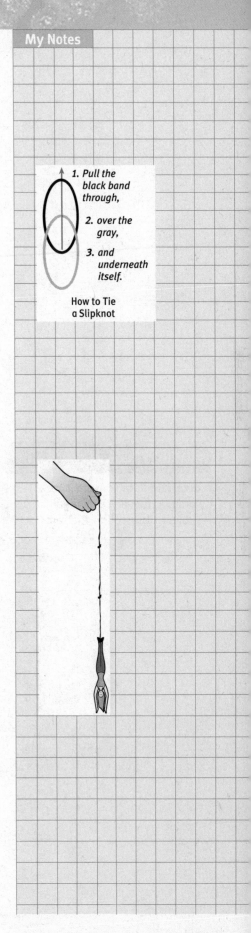

My Notes

1. Pull the black band through,

2. over the gray,

3. and underneath itself.

How to Tie a Slipknot

1. Record the data for your class in the table below. Measure the Length of Bungee Jump from the 0 point of the tape measure.

Number of Rubber Bands Attached to the Sue Doll	Length of Bungee Jump
1	
2	
3	
4	
5	
6	
7	
8	
9	
10	

The data you have recorded is an example of **bivariate data**.

Bivariate data are data that list two variables for each subject or observation (for example, number of rubber bands *and* length of jump, a person's height *and* weight, someone's favorite food *and* state of residence, and so on.)

MATH TERMS

Bivariate data contains two variables for each individual, subject, observation, trial, etc.

2. **Attend to precision.** Create a scatter plot of the data on the grid below. Adjust the scale of the *y*-axis according to your unit of measurement and the number of your rubber bands.

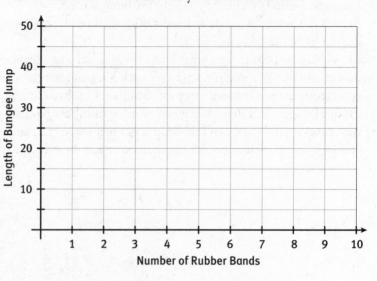

My Notes

3. Do the data indicate a linear relationship between the number of rubber bands and the length of bungee jump? Explain your answers using both the scatter plot and the table.

4. Describe how the length of the bungee jump changes as the number of rubber bands increases. What are the direction and strength of this association?

A scatterplot displays data so that you can visually see the distribution of the data. In earlier grades, you have calculated the mean, median, and mode of data as measures of variability in the data. Another measure of the spread of a distribution is the ***mean absolute deviation*** (MAD). The MAD is the average distance that the observations are from the mean of the distribution.

For example, if the mean of the bungee-jumping results for your class is 18 inches and your result was 22 inches, then your result is a distance of 4 from the mean—the distance between 18 and 22.

Assume that 10 of your classmates had the following distribution of results for the bungee jumping contest (in inches).

2 18 22 14 17 18 26 29 23 21

5. What is the mean for this distribution?

6. Create a table showing the results above. List the results in one column, and then calculate the distance from the mean for each data point in the second column. Add the distances from the mean to find a total.

7. Now find the mean absolute deviation (MAD) by finding the average, or mean, of the distances in the table.

8. Look back to Item 2 and the data you plotted on a scatter plot for the length of each bungee jump. Notice how the lengths are spread and relate this to the MAD.

My Notes

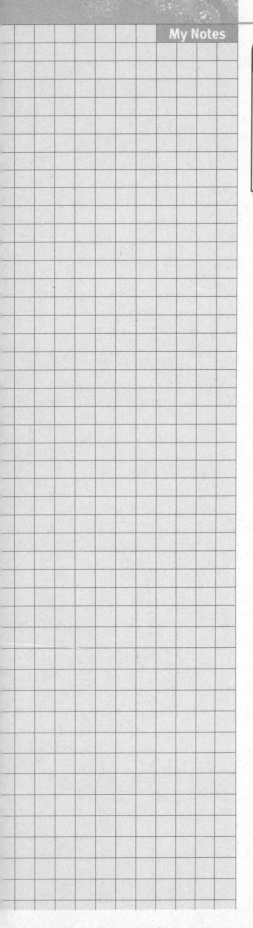

Check Your Understanding

9. Compare your scatter plot and table with the scatter plots and tables of other classmates. How are the scatter plots and tables similar? How are they different? Explain your reasoning.

10. Describe the mean absolute deviation. How does it relate to the mean of a sample of data?

LESSON 33-1 PRACTICE

11. Four data sets are described below. Which of these data sets are bivariate data?

    Data Set 1: Heights of 20 third graders.

    Data Set 2: Prices and sizes of 40 houses.

    Data Set 3: Amounts of fat and numbers of calories for 10 brands of hot dogs.

    Data Set 4: Times to run 1 mile for 12 runners.

12. For each data set in Item 6 that is bivariate data, would you expect the association between the two variables to be positive or negative? Explain your choices.

13. **Make use of structure.** The scatter plot below displays data on height (in inches) and distance jumped (in inches) for twenty high school girls. How would you describe the association between height and distance jumped?

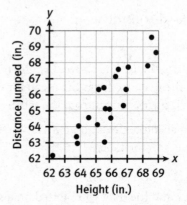

14. **Reason abstractly.** Imagine that you collected data for a new bungee jump experiment and that you did not add a weight to the doll in this experiment. If you were to make a scatter plot for the data from this new experiment, how do you think it would be different from the scatter plot you made in Item 2?

15. Calculate the MAD for the following data points: 22, 34, 21, 12, 40, 37, 27, 19, 23, 25.

Learning Targets:
- Informally fit a line to bivariate data.
- Use a trend line to make a prediction.

SUGGESTED LEARNING STRATEGIES: Activating Prior Knowledge, Think-Pair-Share, Self Revision/Peer Revision, Visualization.

A *trend line* is a line that indicates the general pattern in linearly associated data.

1. **Use appropriate tools strategically.** Place a straightedge like a piece of cardboard or a ruler on the scatter plot in Item 2 in Lesson 33-1 in a position that would seem to indicate the general trend of the data and serve as a good, representative linear model. Trace that linear model on the coordinate grid. The line *does not* have to go through any of the data points you collected. It just needs to represent the general trend of the data.

2. Write an equation in slope-intercept form for the trend line you just created.

3. Explain what the variables in the equation of your trend line represent.

4. **Make sense of problems.** How would you interpret the slope of your trend line in relation to the variable names you used above?

5. In preparation for the competition, make a prediction for the distance your doll will drop based on the number of rubber bands your teacher specifies.

Prediction:

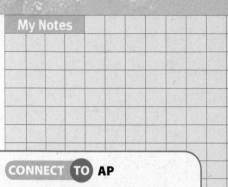

CONNECT TO AP

In AP Statistics, you will find trend lines for bivariate numerical data using a method called *Least Squares Regression*.

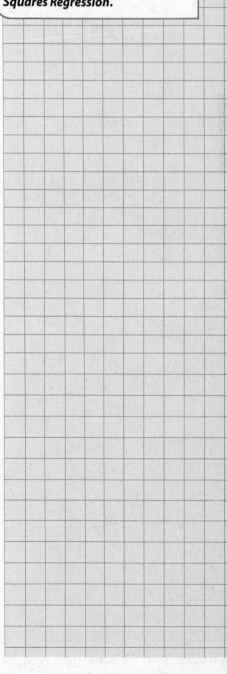

Check Your Understanding

6. Compare your trend line equation with the equations of other classmates. Why would the slopes be similar? Why would they be different?

7. Briefly explain how you chose your trend line model. What characteristics of the data were important to you in determining your equation?

LESSON 33-2 PRACTICE

8. The scatter plot below was constructed using data on age and number of cell phone calls made in a typical day for 10 people. Two trend lines have been added to the scatter plot. Which line does a better job of describing the relationship between age and number of cell phone calls made?

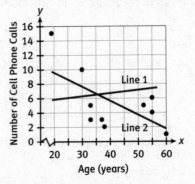

9. **Make sense of problems.** The trend line $y = 492 + 15x$ was determined using data on age, x, and distance walked (in meters), y, for six minutes for boys between the ages of 3 and 18.
   a. Interpret the slope of the trend line.
   b. Based on this trend line, how many meters would you predict a 12-year-old boy would walk in six minutes?

10. The scatter plot below was made using data on $x =$ cost per cup (in cents) and $y =$ amount of fiber per cup (in grams) for 11 breakfast cereals. Graph a trend line on the scatter plot that you think does a good job of describing the relationship between fiber content and cost.

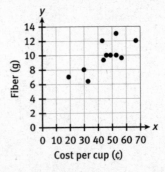

11. Write an equation for the trend line you drew in Item 10.

12. Based on your trend line model from Item 11, how many grams of fiber would you predict for a cereal that costs 40 cents per cup?

Learning Targets:

- Interpret scatter plots.
- Use a trend line to make predictions.

SUGGESTED LEARNING STRATEGIES: Activating Prior Knowledge, Think-Pair-Share, Self Revision/Peer Revision, Visualization

Now it is time to carry out the competition!

1. How close was your prediction in Item 5 in Lesson 33-2 to the actual distance your doll dropped in the competition?

2. **Reason quantitatively.** Since you could technically use the value 3.5 as an input for your equation from Item 2 in Lesson 33-2, would it make sense to use the equation to predict the length of the bungee jump with 3.5 rubber bands? Explain your reasoning.

Suppose that another class hears about the competition and prepares a similar entry. They also decide to collect data during class using another Sue Swandive doll that is the same height and weight as your doll, but they use a much *heavier* rock for their experiments. Assume they use the same kind of rubber bands that you used.

3. **Construct viable arguments.** Do you think that their scatter plot for recording the distance the doll travels on the bungee jump vs. the number of rubber bands will have a similar direction, form, and strength to your graph? Explain your reasoning.

4. Do you think that their trend line will show a slope that is greater than, less than, or about the same as the slope of your trend line? Explain your reasoning.

My Notes

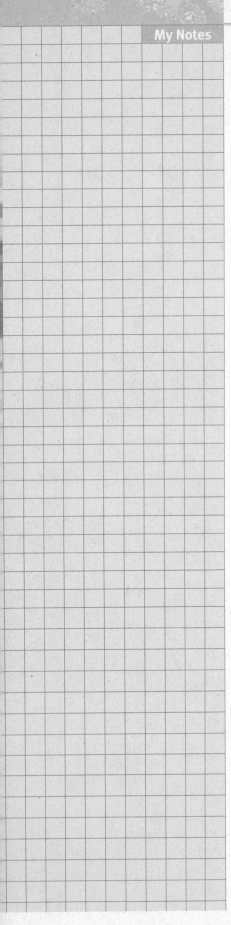

Check Your Understanding

Write your answers on notebook paper. Show your work.
Each of the scatter plots in Items 5, 6, and 7 displays data that show an approximate linear trend. Write an equation for each trend line.

5.

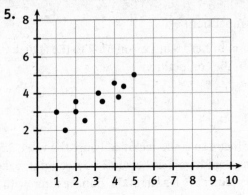

6.

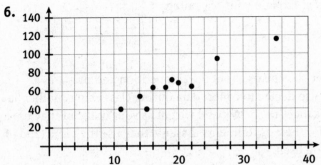

7.

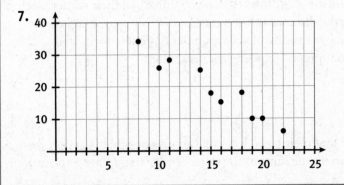

For each trend line equation in Items 8 and 9, briefly interpret the slope in relation to the numerical variables.

8. $y = 75 + .19x$, where x = number of miles traveled and y = the cost of an airline flight in dollars.

9. $y = 100 - 1.2x$, where x = number of hours of TV watched per week and y = test score on last week's test.

10. **Make sense of problems.** What does the direction of the association for a set of bivariate numerical data indicate about the slope of the corresponding trend line?

LESSON 33-3 PRACTICE

11. The scatter plot below shows the data for hours of TV per week and test scores.

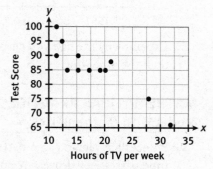

a. Graph a trend line on the scatter plot.
b. Write an equation of the trend line you drew.

12. Do you think every student in your class will have the same equation or trend line in Item 11? Why or why?

13. **Critique the reasoning of others.** In the scatter plot shown below, explain why Jacinda's Line 1 does a better job of describing the trend than Lucas' Line 2.

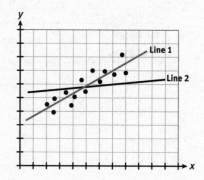

ACTIVITY 33 PRACTICE

1. Three data sets are described below. Which of these data sets are bivariate?

   Data Set 1: Heights and weights of 17 bears.

   Data Set 2: Test scores for 25 students.

   Data Set 3: Scores on a reading test and ages for 50 elementary school children.

2. For each data set in Item 1 that is bivariate data, would you expect the association between the two variables to be positive or negative? Justify your response.

3. The trend line $y = 12 - 0.2x$ was determined using data on $x =$ frying time (in seconds) and $y =$ moisture content (in %) for tortilla chips.
   a. Interpret the slope of the trend line.
   b. Based on this trend line, what moisture content would you predict for a frying time of 40 seconds?

4. The scatter plot below was made using the data from Lesson 32-1 on $x =$ percent homework completed and $y =$ test score for 12 students. Graph a trend line on the scatter plot that you think does a good job of describing the relationship between test score and percent of homework completed.

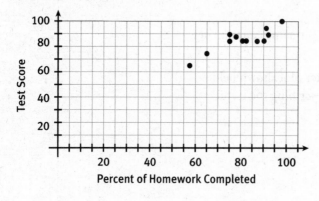

5. Write an equation of the trend line you graphed in Item 4.

6. Based on your trend line equation from Item 5, what test score would you predict for a student who completed 80% of the homework?

7. Two trend lines are shown on the scatter plot below. Which line does a better job of describing the relationship between x and y?

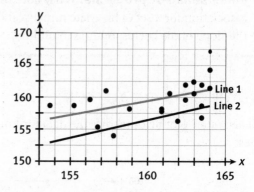

8. Explain why the line you chose in Item 7 is better than the other line.

MATHEMATICAL PRACTICES
Model with Mathematics

9. Frances has planted a new African violet and, as time passes, new leaves are appearing. She has recorded this information in the table below. Create a linear equation that best models Frances's data and can be used to predict the number of leaves Frances should expect after 60 weeks. Let t represent the time (in weeks) and n represent the number of leaves on the plant.

Time in weeks	1	3	6	9	12	15	18	21
Number of leaves	1	2	3	3	4	6	7	9

1. The scatter plot below shows the U.S. population (in millions) from 1790 to 2010 according to data from the U.S. Census Bureau.

   a. What is the *direction* of the association between U.S. Population and Years Since 1790? Briefly state a few characteristics of the data or the graph that support your description.

   b. What is the *form* of the association between U.S. Population and Years Since 1790? Is it linear or non-linear?

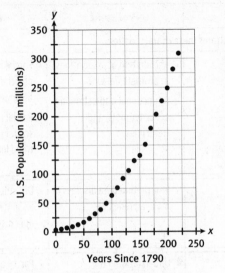

> **MATH TIP**
>
> A *census* occurs when the information of interest is collected on all members of a population. Collecting the survey information from all students is a census.

   c. What is the *strength* of the association between U.S. Population and Years Since 1790? State a characteristic of the graph that supports your description.

   d. Do you think a linear model would be a good model to use to explain the association between U.S. Population and Census Year? Why or why not?

2. Mr. Mokher and his college students went to the local elementary school to collect data. The names of all the students were written on slips of paper and placed into a large container, which was then shaken vigorously. Mr. Mokher and his college students drew 12 slips of paper, one at a time, from the container. After taking a random sample of 12 children from Grade 0 (Kindergarten) through Grade 6, they collected data on each child's grade level and height in inches.

Student	Grade	Height (in.)
1	0	36
2	0	38
3	0	40
4	1	39
5	2	40
6	2	42
7	3	45
8	4	47
9	5	47
10	5	50
11	5	60
12	6	53

   a. Construct a scatter plot of height (*y*-axis) versus grade (*x*-axis).

   b. Describe the overall association between the grade level and the student's height in inches in terms of direction, form and strength.

   c. Graph a trend line on your scatter plot.

   d. Write an equation for the trend line.

   e. Interpret the slope of your trend line in the context of this analysis.

   f. Identify any student who substantially deviates from the overall pattern. Describe in context how the student does not fit the overall pattern.

   g. Given the context of the data set and the trend line model you have created, do you think your model will be applicable for later grades (e.g., middle school, high school, college)? Justify your response.

Scoring Guide	Exemplary	Proficient	Emerging	Incomplete
	The solution demonstrates these characteristics:			
Mathematics Knowledge and Thinking (Items 1a-d, 2a-g)	• Clear and accurate understanding of associations in bivariate data. • Clear and accurate understanding of scatter plots and trend lines.	• Recognition of associations in bivariate data. • A functional understanding of scatter plots, and trend lines.	• Partial recognition of associations in bivariate data. • Partial understanding of scatter plots, and trend lines.	• Little or no understanding of associations in bivariate data. • Little or no understanding of scatter plots, and trend lines.
Problem Solving (Item 2g)	• Clear and accurate interpretation of data displays to make a prediction.	• Interpreting data displays to make a prediction.	• Difficulty making an accurate prediction from data displays.	• Inaccurate interpretation of data displays.
Mathematical Modeling / Representations (Items 1d, 2a, 2c-d)	• Clear and accurate understanding of linear and non-linear models. • Clear and accurate understanding of plotting data, drawing a trend line, and writing an equation from a trend line.	• Understanding the difference between linear and non-linear models. • Mostly correct plotting of data, drawing a trend line, and writing an equation from a trend line.	• Partial understanding of linear and non-linear models. • Partial understanding of plotting data, drawing a trend line, and writing an equation from a trend line.	• Little or no understanding of linear and non-linear models. • Inaccurate or incomplete understanding of plotting data, drawing a trend line, or writing an equation.
Reasoning and Communication (Items 1a, 1c, 2b, 2e-g)	• Precise use of appropriate math terms and language to characterize associations in bivariate data using a scatter plot or trend line. • Making clear and accurate predictions from a graph.	• Correct characterization of associations in bivariate data using a scatter plot or trend line. • Making reasonable predictions from a graph.	• Misleading or confusing characterization of associations in bivariate data using a scatter plot or trend line. • Making partially correct predictions from a graph.	• Incomplete or inaccurate characterization of associations in bivariate data using a scatter plot or trend line. • Making incomplete or inaccurate predictions from a graph.

Median-Median Line

Homework Help Line
Lesson 34-1 Finding the Median-Median Line

Learning Targets:

- Determine if a linear model is a good fit for a scatter plot.
- Find the median-median line for bivariate numerical data.

> **SUGGESTED LEARNING STRATEGIES:** Activate Prior Knowledge, Think-Pair-Share, Quickwrite

Ms. Windle wants to examine the relationship between a student's percent of homework completed and the grade earned on the unit test. Below is a table showing the percent of homework completed and the earned test grade for each student in her class.

Percent of Homework Completed	Unit Test Grade
26	39
29	54
42	61
46	50
52	53
56	62
63	76
70	77
71	64
74	83
82	66
87	70
92	87
95	78
100	91

1. Let *x* represent the percent of homework completed and *y* represent the unit test grade. Construct a scatter plot of the data.

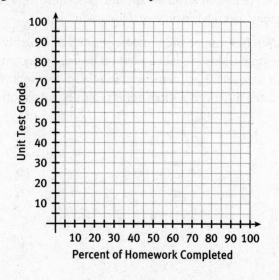

My Notes

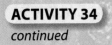

My Notes

2. **Make use of structure.**
   a. Describe the overall association between the two variables in terms of direction, form, and strength.

   b. Why might Ms. Windle want to display the scatter plot to her students?

3. Would a linear model such as a trend line be appropriate here? If so, how well do you think the data would fit such a model? Explain.

4. If each student in your class were to fit a trend line by drawing a line on the scatter plot, would everyone get the same line?

Check Your Understanding

Imagine a scatter plot where you decide that a linear model will **not** fit the data well. Consider the characteristics of such a scatter plot.

5. What kind of form in a scatter plot would lead you to say that a linear model will *not* fit the data well?

6. Even with a linear form of association, what kind of strength would lead you to say that a linear model will *not* fit the data well?

When there is a strong linear association visible in a scatter plot, a trend line developed by visual examination tends to be a very good model. However, it would be better if we had an effective, specific procedure for developing such a model rather than just relying on visual judgment.

A *median-median line* can be used to describe and analyze bivariate data. Ms. Windle likes to use this modeling method because it is convenient to use with smaller data sets. Also, compared to other linear modeling methods, calculating the line's slope and *y*-intercept is typically not as influenced by outliers.

7. Keeping the *x*-coordinates of the points in increasing order, use the *x*-coordinates (in this case, Percent of Homework Completed) to divide the data set into three similarly sized groups.

Lower Group		Middle Group		Greatest Group	
Percent of Homework Completed	Unit Test Grade	Percent of Homework Completed	Unit Test Grade	Percent of Homework Completed	Unit Test Grade

8. For each group:
- Find the median of the *x*-values.
- Find the median of the *y*-values.
- Use these median values to write one ordered pair from each group.

  L: *M*:   *G*:

9. Add points *L*, *M*, and *G* to the scatter plot you constructed in Item 1.

10. Write the equation of the line containing points *L* and *G*.

MATH TIP

When a set of numbers is listed in order, the median is the middle term. If the set contains an even number of terms, the median is the average of the two middle terms.

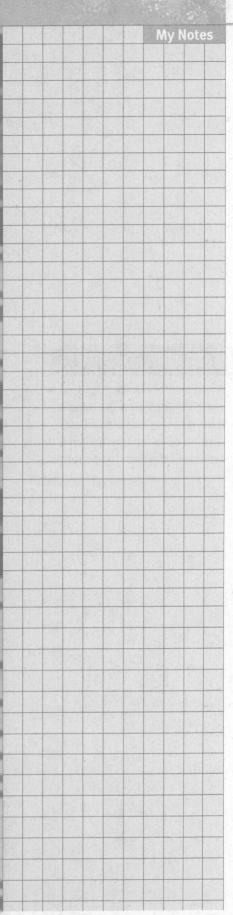

My Notes

11. Write the equation of the line that goes through point *M* and is parallel to the line that contains points *L* and *G*.

12. Compute the *y*-intercept of the median-median line by averaging the three *y*-intercept values for the lines that are associated with points *L*, *M*, and *G*. This averaging gives equal weight to each of the three ordered pairs of *L*, *M*, and *G* in the *y*-intercept computation. (*Note:* The *y*-intercept value associated with *L* and the *y*-intercept value associated with *G* will be the same.)

13. Write the equation of the median-median line for Ms. Windle's class data and draw this line on your scatter plot in Item 1.

14. **Reason abstractly.** Based on visual inspection of your scatter plot, does the median-median line appear to yield a reasonable, well-fitting model? Justify your response.

Check Your Understanding

15. Compare your median-median line equation with a classmate's equation. Did each of you obtain the same equation? If not, determine where you differed in your process. Do you both agree that the model is reasonable or unreasonable?

LESSON 34-1 PRACTICE

Model with mathematics. For each of the following data sets in Items 16–17:

    a. Construct a scatter plot of the data.
    b. Find the equation of the median-median line.
    c. Draw the median-median line on the scatter plot.

16. Eighteen middle school students were asked how many hours they spent playing video games in a typical week. Then each student was asked to play a new video game that none of the other students had played before. For these 18 students, the table below gives the number of hours spent playing video games per week and the score received on the first attempt at the new game.

$x =$ Time Spent Playing	$y =$ Score on New Game
0	80
0	84
2	85
5	99
8	115
9	120
9	118
10	114
11	125
12	130
13	139
14	150
15	168
16	171
16	174
16	174
17	184
20	196

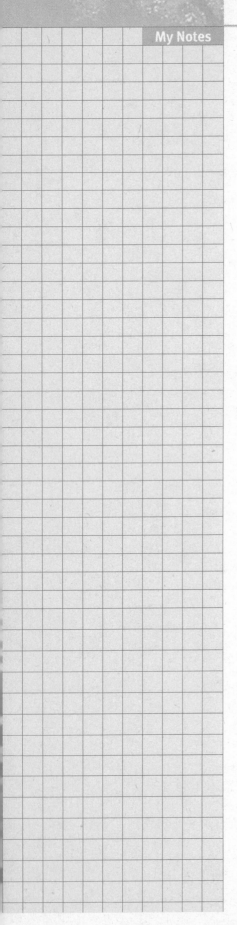

My Notes

17. Fifteen high school boys were measured for height (in inches) and arm span (in inches).

x = Height	y = Arm Span
66	65
67	66
68	67
68	68
68	68
69	69
69	69
69	70
69	70
71	70
71	70
71	70
72	70
73	71
75	71

18. From the scatter plot you constructed in Item 16, describe the association between hours spent playing video games per week and score in terms of direction, form, and strength.

19. From the scatter plot you constructed in Item 16, would a linear model be appropriate to describe the relationship between hours spent playing video games per week and score? Explain your reasoning.

20. Draw a scatter plot with 20 points where a linear model would not be a good way to describe the relationship.

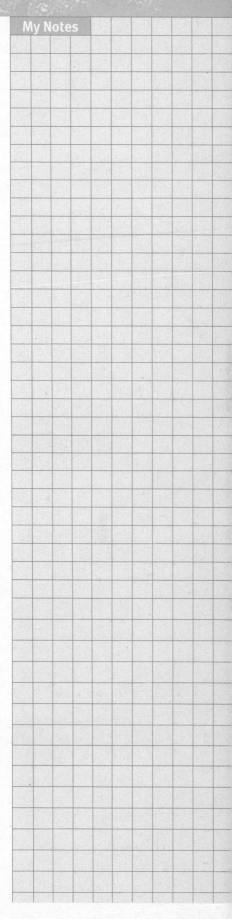

Learning Targets:

- Find the median-median line for bivariate numerical data.
- Use the median-median line to make predictions.

> **SUGGESTED LEARNING STRATEGIES:** Think-Pair-Share, Create Representations, Quickwrite

Use the equation for the median-median line that you wrote in Item 13 in Lesson 34-1 to answer each of the following:

1. **Make sense of problems.** Explain the meaning of the slope of the median-median line in the context of Ms. Windle's algebra class.

2. Explain the meaning of the *y*-intercept of the median-median line in the context of Ms. Windle's algebra class. Does this value seem reasonable in the context of these data?

3. What is the risk in assuming that the pattern of the median-median line you've developed will be appropriate for homework completion percentages less than 25% (the lowest value in your data set)?

4. Use the median-median line to predict the unit test score for a student who completes 72% of the homework.

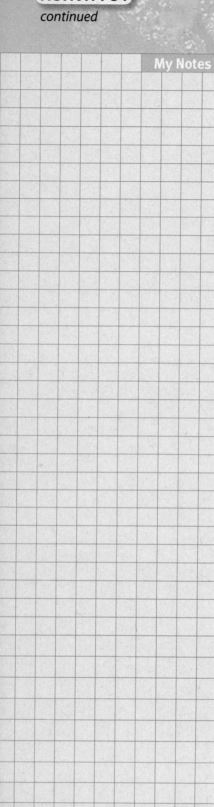

My Notes

Check Your Understanding

Write your answers on notebook paper or grid paper. Show your work.

A local car dealership recently received its shipment of a highly anticipated new model of car. Many customers needed to borrow some money in order to purchase one of these new cars. The data set below shows the amount borrowed (in dollars) by 11 customers to purchase their new car as well as the number of months that each customer had been saving up for purchasing his or her new car.

Number of Months Spent Saving for the Purchase	Amount Borrowed (in dollars)
0	21,500
1	18,000
1	17,380
2	17,500
4	14,600
5	13,958
8	12,100
10	11,000
11	9,870
16	7,300
18	5,120

5. Make a scatter plot of amount borrowed to purchase the car (y-axis) in dollars versus the number of months the customer had been saving up for the car (x-axis). Does a linear model seem appropriate? Justify your response.

6. Write the equation of the median-median line that estimates the amount borrowed (y) based on the number of months spent saving up for the car (x) for these 11 customers.

7. Use this equation to predict the amount borrowed by a customer who had been saving up for 7 months.

8. **Reason abstractly.** What graphical and numerical results can be used to determine if using a linear model is appropriate? Explain.

LESSON 34-2 PRACTICE

Here are the data on hours of TV per week and test scores from Activity 32.

x = Hours of TV per Week	y = Test Score
11	100
11	90
12	95
13	85
15	85
15	90
17	85
19	85
20	85
21	88
28	75
32	66

9. Construct a scatter plot for this data set.

10. Write the equation of the median-median line.

11. Graph the median-median line on your scatter plot.

12. Using the median-median line, what test score would you predict for someone who watches 25 hours of TV per week?

13. Using the median-median line, what test score would you predict for someone who watches 10 hours of TV per week?

14. **Construct viable arguments.** Explain why it is not a good idea to use the median-median line to predict the test score for someone who watchers TV 0 hours per week or someone who watches TV 60 hours per week.

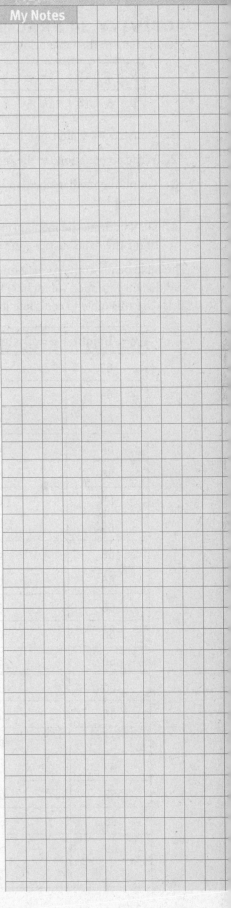

ACTIVITY 34 PRACTICE

Use the data in the table below to complete Items 1–4.

x	4	2	1	8	3	5	9	13
y	6	14	11	5	8	2	4	3

1. Construct a scatter plot for the data set.

2. Write an equation for the median-median line.

3. Graph the median-median line on your scatter plot.

4. Do you think the median-median line is a good fit for the data? Justify your response.

The table below contains data on height (in inches) and distance jumped (in inches) for 20 high school girls. Use this table to complete Items 5–9.

x = Height	y = Distance Jumped
62	62
64	63
64	63
64	64
65	66
65	65
65	64
66	67
66	65
66	63
66	64
66	68
66	65
66	66
67	66
67	65
67	68
68	68
69	69
69	70

5. Construct a scatter plot for this data set.

6. Write an equation for the median-median line.

7. Graph the median-median line on your scatter plot.

8. Using the median-median line, how far would you predict a girl who is 66 inches tall would be able to jump?

9. Do you think the median-median line is a good fit for the data? Justify your response.

The following table describes the federal minimum hourly wage since 1955. Use this table to complete Items 10–14.

# of Year	0	6	10	12	15	22	31	45
Hourly Wage	0.75	1.15	1.25	1.40	1.60	2.30	3.35	5.15

10. Construct a scatter plot for this data set.

11. Write an equation for the median-median line.

12. Graph the median-median line on your scatter plot.

13. Using the median-median line, predict what the federal minimum hourly wage will be in the year 2020.

14. Do you think the median-median line is a good fit for the data? Justify your response.

MATHEMATICAL PRACTICES
Attend to Precision

15. Chuck has made a mistake in finding the equation for a median-median line. He knows he has the correct coordinates for the points *L*, *M*, and *G*. The slope of his line is correct but the *y*-intercept is not. Which calculations should Chuck go back and check to find where he made his mistake?

Two-Way Tables and Association

Student Opinions

Lesson 35-1 Two-Way Tables

Learning Targets:

- Analyze two-way tables and find relative frequencies.
- Construct segmented bar graphs to display association.

> SUGGESTED LEARNING STRATEGIES: Activate Prior Knowledge, Look for a Pattern, Think-Pair-Share

Prior to an upcoming school election, Greg is curious about students' opinions on some school issues. He is hoping that by carrying out a survey of the students, he will learn about student opinions before he runs for office.

Greg is particularly interested in two questions—one regarding recent changes in the food served in the cafeteria, the other regarding a recent Spirit Day held at the school. Since Greg suspects that students from different grades may feel differently about these issues, he develops a survey with the following questions:

Student Survey	(circle one answer for each)		
Do you support the new policy of healthier choices being served in the school cafeteria?	Support	Oppose	Not Sure
Do you feel the recent Spirit Day was a success in terms of raising school spirit?	Success	Not a Success	Not Sure
What grade are you in?	Seventh	Eighth	

Every student in the school completes the survey.

My Notes

MATH TERMS

A **two-way table** is used for identifying each observation, response, etc., in a data set according to two categorical variables.

Categorical variables are used to represent categorical (as opposed to numerical) data.

Greg summarizes the data from his first question using a ***two-way table*** as shown below. It is called a two-way table because each student's response is identified according to two ***categorical variables***.

Do you support the new policy of healthier choices being served in the school cafeteria?

	Support	Oppose	Not Sure	Total
Seventh	111	30	9	150
Eighth	180	55	15	250
Total	291	85	24	400

The table shows that there are 250 eighth graders in the school, and that 291 seventh- and eighth-grade students in the entire student body support the new policy of healthier choices being served in the school cafeteria.

1. What percentage of the seventh graders support the new policy of healthier choices being served in the school cafeteria?

2. What percentage of the eighth graders support the new policy of healthier choices being served in the school cafeteria?

3. **Reason quantitatively.** Are the percentages you computed in Items 1 and 2 similar or very different? From a percentage standpoint, does one grade seem to be much more in favor of the healthier choices being served in the school cafeteria, or are the two groups' percentages about the same in terms of supporting the healthier choices?

A *segmented bar graph* is helpful for visualizing the similarities and differences between groups in a case like this. The first step to making a segmented bar graph involves computing the percentages of each response for each group of interest.

4. In the table below, write the percentages you computed in Items 1 and 2. Also, compute and record the percentages of Oppose and Not Sure for each grade.

Do you support the new policy of healthier choices being served in the school cafeteria?

	Support	Oppose	Not Sure	Total
Seventh				
Eighth				

5. Find the sum of the percentages in each row. These percentages are called *row percentages* (or relative frequencies) because the percentages are relative to each row category.

Based on the row percentages in the table, construct a segmented bar graph.

6. Draw one bar for seventh grade and one bar for eighth grade. What is the total height of each bar?

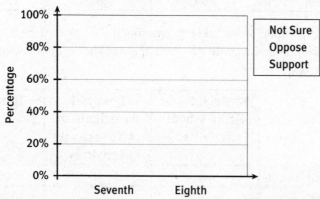

Response Percentage for Seventh and Eighth Graders - Healthier Choices

7. **Model with mathematics.** Use the row percentages for each response to divide each bar into segments.

8. Include a key with your graph to distinguish the segments.

Note that the order of stacking is the same for both the seventh-grade and eighth-grade bars.

MATH TERMS

A **segmented bar graph** compares how two or more groups are divided into categories.

MATH TERMS

In a two-way table, **row percentages** communicate the relative frequencies of column categories within a given row category.

My Notes

CONNECT TO AP

In AP Statistics, you will learn formal methods for testing whether or not the two variables in a two-way table are associated.

Check Your Understanding

9. Does grade level seem to matter in terms of the response percentages?

10. In the analysis of the "healthier options" survey question above, the percentages for each response were fairly similar for each grade. If many seventh graders switched from Support to Oppose, how might the row percentages change, and how might the segmented bar graph above look different? How would the graph remain the same?

LESSON 35-1 PRACTICE

Students at a large middle school were surveyed, and each student responded to a question about after-school activities. The data are given in the two-way table below.

	Participates in After-School Activities	Does Not Participate in After-School Activities	Total
Sixth Grade	160	90	250
Seventh Grade	150	150	300
Eighth Grade	50	150	200
Total	360	390	750

11. Complete the following table by entering the missing percentages for those who do and who do not participate in after-school activities for each grade.

	Participates in After-School Activities	Does Not Participate in After-School Activities	Total
Sixth Grade			100%
Seventh Grade			100%
Eighth Grade			100%

12. How many segments will each bar have?

13. Construct a segmented bar graph for each grade that shows the percentages who do and who do not participate in after-school activities.

14. **Make use of structure.** Do the three grades appear to be different with respect to the percentages that participate in after-school activities?

Learning Targets:

- Understand association between two categorical variables.
- Describe association between two categorical variables.

> **SUGGESTED LEARNING STRATEGIES:** Look for a Pattern, Think-Pair-Share

Like numerical variables, two categorical variables can also exhibit association. For Greg's first survey question regarding the healthier cafeteria menu, there does not appear to be an association between the response and the student's grade level.

For the second survey question regarding the Spirit Day activities, Greg makes another two-way table to summarize the results.

Do you feel the recent Spirit Day was a success in terms of raising school spirit?

	Success	Not a Success	Not Sure	Total
Seventh	96	45	9	150
Eighth	130	109	11	250
Total	226	154	20	400

1. Compute the row percentages for each grade and complete the table below.

Do you feel the recent Spirit Day was a success in terms of raising school spirit?

	Success	Not a Success	Not Sure	Total
Seventh				100%
Eighth				100%

2. Based on your work in Item 1, do you think that there is an association between a student's response and his or her grade level? For example, do you think that a seventh grader is more likely (or less likely) to claim that Spirit Day was a success compared to an eighth grader? Explain your reasoning.

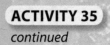

3. Based on the table above, construct a segmented bar graph.

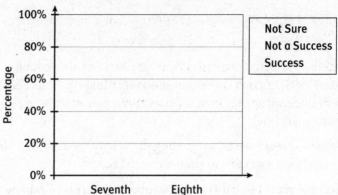

Response Percentage for Seventh and Eighth Graders - Spirit Day

4. Construct viable arguments. Does your graph in Item 3 support your response to Item 2? Explain.

The following information presents the results of a survey where men and women were asked a question to which the only possible answers were Support or Oppose.

In the survey, 44% of men stated they support the new law, while only 28% of women said they support the new law.

5. Make sense of problems. Can you compute the overall percentage of people in the survey who answered Support from this information alone? Explain why or why not.

Check Your Understanding

Write your answers on notebook paper. Show your work.

6. What are two categorical and two numerical variables that describe students at your school?

7. What characteristics of a two-way table and a segmented bar graph can be used to assess if an association exists between two categorical variables? Explain.

LESSON 35-2 PRACTICE

Susan wondered if soccer players have more injuries than students who play football or basketball. She went to the local high school and asked 40 students who play soccer if they had been injured in the last year. She also asked 50 students who play football and 30 students who play basketball. Susan's data are summarized in the table below.

	Injured	Not Injured	Can't Remember	Total
Soccer	8	30		40
Football	12		3	50
Basketball	6		1	30
Total	26	88	6	120

8. Fill in the remaining cells in the table.

9. What percentage of soccer players were injured in the last year? What percentage of football players were injured?

10. Complete the table below by entering the row percentages.

	Injured	Not Injured	Can't Remember	Total
Soccer				100%
Football				100%
Basketball				100%

11. Use the percentages from Item 10 to create a segmented bar graph that compares injuries for each sport.

12. **Make use of structure.** Is there evidence of an association between whether a student is injured and the sport played? Justify your response.

ACTIVITY 35 PRACTICE

1. A football team manager took a team survey regarding where to have the team dinner after the final game of the season. The players play on either offense or defense only, and all players on the team were assigned to an offensive or defensive position.

   Based on the table below, what percentage of defensive players preferred Burger Bungalow?

	Pizza Palace	Burger Bungalow
Offense	23	21
Defense	35	9

   a. 52.3%
   b. 47.7%
   c. 79.5%
   d. 20.5%

One thousand adults were asked about seat belt usage. Gender was also recorded for each person. The data are summarized in the table below.

	Never Use Seat Belt	Sometimes Use Seat Belt	Always Use Seat Belt	Total
Males	50	120	330	500
Females	75	100	325	500
Total	125	220	655	1000

2. What percentage of males always wore seat belts?

3. Complete the following table by calculating row percentages.

	Never Use Seat Belt	Sometimes Use Seat Belt	Always Use Seat Belt	Total
Males				100%
Females				100%

4. Construct a segmented bar graph using the row percentages you calculated in Item 3.

5. Does seat belt use seem to differ for males and females? If so, how does it differ?

6. Is there evidence of an association between gender and seat belt usage? Justify your response.

A class survey at a local college asked students to provide their class level and political party affiliation. Some of the results of this survey are shown in the table below.

	Political Party			
	Democrat	Republican	Other	Total
Freshman	1		1	6
Sophomore	4	8		15
Junior		4	3	12
Senior	3		2	7
Total	13	18	9	40

7. Complete the two-way table.

8. What percentage of sophomores in the class affiliate themselves as "Other"?

9. What percentage of juniors in the class affiliate themselves as "Democrat"?

10. Calculate row percentages to complete the table below.

	Political Party			
	Democrat	Republican	Other	Total
Freshman				100%
Sophomore				100%
Junior				100%
Senior				100%

11. Construct a segmented bar graph using the row percentages you calculated in Item 10.

12. Is there evidence of an association between class level and political party affiliation? Justify your response.

MATHEMATICAL PRACTICES
Create Viable Arguments and Critique the Reasoning of Others

13. Chuck's group is creating a segmented bar graph involving sixth, seventh, and eighth graders. Since there are more seventh graders, Chuck believes the group should begin with the bar representing the seventh grade because that bar will be the tallest. Do you agree or disagree with Chuck? Explain why.

1. After taking a random sample of 12 children from Grade 0 (Kindergarten) through Grade 6, Mr. Mokher and his students collected data on each child's grade level and weight in pounds.

    a. Construct a scatter plot of weight (y-axis) versus grade (x-axis).

    b. Describe the overall association between grade level and weight in pounds in terms of direction, form, and strength. If necessary, identify any observations that substantially deviate from the overall pattern.

    c. Write the equation of a median-median line for this relationship that could be used to predict weight based on grade level. Graph the line on your scatter plot and comment on how well the model seems to fit the data.

    d. Interpret the slope of the median-median line in the context of this problem.

    e. Interpret the y-intercept of the median-median line in the context of this problem.

    f. Using the median-median line, what is the predicted weight of a third grader?

Student	Grade	Weight (lbs.)
1	0	39
2	0	40
3	0	42
4	1	45
5	2	47
6	2	52
7	3	57
8	4	62
9	5	68
10	5	72
11	5	63
12	6	75

2. A survey conducted by the Pew Research Center in April–May 2010 as part of their "Internet & American Life Project" obtained the following results based on a sample of individuals:

Survey Question: Do you use the Internet, at least occasionally?

Age	Yes	No	Total
18–29	1,845	143	1,988
30–49	2,459	1,657	4,116
50–64	937	508	1,445
65 and older	559	810	1,369
Total	5800	3,118	8,918

    a. Calculate the row percentages for each row category above. Then create a table showing the row percentages. Round your percentages to the nearest tenth of a percent.

b. Create a segmented bar graph that compares the Yes and No response percentages for each age group based on the row percentages above. Be sure to include a key.

c. Is there evidence of an association between age and response to the question? Justify your response, referencing your work in parts a and b in your explanation.

Scoring Guide	Exemplary	Proficient	Emerging	Incomplete
	The solution demonstrates these characteristics:			
Mathematics Knowledge and Thinking (Items 1a-f, 2a-c)	• Clear and accurate understanding of scatter plots, median-median lines, and other data displays.	• A functional understanding of scatter plots, median-median lines, and other data displays.	• Partial understanding of scatter plots, median-median lines, and other data displays.	• Little or no understanding of scatter plots, median-median lines, and other data displays.
Problem Solving (Items 1f, 2c)	• Clear and accurate interpretation of data displays to make a prediction and to characterize an association.	• Interpreting data displays to make a prediction and to characterize an association.	• Difficulty making an accurate prediction or characterizing an association using data displays.	• Inaccurate interpretation of data displays.
Mathematical Modeling / Representations (Items 1a, c, 2a-b)	• Clear and accurate understanding of creating tables and graphs from data.	• Creating tables and graphs from data that are mostly correct.	• Errors in creating tables and graphs from data.	• Inaccurate or incomplete tables and graphs
Reasoning and Communication (Items 1b-f, 2c)	• Precise use of appropriate math terms and language to characterize associations in bivariate data.	• Correct characterization of associations in bivariate data.	• Misleading or confusing characterization of associations in bivariate data.	• Incomplete or inaccurate characterization of associations in bivariate data.

Personal Financial Literacy

Unit Overview

Many Americans—both teenagers and adults—do not make responsible financial decisions. Learning to be responsible with money means looking at what you earn compared to what you spend. Learning to invest for future needs is also part of being financially responsible. In this unit, you will discover how to apply your knowledge of mathematics to help you make wise financial decisions both now and in the future. As you study this unit, you will apply what you have learned to real-world issues in saving, borrowing, and planning for a college education.

Key Terms

As you study this unit, add these and other terms to your math notebook. Include in your notes your prior knowledge of each word, as well as your experiences in using the word in different mathematical examples. If needed, ask for help in pronouncing new words and add information on pronunciation to your math notebook. It is important that you learn new terms and use them correctly in your class discussions and in your problem solutions.

Academic Vocabulary

- installment credit
- revolving credit
- principal
- interest
- term
- simple interest
- compound interest

ESSENTIAL QUESTIONS

? Why is regular saving important to your future?

? How can you learn to make financially responsible decisions?

Write your answers on notebook paper.
Show your work.

1. Calculate.
   a. 0.19×980
   b. 0.06×750
   c. 0.055×1800

2. Write each percent as a decimal.
   a. 5.2%
   b. 4.8%
   c. 18.4%
   d. 19.7%

3. Write each decimal as a percent.
   a. 0.046
   b. 0.035
   c. 0.059
   d. 0.195

4. Explain how fractions and decimals are related.

5. Compute. Use what you know about order of operations.
   a. $0.07 \times 840 + 40$
   b. $50 + 8\% \times 720$
   c. $1800 \times 0.197 + 60$
   d. $0.058 \times 920 + 75 + 38$

6. Calculate the percentages.
   a. 46.75% of 850
   b. 79.44% of 1324

7. Divide.
   a. $670 \div 0.05$
   b. $885 \div 0.07$

8. Subtract.
   a. $408.20 - 124.12 - 38.42$
   b. $520.50 - 70.55 - 29.48$
   c. $105.30 - 12.79 - 19.24 - 46.75$

Managing Money

To Charge or Not
Lesson 36-1 The Cost of Borrowing

Learning Targets:

- Analyze the factors that affect the cost of a loan.
- Calculate and compare the costs of different types of loans.
- Explain the advantages and disadvantages of different methods of repayment.

SUGGESTED LEARNING STRATEGIES: Marking the Text, Create Representations

An important part of personal financial literacy is learning how to use credit wisely. Overuse of credit is not good, but at some point most people need to make a large purchase, such as a house or car. That usually involves borrowing money by taking out a loan. Other reasons to borrow include money for college or to start a business.

Whether you are borrowing a small amount or a large one, there are costs to using credit. Two popular types of credit are *installment credit*, which requires set payments, and *revolving credit*, in which payments may vary each month. Personal loans and mortgages are examples of installment credit, while credit card balances are an example of revolving credit. The cost of using credit depends on the amount borrowed, the interest rate, and the length of the loan.

The *principal* (*P*) is the total money borrowed.
Interest rates (*R*) are fixed or variable. A *fixed* rate stays the same for the term of the loan. A *variable* rate changes as other interest rates in the economy change. It can go up or down. Variable rates are often used for home mortgages.
The *term* (*T*) is the length of time for which you borrow the money. Most personal loans have a term of 1 to 5 years. Mortgage loans (for buying a house or condominium) are commonly made for 15, 20, or 30 years.

There are several ways to calculate interest. One is *simple interest*, for which the formula is $I = P \times R \times T$, or $I = PRT$.

ACADEMIC VOCABULARY

An *installment loan* is one in which the borrower makes fixed payments, such as a monthly payment. With *revolving credit*, the amount paid each month can vary based on additional charges, as with a credit card.

ACADEMIC VOCABULARY

The *principal* is the amount of a loan. *Interest* is a percentage of the loan amount paid to the lender in addition to the principal. Interest rates are stated as a percentage. The *term* is the length of the loan, usually stated in months or years. *Simple interest* is paid only on the principal of the loan.

Example A

You want to borrow $800 to take a vacation. You plan to pay the loan back in 6 months. The interest rate is 4.5% per year. What is your total cost?

Step 1: Convert the interest percent to a decimal.   0.045

Step 2: Apply the interest formula. $800 \times 0.045 \times 0.5 = 18$

Step 3: Add the principal and interest. $800 + 18 = 818$

Try These A

a. Calculate the interest on $1200 at 3.9% for a year.
b. What is the principal if you have interest of $75 and a rate of 5%?
c. What is the interest on $2400 at 5.5% for 8 months?

CONNECT TO FINANCE

The Consumer Credit Act of 1968, which is also called the Truth in Lending Act, requires lenders to calculate the Annual Percentage Rate (APR) and any finance charges for a loan so that borrowers can more easily compare the costs of borrowing.

ACADEMIC VOCABULARY

A *compound interest* is one paid on the principal, loan fees, and interest.

If you look at advertisements in local papers, you may see stores offering credit to customers. Some stores do not charge interest if you repay the loan within a specific time, such as in 3 months. This is sometimes advertised as "90 days same as cash." Others may charge interest, which will be stated as a annual rate, such as 3.4 % per year. Lenders check your credit history and whether you are a good credit risk before deciding to give you a loan. If you have a poor credit history, you may have to pay a higher interest rate.

1. **Apply mathematics to everyday life.** You want to buy a large-scree television for $1500 on credit. The interest rate is 4.2%, and you will need to pay off the loan in 6 months.
   a. How much interest will you pay for 6 months if you are paying simple interest?

   b. What will be your monthly payment to repay the loan plus interest?

2. If you changed the term of the loan to 18 months, what is the effect on the interest cost and on your monthly payments?

3. A borrower takes out a loan of $1500 at 6% for one year. But this loan is *compounded* quarterly (every three months). The borrower plans to repay the principal and interest at the end of the year. Part of the table has been filled in. Complete the table to figure out the cost of this loan.

Time	Balance	Interest @ 6%	New Balance
March	1500.00	22.50	1522.50
June	1522.50		
September			
December			

4. Compare the cost of a loan with simple interest to the cost of a loan with compound interest. What do you notice about the differences in the two ways of calculating interest?

Credit cards charge compound interest if you do not pay the full balance each month. Each month's bill includes the balance remaining from the previous bill, interest, and new purchases. (In addition, some cards also charge a yearly fee.) You are required to pay only a minimum amount (about 2% plus any interest and fees) each month. However, paying only the minimum each month is not a wise credit decision, because the interest costs will add up quickly, adding to the cost of your original purchase.

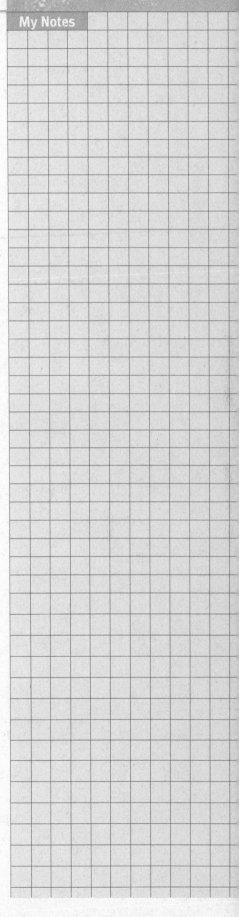

Sample Credit Card Statement			
Bank Name	**Send payments to:** Bank Name, Bank Address		
Account Number 588-421387	**Name** Your Name	**Statement Date** 06/06/xx	**Payment Due Date** 06/27/xx
Previous Balance $288.40	**New Balance** $242.20	**Annual Percentage Rate** 19.8%	**Minimum Payment Due:** $5.00

This Month's Activity:

Transaction Date	Description	Amount
05/12/xx	Payment	−288.40
05/13/xx	Marnie's Gift Shop	58.66
05/20/xx	Pizza Pizza	15.50
06/02/xx	Blue's Department Store	78.82
06/03/xx	Fresh Foods Store	68.22

Statement Summary:		Daily Balance	
Credit Limit	2000.00	− Payments/Credits	288.40
Available Credit	1757.80	**+ Finance Charges**	0
Past Due	0	= New Balance	242.20

An important date on this statement is the payment due date. The credit card company must receive payment by this date or a late fee will be charged. If you write a check, you should mail it several days before the due date to avoid late fees. Late payments also affect your credit record and may make financial institutions wary about giving you a loan or a credit card.

5. What is the minimum payment for this statement?

6. How does this credit card statement show financial responsibility by the credit card holder? Explain your reasoning.

7. Assume you have a credit card balance of $954.96. The minimum payment due is $21.20. What balance will be carried over to the next month's statement?

8. If you pay only the minimum on the balance in Item 7 each month and do not make additional charges, how long will it take you to pay off the balance? Assume an 18% annual percentage rate (APR) and a minimum monthly payment of 2% of the balance plus interest. Create a table to show the interest and each monthly payment.

My Notes

9. Analyze the situation in Item 8 in terms of financial responsibility. What is the most responsible decision you could make in this case? The least responsible?

10. What are the benefits of being financially responsible? What are the costs of financial irresponsibility?

Credit cards and personal loans are a form of short-term borrowing. People also borrow for much longer periods of time of buy cars or homes. Like credit cards, the interest rates are stated as annual percentage rates (APR). The APR includes both the interest and any fees and costs added to the amount of the principal. For example, home mortgage loans have application fees and other costs in addition to the amount of the principal.

APRs give borrowers the true cost of borrowing because they include all the costs related to the loan. Comparing the APRs of different lenders allows borrowers to compare the true costs of a loan and to select the one with the lowest cost. Lenders are required to calculate a loan's APR and provide borrowers with that information.

You can also use free online calculators to enter the amount you want to borrow, the term, and the interest rate. These online calculators will determine the monthly payments you need to make to repay the loan. A number of websites provide an online calculator. The online calculator includes tools that let you check the costs of loans at different rates and terms. An example is www.thecalculatorsite.com. Your teacher may suggest others, or you may search for online loan calculators. Some sites have specific calculators for loan repayments, car loans, and credit card payments.

11. **Select and use tools.** Use an online calculator to calculate the monthly payments and total cost of these cases.
    a. $5500 car loan for two years at 4% interest

    b. $4000 loan for four years at 6% interest compounded quarterly with an extra yearly payment of $50

    c. Months to pay off a credit card balance of $2,485 and total interest paid at 19% APR with monthly payments of $40

My Notes

You can pay for purchases with cash or different forms of credit. The advantage of cash is lower cost because you pay no interest. The disadvantage is that you may need a repair, for example, and not have the cash to pay for it. Credit allows you to buy items and pay for them over time. Disadvantages are the interest cost if balances are not paid off each month and buying more than you can afford. Late payments or non-payments also affect your ability to get credit.

12. Identify when you would use cash and credit for purchases. Explain each method and why it is an advantage or disadvantage in the situation.

Check Your Understanding

13. Both the interest rate and the loan length affect the cost of borrowing. Use online calculators as needed for the following calculations.
    a. You borrow $3000 for five years (60 months) at an interest rate of 6%. If you make monthly payments of $58, what is the total cost of your loan?
    b. You borrow $3000 for five years at an interest rate of 8.5%. Your monthly payments are $61.55. What is the total cost of this loan?
    c. You borrow $3000 for three years at an interest rate of 6%. Your monthly payments are $91.27. How does the term affect the total cost of your loan?

14. Explain how interest rate and the term of the loan affect the cost of credit.

15. Write an explanation of the cost of using credit irresponsibly.

LESSON 36-1 PRACTICE

16. Compare how simple interest and compound interest affect the total interest on a loan.

17. Identify and explain the advantages and disadvantages of different methods of paying for purchases.

18. **Use a problem-solving model.** You borrow $2500 for five years (60 months) at an interest rate of 5%. Your monthly payment is $47.18.
    a. What will be the total cost of your loan?
    b. You borrow $2500 for three years (36 months) at the same 5% interest rate. Now your monthly payment is $74.93. What will be the total cost of this loan?

19. Your credit card statement has a balance of $295.60.
    a. What would the minimum payment be at 18% interest?
    b. How much would you pay if you pay the full balance by the due date?
    c. Think about this situation with a much larger debt, such as a credit card balance of $12,800. How would paying a larger amount each month affect the total interest paid and the length of time to pay off the balance? What would be financially responsible?

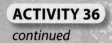

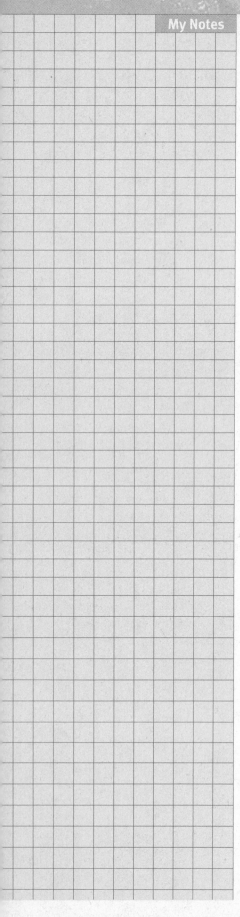

My Notes

Learning Targets:

- Compare simple and compound interest and how they affect savers and borrowers.
- Explain the importance of regular saving for the future.
- Outline a financial plan to pay for college.

> **SUGGESTED LEARNING STRATEGIES:** Marking the Text, Create a Plan, Graphic Organizer

In the previous lesson, you used simple interest to calculate the cost of using credit. Interest is also paid on savings accounts. You might save money through a savings account, through investments in the stock market, or through investments in college savings accounts.

If a bank quotes a rate of 4 percent on a savings account, then money in the account is earning interest at a rate of 4 percent per year. Most banks, though, use a compound rate, which means that they add the interest to savings several times a year.

Example A

You have a savings account with $400 in it. The account earns 3.5% per year. The bank compounds—that is, adds the interest—4 times a year.

Step 1: Calculate the simple interest on $400. $I = 400 \times .035 \times 1 = 14$

Step 2: For the first quarter, divide $14 by 4. $14 \div 4 = 3.50$

Step 3: Add the principal and interest. $400 + 3.50 = 403.50$

Step 4: Calculate interest on the new principal. $403.50 \times .035 = 14.12$

With compounding, the interest on your savings also earns interest throughout the year. The more frequent the compounding, the more interest you earn.

Try These A

a. Calculate the simple interest for a year on $5000 invested at 4.5%.
b. Calculate the compound interest on $5000 invested at 4.5% when the interest is compounded each quarter.
c. How does compounding interest benefit a saver?

Although you must be at least 16 or 18 years old to have your own checking account, you can start a savings account at any age.

Whether you are borrowing or saving, two things are true:

- Simple interest grows slowly.
- Compound interest can grow much faster, depending on how often the interest is compounded. Interest is often compounded monthly, quarterly, or semiannually.

Compound interest makes borrowing expensive, but it works in your favor when you save over a long period of time. Saving or investing even small amounts of money over time can build up a sizable amount of money for your future.

1. Suppose you start saving for college by putting some of your allowance and money earned from chores into a savings account. If you save $15 a month for 5 years, how much money would you have if your account earns simple interest of 4% per year?

2. What conclusions can you draw about the advantages of saving a specific amount of money each month?

3. You have decided to save $40 every month, starting at the beginning of the year. The account carries a 4% interest rate, compounded twice a year. Complete the table to find savings and interest for two years. (Remember that interest is 4% per year, not 4% per 6 months.)

Year	Deposit	Balance	Interest	Total
[1] June	$240 ($40 × 6)	$240	$4.80	$244.80
[1] December	$240	$484.80	$9.70	
[2] June	$240			
[2] December	$240			

For long-term savings, most people look for a savings account that pays compound interest. When calculating compound interest over several years, it is easier to use an online interest calculator. An example of such a calculator may be found at www.thecalculatorsite.com. Choosing the compound interest calculator at that website will allow you to experiment with different savings plans. You will need to enter the following information:

- *Base amount*: This amount is the beginning savings you have when you open a savings account, for example, $100. If you are starting with no savings, enter 0.
- *Annual interest rate*: Put in the interest rate offered by a local bank or other financial institution.
- *Calculation period*: This number is the number of years you plan to save. The default is years, but you can also change this to months.
- *Regular monthly deposit*: This number is the amount you plan to deposit in your savings account each month.
- *Compounding interval*: This space allows you to enter the frequency of compounding, whether daily, monthly, quarterly, half yearly, or yearly.

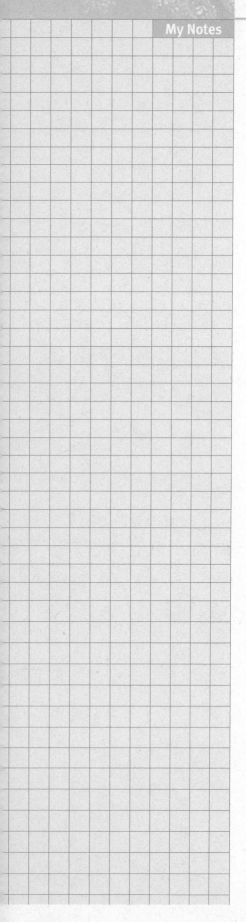

My Notes

4. Use the online interest calculator to evaluate long-term savings plans.

  a. If you save $20 per month for 10 years at 4.5% compounded quarterly, how much will you have at the end of 10 years?

  b. If you change your monthly savings to $40, how much would you have at the end of 10 years?

  c. Change the number of years to 15, and recalculate the savings.

Saving for college or for retirement are long-term goals for many people. To help determine a savings plan, it is important to know approximately what your college costs will be or the amount of money you will need for retirement. Both require regular savings and wise money management.

You may be interested in saving for college. Keep in mind that most people also use other ways than just savings for paying college costs, such as student loans, work-study programs, and grants and scholarships.

5. Create and use representations. Choose three schools you think you might like to attend. Choose one two-year school, such as a community college, and two different kinds of four-year schools—a public, state-supported university and a private college or university. Remember in choosing public schools that costs will be different for in-state students (meaning you are a resident of the state) versus out-of-state students.

  a. Research (online or in person) the estimated costs for tuition, room and board, and other expenses at each of the three schools. Then make a plan for at least your first year.

  b. Discuss with your family the kind of financial help they can give. You might suggest that you both begin a savings plan now, if you have not already done so. Estimate the amount of family contribution and create a plan for saving that amount.

Research Tip: If you are researching online, the College Board has information that you may find useful in estimating costs. Remember that the costs listed at this site are averages. The costs for the specific schools that you may want to attend will vary.

See https://bigfuture.collegeboard.org/pay-for-college/college-costs/college-costs-faqs

c. Create a chart similar to this to record costs and possible savings.

COSTS	Tuition	Room/board	Other/fees	Totals
Two-year college				
Public university				
Private college				

SAVINGS PLAN	Weekly	Monthly	Yearly	
Mine				
Family or other				

OTHER INCOME				
Grants/scholarships				
Work-study jobs				
Student loans				

Check Your Understanding

6. Explain how simple and compound interest are calculated.

7. Explain how saving even small amounts each month can build to substantial amounts over a period of years.

8. What items should you include in making a plan for your education?

LESSON 36-2 PRACTICE

9. If you save $50 a month, but keep it in cash or a box in your house, how much will you have at the end of three years?

10. If you save $50 a month in a savings account that pays simple interest of 2%, what will your balance be at the end of one year?

11. **Select and use tools.** If you save $50 a month in a bank savings account that pays 2%, compounded semiannually (twice a year), how much will you have at the end of three years? Use an online calculator.

12. Calculate the simple interest on a one-year loan for $1800 at 4.4%.

13. **Communicate mathematical ideas.** In Items 9–11, which approach would be the most financially responsible? Explain your reasoning and give examples to support it.

14. Who benefits most from compound interest?
    - **A.** borrowers
    - **B.** savers
    - **C.** lenders
    - **D.** both b and c

ACTIVITY 36 PRACTICE

1. What factors influence the cost of a loan to a borrower?

2. Calculate simple interest on a loan of $4500 at a rate of 5.5% for 6 months.

3. You borrow $3000 for five years (60 months) at a simple interest rate of 4%. Your monthly payment is $55.25.
   a. What will be the total cost of your loan?
   b. You borrow $3000 for three years (36 months) at the same 4% interest rate. Now your monthly payment is $88.57. What will be the total cost of this loan?
   c. Which factor made the most difference in the cost of this loan?

4. Explain the difference between simple and compound interest.

5. Who benefits most from compound interest—lenders, borrowers, or savers? Explain.

6. Complete this table to calculate the interest on an account of $1,000 at 6% interest compounded quarterly for two years with no additional deposits. How much will this saver have earned at the end of two years?

Year	Balance	Interest @ 6%	New Balance
[1] March	1000	15	1015
June	1015	15.23	1030.23
September			
December			
[2] March			
June			
September			
December			

7. Describe the different methods you might use to pay for purchases, and explain the advantages and disadvantages of each.

8. Give an example of being financially responsible and describe the benefits. Give an example of being financially irresponsible and describe the potential costs.

MATHEMATICAL PRACTICES
Use a Problem-Solving Model

9. Assume that you will need some savings to attend a college of your choice. Estimate the costs and create different savings plans to reach a savings goal for each of these situations.
   a. Two-year public college with annual tuition and fees of $2,713. Books and supplies are $1,133. Assume living at home rather than in a dorm or apartment. Transportation to and from school will be $1,500 a year.
   b. Four-year public college with annual tuition of $7,605 plus books and supplies of $1,200 per year. Assume living at home and transportation costs of $1,500 per year.
   c. Determine how much more you would need to save for college if you added a cost for room and board of $7,500 per year.

Symbols

$<$	is less than
$>$	is greater than
$\leq$	is less than or equal to
$\geq$	is greater than or equal to
$=$	is equal to
$\neq$	is not equal to
$\approx$	is approximately equal to
$\lvert a \rvert$	absolute value: $\lvert 3 \rvert = 3$; $\lvert -3 \rvert = 3$
$\sqrt{}$	square root
$\%$	percent
$\perp$	perpendicular
$\parallel$	parallel
(x, y)	ordered pair
$\overset{\frown}{AB}$	arc AB
$\overleftrightarrow{AB}$	line AB
$\overrightarrow{AB}$	ray AB
$\overline{AB}$	line segment AB
$\angle A$	angle A
$m\angle A$	measure of angle A
$\triangle ABC$	triangle ABC
π	pi; $\pi \approx 3.14$; $\pi \approx \dfrac{22}{7}$

Formulas

Perimeter	
P	= sum of the lengths of the sides
Rectangle	$P = 2l + 2w$
Square	$P = 4s$
Circumference	$C = 2\pi r$

Area	
Circle	$A = \pi r^2$
Parallelogram	$A = bh$
Rectangle	$A = lw$
Square	$A = s^2$
Triangle	$A = \frac{1}{2}bh$
Trapezoid	$A = \frac{1}{2}h(b_1 + b_2)$

Surface Area	
Cube	$SA = 6e^2$
Rectangular Prism	$SA = 2lw + 2lh + 2wh$
Cylinder	$SA = 2\pi r^2 + 2\pi rh$
Cone	$SA = \pi r^2 + \pi rl$
Regular Pyramid	$SA = B + \frac{1}{2}pl$
Sphere	$SA = 4\pi r^2$

Volume

Cylinder	$V = Bh, B = \pi r^2$
Rectangular Prism	$V = lwh$
Triangular Prism	$V = Bh, B = \frac{1}{2}bh$
Pyramid	$V = \frac{1}{3}Bh$
Cone	$V = \frac{1}{3}\pi r^2 h$
Sphere	$V = \frac{4}{3}\pi r^3$

Linear function

Slope	$m = \dfrac{y_2 - y_1}{x_2 - x_1}$
Slope-intercept form	$y = mx + b$
Point-slope form	$y - y_1 = m(x - x_1)$
Standard form	$Ax + By = C$

Quadratic Equations

Standard Form	$ax^2 + bx + c = 0$
Quadratic Formula	$x = \dfrac{-b \pm \sqrt{b^2 - 4ac}}{2a}$

Other Formulas

Pythagorean Theorem	$a^2 + b^2 = c^2$, where c is the hypotenuse of a right triangle
Distance	$d = \sqrt{(x_2 - x_1)^2 + (y_2 - y_1)^2}$
Direct variation	$y = kx$
Inverse variation	$y = \dfrac{k}{x}$

Temperature

Celsius	$C = \frac{5}{9}(F - 32)$
Fahrenheit	$F = \frac{9}{5}C + 32$

Properties of Real Numbers

Reflexive Property of Equality	For all real numbers a, $a = a$.
Symmetric Property of Equality	For all real numbers a and b, if $a = b$, then $b = a$.
Transitive Property of Equality	For all real numbers a, b, and c, if $a = b$ and $b = c$, then $a = c$.
Substitution Property of Equality	For all real numbers a and b, if $a = b$, then a may be replaced by b.
Additive Identity	For all real numbers a, $a + 0 = 0 + a = a$.
Multiplicative Identity	For all real numbers a, $a \cdot 1 = 1 \cdot a = a$.
Commutative Property of Addition	For all real numbers a and b, $a + b = b + a$.
Commutative Property of Multiplication	For all real numbers a and b, $a \cdot b = b \cdot a$.
Associative Property of Addition	For all real numbers a, b, and c, $(a + b) + c = a + (b + c)$.
Associative Property of Multiplication	For all real numbers a, b, and c, $(a \cdot b) \cdot c = a \cdot (b \cdot c)$.
Distributive Property of Multiplication over Addition	For all real numbers a, b, and c, $a(b + c) = a \cdot b + a \cdot c$.
Additive Inverse	For all real numbers a, there is exactly one real number $-a$ such that $a + (-a) = 0$ and $(-a) + a = 0$.
Multiplicative Inverse	For all real numbers a and b where $a \neq 0$, $b \neq 0$, there is exactly one number $\frac{b}{a}$ such that $\frac{b}{a} \cdot \frac{a}{b} = 1$ and $\frac{a}{b} \cdot \frac{b}{a} = 1$.
Multiplication Property of Zero	For all real numbers a, $a \cdot 0 = 0$ and $0 \cdot a = 0$.
Addition Property of Equality	For all real numbers a, b, and c, if $a = b$, then $a + c = b + c$.
Subtraction Property of Equality	For all real numbers a, b, and c, if $a = b$, then $a - c = b - c$.
Multiplication Property of Equality	For all real numbers a, b, and c, if $a = b$, then $a \cdot c = b \cdot c$.
Division Property of Equality	For all real numbers a, b, and c, $c \neq 0$ if $a = b$, then $\frac{a}{c} = \frac{b}{c}$.
Zero Product Property of Equality	For all real numbers a and b, if $a \cdot b = 0$ then $a = 0$ or $b = 0$ or both a and b equal 0.
Addition Property of Inequality*	For all real numbers a, b, and c, if $a > b$, then $a + c > b + c$.
Subtraction Property of Inequality*	For all real numbers a, b, and c, if $a > b$, then $a - c > b - c$.
Multiplication Property of Inequality *	For all real numbers a, b, and c, $c > 0$, if $a > b$, then $a \cdot c > b \cdot c$. For all real numbers a, b, and c, $c < 0$, if $a > b$, then $a \cdot c < b \cdot c$.
Division Property of Inequality*	For all real numbers a, b, and c, $c > 0$ if $a > b$, then $\frac{a}{c} > \frac{b}{c}$.
	For all real numbers a, b, and c, $c < 0$ if $a > b$, then $\frac{a}{c} < \frac{b}{c}$.

*These properties are also true for $<$, $\leq$, $\geq$.

Table of Measures

Customary	Metric
Distance/Length 1 foot (ft) = 12 inches (in.) 1 yard (yd) = 3 feet (ft) = 36 inches (in.) 1 mile (mi) = 5280 feet (ft)	1 centimeter (cm) = 10 millimeters (mm) 1 meter (m) = 100 centimeters (cm) 1 kilometer (km) = 1000 meters (m)
Volume 1 cup (c) = 8 fluid ounces (fl oz) 1 pint (pt) = 2 cups (c) 1 quart (qt) = 2 pints (pt) 1 gallon (gal) = 4 quarts (qt)	1 liter (L) = 1000 milliliters (mL)
Weight/Mass 1 pound (lb) = 16 ounces (oz)	1 gram (g) = 1000 milligrams (mg) 1 kilogram (kg) = 1000 grams (g)
Time 1 minute (min) = 60 seconds (sec) 1 hour (hr) = 60 minutes (min) 1 day (d) = 24 hours (hr) 1 week (wk) = 7 days (d)	1 year (yr) = 365 days (d) 1 year (yr) = 52 weeks (wk) 1 year (yr) = 12 months (mo)

SpringBoard Learning Strategies

READING STRATEGIES

STRATEGY	DEFINITION	PURPOSE
Activating Prior Knowledge	Recalling what is known about a concept and using that information to make a connection to a new concept	Helps students establish connections between what they already know and how that knowledge is related to new learning
Chunking the Activity	Grouping a set of items/questions for specific purposes	Provides an opportunity to relate concepts and assess student understanding before moving on to a new concept or grouping
Close Reading	Reading text word for word, sentence by sentence, and line by line to make a detailed analysis of meaning	Assists in developing a comprehensive understanding of the text
Graphic Organizer	Arranging information into maps and charts	Builds comprehension and facilitates discussion by representing information in visual form
Interactive Word Wall	Visually displaying vocabulary words to serve as a classroom reference of words and groups of words as they are introduced, used, and mastered over the course of a year	Provides a visual reference for new concepts, aids understanding for reading and writing, and builds word knowledge and awareness
KWL Chart (Know, Want to Know, Learn)	Activating prior knowledge by identifying what students know, determining what they want to learn, and having them reflect on what they learned	Assists in organizing information and reflecting on learning to build content knowledge and increase comprehension
Marking the Text	Highlighting, underlining, and /or annotating text to focus on key information to help understand the text or solve the problem	Helps the reader identify important information in the text and make notes about the interpretation of tasks required and concepts to apply to reach a solution
Predict and Confirm	Making conjectures about what results will develop in an activity; confirming or modifying the conjectures based on outcomes	Stimulates thinking by making, checking, and correcting predictions based on evidence from the outcome
Levels of Questions	Developing literal, interpretive, and universal questions about the text while reading the text	Focuses reading, helps in gaining insight into the text by seeking answers, and prepares one for group and class discussions
Paraphrasing	Restating in your own words the essential information in a text or problem description	Assists with comprehension, recall of information, and problem solving
Role Play	Assuming the role of a character in a scenario	Helps interpret and visualize information in a problem
Shared Reading	Reading the text aloud (usually by the teacher) as students follow along silently, or reading a text aloud by the teacher and students	Helps auditory learners do decode, interpret, and analyze challenging text
Summarizing	Giving a brief statement of the main points in a text	Assists with comprehension and provides practice with identifying and restating key information
Think Aloud	Talking through a difficult text or problem by describing what the text means	Helps in comprehending the text, understanding the components of a problem, and thinking about possible paths to a solution
Visualization	Picturing (mentally and/or literally) what is read in the text	Increases reading comprehension and promotes active engagement with the text
Vocabulary Organizer	Using a graphic organizer to keep an ongoing record of vocabulary words with definitions, pictures, notes, and connections between words	Supports a systematic process of learning vocabulary

SpringBoard Learning Strategies
COLLABORATIVE STRATEGIES

STRATEGY	DEFINITION	PURPOSE
Critique Reasoning	Through collaborative discussion, respond to the arguments of others; question the use of mathematical terminology, assumptions, and conjectures to improve understanding and to justify and communicate conclusions	Helps students learn from each other as they make connections between mathematical concepts and learn to verbalize their understanding and support their arguments with reasoning and data that make sense to peers
Debriefing	Discussing the understanding of a concept to lead to consensus on its meaning	Helps clarify misconceptions and deepen understanding of content
Discussion Groups	Working within groups to discuss content, to create problem solutions, and to explain and justify a solution	Aids understanding through the sharing of ideas, interpretation of concepts, and analysis of problem scenarios
Group Presentation	Presenting information as a collaborative group	Allows opportunities to present collaborative solutions and to share responsibility for delivering information to an audience
Jigsaw	Reading different texts or passages, students become "experts" and then move to a new group to share their information; after sharing, students go back to the original group to share new knowledge	Provides opportunities to summarize and present information to others in a way that facilitates understanding of a text or passage (or multiple texts or passages) without having each student read all texts
Sharing and Responding	Communicating with another person or a small group of peers who respond to a piece of writing or proposed problem solution	Gives students the opportunity to discuss their work with peers, to make suggestions for improvement to the work of others, and/or to receive appropriate and relevant feedback on their own work
Think-Pair-Share	Thinking through a problem alone, pairing with a partner to share ideas, and concluding by sharing results with the class	Enables the development of initial ideas that are then tested with a partner in preparation for revising ideas and sharing them with a larger group

WRITING STRATEGIES

Drafting	Writing a text in an initial form	Assists in getting first thoughts in written form and ready for revising and refining
Note Taking	Creating a record of information while reading a text or listening to a speaker	Helps in organizing ideas and processing information
Prewriting	Brainstorming, either alone or in groups, and refining thoughts and organizing ideas prior to writing	Provides a tool for beginning the writing process and determining the focus of the writing
Quickwrite	Writing for a short, specific amount of time about a designated topic	Helps generate ideas in a short time
RAFT (Role of Writer, Audience, Format, and Topic)	Writing a text by consciously choosing a viewpoint (role of the writer), identifying an audience, choosing a format for the writing, and choosing a topic	Provides a framework for communicating in writing and helps focus the writer's ideas for specific points of communication
Self Revision / Peer Revision	Working alone or with a partner to examine a piece of writing for accuracy and clarity	Provides an opportunity to review work and to edit it for clarity of the ideas presented as well as accuracy of grammar, punctuation, and spelling

SpringBoard Learning Strategies
PROBLEM-SOLVING STRATEGIES

Construct an Argument	Use mathematical reasoning to present assumptions about mathematical situations, support conjectures with mathematically relevant and accurate data, and provide a logical progression of ideas leading to a conclusion that makes sense	Helps develop the process of evaluating mathematical information, developing reasoning skills, and enhancing communication skills in supporting conjectures and conclusions
Create a Plan	Analyzing the tasks in a problem and creating a process for completing the tasks by finding information needed for the tasks, interpreting data, choosing how to solve a problem, communicating the results, and verifying accuracy	Assists in breaking tasks into smaller parts and identifying the steps needed to complete the entire task
Create Representations	Creating pictures, tables, graphs, lists, equations, models, and /or verbal expressions to interpret text or data	Helps organize information using multiple ways to present data and to answer a question or show a problem solution
Guess and Check	Guessing the solution to a problem, and then checking that the guess fits the information in the problem and is an accurate solution	Allows exploration of different ways to solve a problem; guess and check may be used when other strategies for solving are not obvious
Identify a Subtask	Breaking a problem into smaller pieces whose outcomes lead to a solution	Helps to organize the pieces of a complex problem and reach a complete solution
Look for a Pattern	Observing information or creating visual representations to find a trend	Helps to identify patterns that may be used to make predictions
Simplify the Problem	Using "friendlier" numbers to solve a problem	Provides insight into the problem or the strategies needed to solve the problem
Work Backward	Tracing a possible answer back through the solution process to the starting point	Provides another way to check possible answers for accuracy
Use Manipulatives	Using objects to examine relationships between the information given	Provides a visual representation of data that supports comprehension of information in a problem

Glossary
Glosario

A

absolute value (p. 12)   The distance of a number from zero on a number line. Distance or absolute value is always positive. For example, the absolute value of both −6 and 6 is 6.

valor absoluto (pág. 12)   Distancia entre un número y el cero en una recta numérica. La distancia o valor absoluto es siempre positivo. Por ejemplo, el valor absoluto tanto de −6 como de 6 es 6.

alternate (p. 211)   As a verb, the word alternate means to shift back and forth between one state and another.

alternar (pág. 211)   Como verbo, la palabra *alternar* significa cambiar sucesivamente de un estado a otro.

alternate exterior angles (p. 211)   A pair of angles that are formed by two lines and a transversal and that are outside the two lines and on opposite sides of the transversal. When the two lines crossed by a transversal are parallel, the alternate exterior angles are congruent.

ángulos alternos externos (pág. 211)   Par de ángulos formados por dos rectas y una transversal y que están fuera de las dos rectas y en lados opuestos de la transversal. Cuando las dos rectas cruzadas por una transversal son paralelas, los ángulos alternos externos son congruentes.

alternate interior angles (p. 211)   A pair of angles that are formed by two lines and a transversal and that are inside the two lines and on opposite sides of the transversal. When the two lines crossed by a transversal are parallel, the alternate interior angles are congruent.

ángulos alternos internos (pág. 211)   Par de ángulos formados por dos rectas y una transversal y que están dentro de las dos rectas y en lados opuestos de la transversal. Cuando las dos rectas cruzadas por una transversal son paralelas, los ángulos alternos internos son congruentes.

angle (p. 204)   The union of two rays with a common endpoint.

ángulo (pág. 204)   Unión de dos rayos con un extremo en común.

association (p. 446)   A collection of data points has a *positive association* if it has the property that y tends to increase as x increases. It has a *negative association* if y tends to decrease as x increases. An association is also known as a **correlation.**

correlación (pág. 446)   Una colección de datos tiene una *correlación positiva* si tiene la propiedad de que y tiende a aumentar a medida que x aumenta y tiene una *correlación negativa* si y tiende a disminuir a medida que x aumenta. Una correlación también se conoce como **asociación.**

B

bivariate data (p. 456)   Data that can be written as ordered pairs, where each numerical quantity represents measurement information recorded about a particular subject.

datos bivariados (pág. 456)   Datos que pueden escribirse como pares ordenados, donde cada cantidad numérica representa información de las medidas registradas acerca de un tema en particular.

C

categorical variable (p. 478)   A variable that describes an attribute; gender and eye color are examples of categorical data.

variable categórica (pág. 478)   Variable que describe un atributo; el género y el color de los ojos son ejemplos de datos categóricos.

center of dilation (p. 281, 287)   A fixed point in the plane about which all points are expanded or reduced. It is the only point under a dilation that does not move.

centro de una dilatación (págs. 281, 287)   Un punto fijo en el plano a partir del cual todos los demás puntos se dilatan positiva o negativamente. Es el único punto que no se mueve en una dilatación.

center of rotation (p. 241)   The fixed point around which a figure is rotated, or turned. The preimage point and the image points are all equidistant from the origin.

punto de rotación (pág. 241)   El punto fijo alrededor del cual gira o rota una figura. Los puntos de la imagen original y de la imagen rotada están a la misma distancia del origen.

cluster (p. 450)   In statistics, a group in which the points (or data) are dense and have small spaces between them.

cluster (pág. 450)   En estadística, un grupo de puntos (o datos) con alta densidad y pequeños espacios entre sí.

coefficient (p. 148)   A number by which a variable is multiplied. For example, in the term 6x, 6 is the coefficient.

coeficiente (pág. 148)   Número por el cual se multiplica una variable. Por ejemplo, en el término 6x, 6 es el coeficiente.

coincide (p. 184, 231)   To occur at the same time or to occupy the same place in space or time.

coincidir (págs. 184, 231)   Ocurrir al mismo tiempo y/u ocupar el mismo lugar en tiempo o espacio.

complementary angles (p. 204)   Two angles whose measures have a sum of 90°.

ángulos complementarios (pág. 204)   Dos ángulos cuyas medidas suman 90º.

composite solid (p. 348)   A solid that consists of two or more simpler solids, such as prisms, pyramids, cylinders, cones, or hemispheres.

cuerpo geométrico compuesto (pág. 348)   Un cuerpo geométrico formado por dos o más cuerpos geométricos más simples, como prismas, pirámides, cilindros, conos o hemisferios.

composition of transformations (p. 252)   The result of performing two or more transformations on a figure.

composición de transformaciones (pág. 252)   El resultado de realizar dos o más transformaciones a una figura.

compound interest (p. 490)   Interest calculated on the total principal plus the interest earned or owed during the previous time period.

interés compuesto (pág. 490)   Interés calculado sobre el capital total más el interés devengado o adeudado durante el período anterior.

congruent (p. 207)   When two or more figures are the same shape and size, they are congruent.

congruentes (pág. 207)   Cuando dos o más figuras tienen la misma forma y el mismo tamaño, son congruentes.

congruent figures (p. 249)   Figures that have corresponding angles as well as corresponding sides.

figuras congruentes (pág. 249)   Figuras cuyos ángulos y y lados correspondientes son congruentes.

conjecture (p. 4)   An unproved statement that seems to be true.

conjetura (pág. 4)   Enunciado no demostrado que parece ser verdadero.

consecutive terms (p. 107)   Terms that follow one after the other in a sequence.

términos consecutivos (pág. 107)   Términos que van uno a continuación el otro en una secuencia.

constant difference (p. 107)   The difference between successive terms in a sequence.

diferencia constante (pág. 107)   La diferencia entre dos términos sucesivos de una sucesión.

constant term (p. 148)   A term in an expression that does not change in value because it does not contain a variable. For example, the constant term in the expression $3n + 6$ is 6.

término constante (pág. 148)   Término cuyo valor no cambia en una expresión, pues no contiene variables. Por ejemplo, el término constante en la expresión $3n + 6$ es 6.

continuous data (p. 148, 372)   A set of data with no breaks in its domain or range; the graph of a continuous data has no holes or gaps.

datos continuos (págs. 148, 372)   Conjunto de datos sin interrupciones en su dominio o rango; la gráfica de los datos continuos no tiene espacios vacíos ni brechas.

corresponding angles (p. 212)   A pair of nonadjacent angles that are formed by two lines and a transversal such that the angles are on the same side of the transversal and one of the angles is outside the two lines while the other angle is between the two lines. When the two lines crossed by a transversal are parallel, the corresponding angles are congruent.

ángulos correspondientes (pág. 212)   Par de ángulos no adyacentes formados por dos rectas y una transversal y que están al mismo lado de la transversal, con uno de los ángulos fuera de las dos rectas y el otro ángulo entre las dos rectas. Cuando las dos rectas cruzadas por una transversal son paralelas, los ángulos correspondientes son congruentes.

cube root (p. 39)   The cube root of a number, n, is the number that when used as a factor three times gives a product of n.

raíz cúbica (pág. 39)   La raíz cúbica de un número n, es el número que usado tres veces como factor da un producto de n.

cubing a number (p. 39)   Raising a number to the third power.

elevar un número al cubo (pág. 39)   Elevar un número a la tercera potencia.

D

deviate (p. 450)   To stray or depart from an established course or to digress from a line of thought or reasoning.

desviar (pág. 450)   Alejar o apartar del rumbo establecido o apartar un pensamiento o razonamiento de una línea de pensamiento.

diagonal (p. 225)   A line segment connecting two nonconsecutive vertices of a polygon.

diagonal (pág. 225)   Segmento de recta que conecta dos vértices no consecutivos de un polígono.

dilation (p. 281, 286)   A transformation in which the image is similar (but not congruent) to the pre-image.

dilatación (págs. 281, 286)   Transformación en la que la imagen es semejante (pero no congruente) a la preimagen.

direct variation (p. 166)   A relationship between two variables x and y such that $y = kx$, where k is any constant other than zero.

variación directa (pág. 166)   Relación entre dos variables x e y, tal que $y = kx$, donde k es cualquier constante distinta de cero.

discrete data (p. 148, 372)   A set of data with a finite number of data values; the graph of discrete data shows as a individual points on a number line or coordinate plane.

datos discretos (págs. 148, 372)   Conjunto de datos con un número finito de valores; la gráfica de datos discretos muestra puntos individuales sobre una recta numérica o plano de coordenadas.

distributive property (p. 122)   The property that states that the result of multiplying a number by the sum of two numbers is the same as the result of multiplying each addend by the number; for example, $4 \times (3 + 5) = (4 \times 3) + (4 \times 5)$.

propiedad distributiva (pág. 122)   Propiedad que establece que el resultado de multiplicar un número por la suma de dos números es igual al resultado de multiplicar cada sumando por el número y luego sumar los productos; por ejemplo, $4 \times (3 + 5) = (4 \times 3) + (4 \times 5)$.

domain (p. 366)   The set of all input values for a relation or function.

dominio (pág. 366)   Conjunto de todos los valores de entrada de una relación o función.

E

enlargement (p. 286)   If $k > 1$, then the image will be larger than the original figure, and dilation is called an enlargement.

ampliación (pág. 286)   Si $k > 1$, entonces la imagen será más grande que la figura original y la dilatación se llama ampliación o dilatación positiva.

equidistant (p. 238)   To be the same distance from a given point or line.

equidistante (pág. 238)   Que está a la misma distancia de una línea o un punto dado.

evaluate (p. 106)   To substitute a given value or values for a variable and simplify.

evaluar (pág. 106)   Reemplazar una variable por un valor o valores dados, y luego simplificar.

exponent (p. 35)   A number that tells how many times another number, called the base, is used as a factor.

exponente (pág. 35)   Un número que expresa las veces que otero número, llamado base, se utiliza como factor.

exponential form (p. 35)   A number written with a base and an exponent. In an expression in exponential form, b^x, b is the base and x is the exponent.

forma exponencial (pág. 35)   Número que se escribe con una base y un exponente. En una expresión en forma exponencial, b^x, b es la base y x es el exponente.

expression (p. 106)   A mathematical phrase that uses numbers, or variables, or both, such as $4 + 3$ or $6n$.

expresión (pág. 106)   Frase matemática que usa números o variables, o ambos, como $4 + 3$ ó $6n$.

exterior angle (p. 223)   The angle formed by extending a side of a triangle.

ángulo exterior (pág. 223)   Ángulo formado al extender un lado de un triángulo.

F

function (p. 359, 362)   A relation that pairs each element of the domain with exactly one element of the range.

función (págs. 359, 362)   Relación que empareja cada elemento del dominio con un solo elemento del rango.

H

hypotenuse (p. 298)   The side of a right triangle that is opposite the right angle.

hipotenusa (pág. 298)   Lado de un triángulo rectángulo que es opuesto al ángulo recto.

I

image (p. 231, 234, 250)   The position of a figure after a transformation.

imagen (págs. 231, 234, 250)   Posición de una figura después de una transformación.

index (p. 39)   In the radical expression, $\sqrt[n]{a}$, n is the root index. $\sqrt[n]{a} = b$ if $b^n = a$.

index (pág 39)   En la expresión radical, $\sqrt[n]{a}$, n es el índice de la raíz. $\sqrt[n]{a} = b$ si $b^n = a$.

installment credit (p. 489)   A type of credit in which the amount is repaid in regular payments.

crédito a plazos fijos/pagos fijos (pág. 489)   Un tipo de crédito en el que la cantidad se paga en pagos iguales.

installment loan (p. 489)   A loan in which the borrower makes fixed payments, such as a monthly payment.

préstamo a plazo fijo/préstamo a pagos fijos (pág. 489)   Un préstamo en el cual el deudor hace pagos fijos, como por ejemplo pagos mensuales.

interest (p. 489)   A percentage of the loan amount charged by the lender as payment for loaning money.

interés (pág. 489)   Un porcentaje de la cantidad prestada que el prestamista cobra por prestar el dinero.

irrational number (p. 59)   A number that cannot be written as the ratio of two integers.

número irracional (pág. 59)   Número que no puede escribirse como razón de dos enteros.

L

lateral area (p. 328)   The sum of the areas of the lateral faces of a solid.

área lateral (pág. 328)   Suma de las áreas de las caras laterales de un cuerpo geométrico.

legend (p. 105)   A story handed down by tradition that is popularly regarded as historical but unverified.

leyenda (pág. 105)   Una historia transmitida por tradición oral que la gente considera histórica, pero que no está verificada.

legs (p. 298)   In a right triangle, the sides that form the right angle.

catetos (pág. 298)   En un triángulo rectángulo, los lados que forman el ángulo recto.

line of reflection (p. 239)   The line across which an object is reflected; a reflection is a transformation that creates a mirror image.

línea de reflexión (pág. 239)   La línea con respecto a la cual se refleja un objeto; una reflexión es una transformación que genera un reflejo o imagen de espejo.

linear (p. 134)   A line representing points on a coordinate plane that lie on a straight line; that is, the rate of change is constant.

lineal (pág. 134)   Una gráfica que representa puntos que se hallan en una línea recta en un plano de coordenadas, es decir, su tasa de cambio es constante.

linear association (p. 449)   An association that occurs when a linear pattern (such as one of the form $y = mx + b$) describes the essential nature of the relationship between two variables.

correlación lineal (pág. 449)   Una asociación que ocurre cuando un modelo lineal (por ejemplo, uno con la forma $y = mx + b$) describe la naturaleza esencial de la relación entre dos variables.

linear model (p. 451)   A model of the form $y = mx + b$ that describes the essential nature of the relationship between y and x.

modelo lineal (pág. 451)   Un modelo con la forma $y = mx + b$ que describe la naturaleza esencial de la relación entre x y y.

M

mapping (p. 362)   A visual representation of a relation in which an arrow associates each input with its output.

mapeo (pág. 362)   Representación visual de una relación en la que una flecha asocia cada entrada con su salida.

mean absolute deviation (p. 457)   The average distance that the observations are from the mean of the distribution.

significa absoluta desviación (pág. 457)   La distancia media que las observaciones son de la media de la distribución.

median-median line (p. 468)   A line that can be used to describe and analyze bivariate data.

recta mediana-mediana (pág. 468)   Una recta que se puede usar para describir y analizar datos bivariados.

N

negative association (p. 449)   Two variables are related in a negative association when values for one variable tend to decrease as values for the other variable increase; an increase in x corresponds with a decrease in y.

correlación negativa (pág. 449)   Dos variables tienen una correlación negativa cuando los valores de una variable tienden a decrecer cuando los valores de la otra variable aumentan; un incremento en x corresponde a un decremento en y.

nonlinear association (p. 449)   An association shown by a nonlinear pattern (such as a curve) that describes the essential nature of the relationship between two variables.

correlación no lineal (pág. 449)   Una correlación mostrada por un modelo no lineal (como una curva) que describe la naturaleza esencial de la relación entre dos variables.

O

ordered pair (p. 357)   Two numbers written in a certain order. Most often, ordered pair refers to the x- and y-coordinates of a point on the coordinate plane, which are written (x,y). Ordered pair may also refer to any values paired together according to a specific order.

par ordenado (pág. 357)   Dos números que se escriben en cierto orden. Más frecuentemente, el par ordenado se refiere a las coordenadas x e y de un punto sobre el plano de coordenadas, que se escriben (x,y). El par ordenado puede también referirse a valores cualesquiera emparejados según un orden específico.

P

perfect square (p. 36)   A number that represents the product of number multiplied by itself.

cuadrado perfecto (pág. 36)   Número que representa el producto de un número multiplicado por sí mismo.

persuasive (p. 143)   Convincing with details, evidence, or examples.

persuasivo (pág. 143)   Que convence con detalles, evidencia o ejemplos.

positive association (p. 449)   Two variables are related in a positive association when values for one variable tend to increase as values for the other variable also increase; an increase in x corresponds with an increase in y.

correlación positiva (pág. 449)   Dos variables tienen una correlación positiva cuando los valores de una variable tienden a aumentar cuando los valores de la otra variable también aumentan; un aumento en x corresponde a un aumento en y.

power (p. 72)   A mathematical expression with two parts, a base and an exponent. For example, in the power 5^3, 5 is the base and 3 is the exponent.

potencia (pág. 72)   Expresión matemática con dos partes, una base y un exponente. Por ejemplo, en la potencia 53, 5 es la base y 3 es el exponente.

pre-image (p. 231, 234, 250)   The original image in a transformation.

preimagen (págs. 231, 234, 250)   Imagen original en una transformación.

principal (p. 489)   The amount of a loan.

principal (pág. 489)   El monto de un préstamo.

proportion (p. 268)   An equation stating that two ratios are equal.

proporción (pág. 268)   Ecuación que establece que dos razones son iguales.

Pythagorean theorem (p. 299)   This theorem states that the sum of the squares of the lengths of the legs of a right triangle equals the square of the length of the hypotenuse.

Teorema de Pitágoras (pág. 299)   Este teorema establece que la suma de los cuadrados de las longitudes de los catetos de un triángulo rectángulo es igual al cuadrado de la longitud de la hipotenusa.

Pythagorean triple (p. 321)   Three integers a, b, and c such that $c^2 = a^2 + b^2$.

triples Pitagóricos (pág. 321)   Tres enteros a, b y c tales que $c^2 = a^2 + b^2$.

R

range (p. 366)   In a relation, the range is the set of all output values. In statistics, the range is the difference between the highest and lowest values in a data set.

rango (pág. 366)   Diferencia entre el valor más alto y el más bajo de un conjunto de datos.

rate of change (p. 411, 426)   In a relationship, the ratio of vertical change in the output to the horizontal change in the input. The output is often represented by the variable y, and the input is often represented by the variable x.

tasa de cambio (págs. 411, 426)   En una relación, razón del cambio vertical en la salida al cambio horizontal en la entrada. La salida se representa habitualmente con la variable y, y la entrada se representa .

rational number (p. 50, 59)   Any number that can be written as the ratio of two integers where the divisor is not zero; for example, 8, 1.5, $\frac{2}{5}$, and -3.

número racional (págs. 50, 59)   Cualquier número que pueda escribirse como la razón entre dos enteros, donde el divisor no es cero; por ejemplo, 8, 1.5, $\frac{2}{5}$ y -3.

ray (p. 223)   A part of a line consisting of an endpoint and all points on one side of that endpoint.

rayo (pág. 223)   Parte de una recta que consta de un extremo y todos los puntos a un lado de ese extremo.

reciprocal (p. 25, 76)   Two numbers are reciprocals if their product is 1. Another name for reciprocal is multiplicative inverse.

recíproco (págs. 25, 76)   Dos números son recíprocos si su producto es 1. Otro nombre para recíprocos es inversos multiplicativos.

reduction (p. 286)   A dilation in which an image described by $0 < k < 1$ is smaller than the original figure.

reducción (pág. 286)   Una dilatación en la cual una imagen descrita por $0 < k < 1$ es más pequeña que la figura original.

reflection (p. 238)   A transformation in which a figure is flipped over a line of reflection. Each point of the image is the same distance from the line of reflection as its corresponding point in the pre-image.

reflexión (pág. 238)   Transformación en la que una figura se invierte sobre un eje de reflexión. Cada punto de la imagen está a la misma distancia del eje de reflexión que el correspondiente punto de la preimagen.

refute (p. 48)   To prove a claim to be wrong; for example, refusing to believe something based on the evidence provided.

refutar (pág. 48)   Demostrar que una afirmación es falsa; por ejemplo, rehusarse a creer algo con base en la evidencia provista.

relation (p. 357)   Any set of ordered pairs.

relación (pág. 357)   Cualquier conjunto de pares ordenados.

remote interior angle (p. 224)   For each exterior angle of a triangle, the two nonadjacent interior angles are its remote interior angles.

ángulo interno remoto (pág. 224)   Para cada ángulo externo de un triángulo, los dos ángulos internos no adyacentes son sus ángulos internos remotos.

repeating decimal (p. 51)   A decimal that has one or more digits following the decimal point that repeat endlessly.

decimal periódico (pág. 51)   Decimal que tiene uno o más dígitos que se repiten sin fin después del punto decimal.

revolving credit (p. 489) A type of credit with which the amount paid each month can vary based on additional charges, as with a credit card.

crédito revolvente (pág. 489) Un tipo de crédito con el cual la cantidad pagada cada mes puede variar en base a cargos adicionales, como en una tarjeta de crédito.

rotation (p. 241) A transformation in which each point of the pre-image travels clockwise or counterclockwise around a fixed point a certain number of degrees.

rotación (pág. 241) Transformación en la que cada punto de la preimagen se mueve un determinado número de grados alrededor de un punto fijo en el sentido de las manecillas del reloj o en el sentido contrario al de las manecillas del reloj.

row percentages (p. 479) In a two-way table, row percentages communicate the relative frequencies of column categories within a given row category.

porcentajes de fila u horizontales (pág. 479) En una tabla de doble entrada, los porcentajes de fila son las frecuencias relativas de las categorías de las columnas en cada categoría de fila.

S

scale factor (p. 271) In similar figures and similar solids, the ratio of the lengths of any pair of corresponding sides or edges.

factor de escala (pág. 271) En figuras semejantes y cuerpos geométricos semejantes, es la razón de las longitudes de cualquier par de lados o aristas correspondientes.

scale factor of a dilation (p. 286) The factor by which each linear measure of the figure is multiplied.

factor de escala de una dilatación (pág. 286) El factor por el cual se multiplica cada medida lineal de la figura.

scatterplot (p. 425) A graphic display of bivariate data on a coordinate plane that may be used to show a relationship between two variables.

diagrama de dispersión (pág. 425) Representación gráfica de datos bivariados sobre un plano de coordenadas, que puede usarse para mostrar una relación entre dos variables.

scientific notation (p. 84) A number is written in scientific notation when it is expressed in the form $a \times 10^n$, where $1 \leq a < 10$ and n is an integer.

notación científica (pág. 84) Un número está escrito en notación científica cuando se expresa en la forma $a \times 10^n$, donde $1 \leq a < 10$ y n es un entero.

segmented bar graph (p. 479) A graphic display of data showing the percentages of each response for each group of interest. A segmented bar graph is helpful for visualizing the similarities and differences between groups.

gráfica de barras segmentadas (pág. 479) Una representación gráfica de datos que muestra los porcentajes de cada respuesta para cada grupo de interés. Una gráfica de barras segmentadas es útil para visualizar similitudes y diferencias entre grupos.

sequence (p. 4) An ordered list of numbers. Each number is called a term of the sequence. For example, {0, 1, 2, 3, …} is a sequence in which the 1st term is 0, the 2nd term is 1, the 3rd term is 2, the 4th term is 3, and so on.

sucesión (pág. 4) Lista ordenada de números. Cada número se llama término de la sucesión. Por ejemplo, {0, 1, 2, 3, …} es una sucesión en que el 1er término es 0, el 2º término es 1, el 3er término es 2, el 4º término es 3, y así sucesivamente.

set (p. 357) A set is a collection of objects, like points, or a type of number, like the real numbers. The symbols {} indicate a set.

conjunto (pág. 357) Un conjunto es una colección de objetos, como puntos o un tipo de número, como los números reales. Los símbolos {} indican un conjunto.

similar figures (p. 268, 281) Figures in which the lengths of the corresponding sides are in proportion and the corresponding angles are congruent.

figuras semejantes (págs. 268, 281) Figuras en que las longitudes de los lados correspondientes están en proporción y los ángulos correspondientes son congruentes.

similarity statement (p. 268) A statement indicating that the corresponding angles are congruent, and the corresponding sides are proportional.

declaración de similitud/semejanza (pág. 268) Una oración que indica que los ángulos correspondientes son congruentes y los lados correspondientes son proporcionales.

simple interest (p. 489) Interest paid only on the principal of the loan.

interés simple (pág. 489) El interés pagado solo sobre el principal del préstamo.

slope (p. 137, 151) The slope of a line is the ratio $\dfrac{\text{change in } y}{\text{change in } x}$ between any two points that lie on the line.

pendiente (págs. 137, 151) La pendiente de una recta es la razón $\dfrac{\text{cambio en } y}{\text{cambio en } x}$ entre cualquier par de puntos que yacen sobre una recta.

slope-intercept form (p. 155) The slope-intercept form of a linear equation is $y = mx + b$, where m is the slope and b is the y-intercept.

forma pendiente-intercepto (pág. 155) La forma pendiente-intercepto de una ecuación lineal es $y = mx + b$, donde m es la pendiente y b es el intercepto en el eje de las y.

solution of a system of linear equations (p. 179) The point or set of points that makes all equations in the system true.

solución de un sistema de ecuaciones lineales (pág. 179) Punto o conjunto de puntos que hace verdaderas todas las ecuaciones del sistema.

solve for y (p. 183) To solve for y use inverse operations to isolate y on one side of the equal sign.

resolver para y (pág. 183) Al resolver para y se usan operaciones inversas para aislar y en un lado del signo de igual.

square root (p.36) A number that when multiplied by itself gives the original number under the radical sign.

raíz cuadrada (pág. 36) Un número que se multiplica por sí mismo y produce el número original debajo del signo radical.

substitution method for solving a system of linear equations (p. 190) A method that involves solving one of the equations for one of the variables and then substituting that value in the other equation(s).

método de sustitución para resolver un sistema de ecuaciones lineales (pág. 190) Método que involucra resolver una de las ecuaciones para una de las variables y luego sustituir ese valor en la otra ecuación o ecuaciones.

supplementary angles (p. 206) Two angles whose measures have a sum of $180°$.

ángulos suplementarios (pág. 206) Dos ángulos cuyas medidas suman $180°$.

surface area (p. 328)   The sum of the areas of the faces of a solid figure.

área superficial (pág. 328)   Suma de las áreas de las caras de un cuerpo geométrico.

symbolic representation (p. 234)   An algebraic way to show the changes to the *x*- and *y*-coordinates of the vertices of the original figure, or preimage.

representación simbólica (pág. 234)   Una manera algebraica de mostrar los cambios en las coordenadas *x* y *y* de los vértices de la figura o imagen original.

system of linear equations (p. 179)   Two or more linear equations using the same variables.

sistema de ecuaciones lineales (pág. 179)   Dos o más ecuaciones lineales que usan las mismas variables.

T

term (p. 489)   The length of a loan, usually stated in months or years.

plazo (pág. 489)   La duración de un préstamo, por lo general expresada en meses o años.

terminating decimal (p. 50)   A decimal that has a finite or limited number of digits following the decimal point.

decimal exacto (pág. 50)   Decimal que tiene un número finito o limitado de dígitos después del punto decimal.

transform (p. 231)   To change.

transformar (pág. 231)   Cambiar.

transformation (p. 231)   A change in the position or size of a figure on a plane.

transformación (pág. 231)   Cambio en la posición o el tamaño de una figura sobre un plano.

translation (p. 234)   A transformation that moves each point of a figure the same distance and in the same direction.

traslación (pág. 234)   Transformación que mueve cada punto de una figura la misma distancia y en la misma dirección.

transversal (p. 208)   A line that intersects two or more lines at different points.

transversal (pág. 208)   Recta que interseca dos o más rectas en diferentes puntos.

trend line (p. 424, 459)   A line that helps explain the relationship between two quantities on a graph. A trend line indicates the general course or tendency of a set of data.

línea de tendencia (págs. 424, 459)   Línea que ayuda a explicar la relación entre dos cantidades en una gráfica. Una línea de tendencia indica el curso general o tendencia de un conjunto de datos.

two-way table (p. 478)   A table used for identifying each observation, response, etc., in a data set according to two categorical variables.

tabla de doble entrada (pág. 478)   Una tabla que se usa para identificar cada observación, respuesta, etc. en un conjunto de datos de acuerdo con dos variables cualitativas o categóricas.

V

verbal description (p. 234)   A description of a translation that includes words such as right, left, up, and down.

descripción verbal (pág. 234)   Una descripción de una traslación que incluye palabras como *derecha, izquierda, arriba* y *abajo*.

vertical angles (p. 213)   A pair of angles formed by two intersecting lines. Vertical angles share a common vertex but no common sides.

ángulos opuestos por el vértice (pág. 213)   Pares de ángulos que se forman cuando dos rectas se intersecan. Los ángulos opuestos por el vértice comparten un vértice en común, pero no rayos comunes.

vertical line test (p. 370)   A visual inspection for checking whether or not a graph represents a function.

prueba de la recta vertical (pág. 370)   Inspección visual para comprobar si una gráfica representa o no una función.

Verbal & Visual Word Association

Definition in Your Own Words	Important Elements

Academic Vocabulary Word

Visual Representation	Personal Association

Word Map

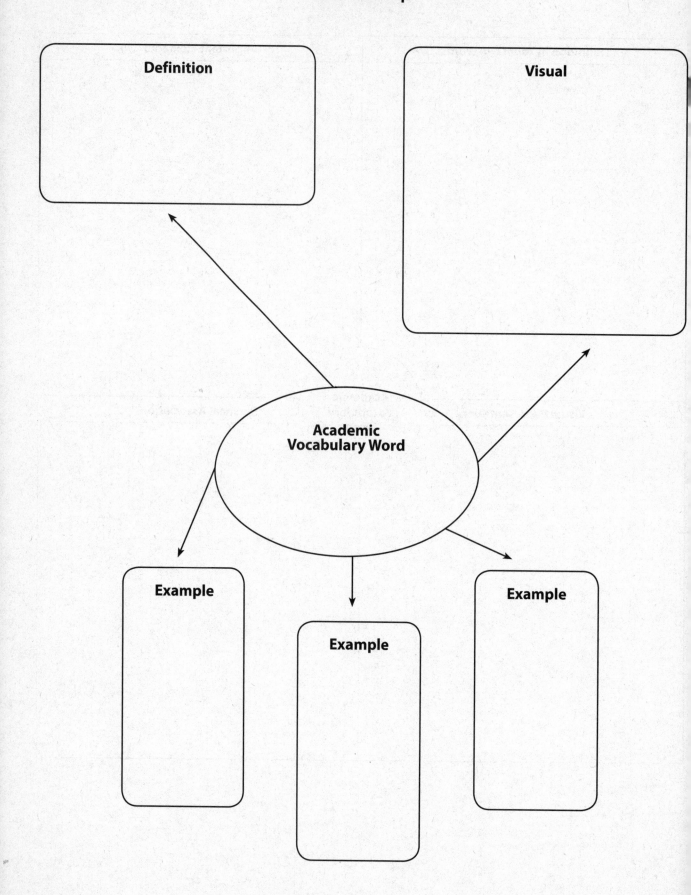

Definition

Visual

Academic Vocabulary Word

Example

Example

Example

Eight Circle Spider

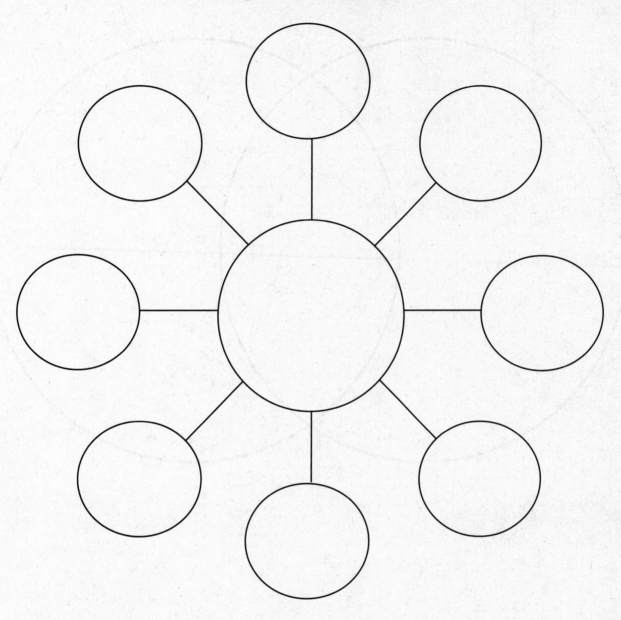

Venn Diagram

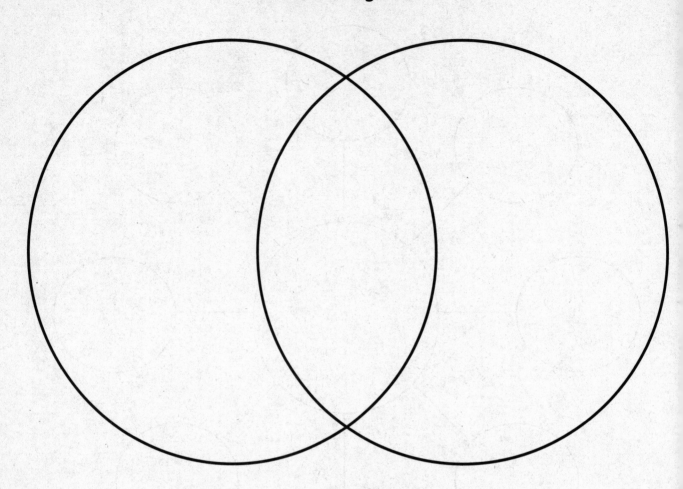

Index

N

Negative association, 449
Negative exponents, 75–77
Nonlinear association, 449
Non-linear functions, 423–436
Numbers
  absolute value, 12
  cubing, 39
  irrational, 59–60
  rational, 50–56, 59–60
  reciprocal of, 25, 76
  rectangular, 114
  scientific notation, 84–87
  standard form, 84–87
  triangular, 114–115

O

Ordered pairs
  defined, 357
  relation and, 357
Order of operations
  exponents and, 41–42
  powers, 41–42
  roots, 41–42
Outliers, 450
Output, function and, 359, 362–365

P

Parallel lines
  angles formed by, 208–214
  symbol for, 209
Parentheses, order of operations and, 42
Patterns
  analyze sequences, 3–10
  consecutive terms, 107
  constant difference, 107–110
  increasing and decreasing sequences,
    11–14
  quantitative reasoning, 31–32
  rectangular numbers, 114
  in scatter plots, 445–448, 449–453
  triangular numbers, 114–115
  writing expressions for, 105–116
Percent
  comparing rational numbers, 53–56
  converting to decimals, 47–49
  converting to fractions, 47–49
  decimal form of, 125
Perfect square, 36
Persuasive, 143
Pi, as irrational number, 59
Pluto, 93
Positive association, 449
Power
  cubes, 38–40
  defined, 35, 72
  order of operations and, 41–42
  of powers, 78–80
  squares, 33–37
  of zero, 78–80, 88–89
Predictions, trend line to make, 459–463
Preimage, 231, 234
Principal, loan, 489
Prisms, volume of, 339–342
Probability and statistics
  association
    cluster, 450
    correlation coefficient, 449

  defined, 446
  direction, 449
  form, 449
  linear, 449
  moderate, 449
  negative, 449
  nonlinear, 449
  outliers, 450
  positive, 449
  strength, 449
  strong, 449
  between two categorical variables,
    481–483
  weak, 449
  bivariate data, collecting, 455–458
  census, 465
  linear model, 451, 467–475
  median-median line, 467–475, 485–486
  row percentages, 479
  scatter plots
    bivariate data, 455–458
    recognize patterns in, 445–448
  segmented bar graph, 479
  trend lines to make prediction, 459–463
  two-way tables, 477–480, 485–486
Profit, 131–132
Properties
  Associative, 94
  Commutative, 94
  Distributive Property, 122
  Multiplicative Identity Property, 121, 124
  of transformations, 247–253
Proportional relationship
  directly proportional relationship,
    166–171
  functions, 391–393
  linear, 161–165
Proportions, similar figures, 268
Propulsion, 379
Pyramids, volume of, 339–342
Pythagoreans, 113, 114
Pythagorean Theorem
  concept of, 297–300
  converse of, 317–320
  coordinate plane and, 311–314
  defined, 299
  find missing lengths, 301–304
  Pythagorean Triple, 321–323
  for two and three dimensions, 307–310
Pythagorean Triple, 321–323

Q

Quadrilaterals, angles of, 225–226
Quantitative reasoning, patterns and,
  31–32

R

Radical sign, 36, 39
Range
  defined, 366
  domain and range, 366–369
  identifying function, 366–369
Rate of change
  defined, 411, 426
  functions, 400–405
  linear equations, 174–175
  linear functions, 411–416
  slope as constant, 137

Ratio
  rate of change as, 135–137
  scale factor, 271–273
  writing, 135
Rational numbers
  compare fractions, decimals, percents,
    53–56
  compare to irrational numbers, 63–66
  defined, 50, 59
  terminating and repeating decimals as,
    50–52
Ray, 223
Reading Math, 35, 51, 135, 137, 179, 205,
  209, 235, 252, 283, 3197
Reciprocal
  defined, 25
  dividing fractions, 25–28
  negative exponent, 76
Rectangles
  area, 33
  Pythagorean Theorem and, 309–310
Rectangular numbers, 114
Rectangular prism
  lateral and surface areas of, 327–332
  volume of, 339–342
Reduction, dilation, 286
Reflection, angle of, 229
Reflections
  coordinates, 238–240
  defined, 231–233
  equidistant and, 238
  line of reflection, 239
  properties of, 247–253
  symbolic representation, 238
Refute, 48
Relation, 357
Remote interior angles, 224
Repeating decimals, 51–52
  comparing rational numbers, 53–56
  converting to fractions, 51
Revenue, 131–132
Revolving credit, 489
Right triangle, Pythagorean Theorem and,
  297–304, 317–320
Roots
  cube, 39–40
  order of operations and, 41–42
  square, 36
Rotations
  coordinates, 241–244
  defined, 231–233
  direction of, 241
  properties of, 247–253
Row percentages, 479

S

Scale factor
  of dilation, 286
  similar triangles, 271–276
Scatter plots
  association, 449–453
  bivariate data, 455–458
  defined, 425
  linear model, 467–475
  median-median line, 467–475
  recognize patterns in, 445–448, 449–453
  trend lines and, 440–441, 459–463
Scientific notation
  addition, 97–98

compare and order numbers in, 88–90
defined, 84
division, 93–96
multiplication, 93–96
negative exponents, 89
power of zero, 88–89
subtraction, 97–98
writing number in, 83–87
Segmented bar graph, 479
Sequence
analyze simple, 3–10
defined, 4
Fibonacci numbers, 11
increasing and decreasing, 11–14
Set, 357
Silo, 415
Similar figures
defined, 281
dilations, 279–291
proportional sides, 268
Similarity statement, 268
Similar triangles, 136
identify, 265–270
properties and conditions of, 271–276
scale factor, 271–273
similarity statement, 268
Simple interest, 489, 494
Slide, 231–232
Slope
as average rate of change, 137
compare different lines, 151–154
concept of, 133–138
as constant rate of change, 137
defined, 137
finding, 137–141
identify, using tables and graphs, 147–150
linear equations and, 133–144
slope-intercept form, 155–158
Slope-intercept form
defined, 155
introduction to, 155–158
Solar system, 93
Solution to system of equations, 179
Spheres, volume of, 343–347
Square
area of, 34
perfect square, 36
as power, 35–36
Pythagorean Theorem and, 307–308
Squared, 35
Square root, 36
Standard form of number, 84–87

Statistics. *See* Probability and statistics
Strength, association, 449
Strong, association, 449
Substitution, to solve linear systems, 190
Subtraction
fractions, 17–22
order of operations and, 42
scientific notation, 97–98
Supplementary angles, 203, 206–207
Supply and demand, 199
Surface area
cylinders, 333–336
defined, 328
prisms, 327–332
Symbolic representation, 234
System of linear equations, 179. *See also*
Linear systems

T

Tables
to find slope, 147–150
rate of change, 412–413
two-way tables, 477–480, 485–486
Term of loan, 489
Terminating decimals, 50
Transform, 231
Transformations
composition of transformations,
252–258
congruency, 249–250
defined, 231
dilations, 279–291
image and preimage, 231, 234
properties of, 247–253
reflections, 238–240
rotations, 241–244
symbolic representation, 234
terms for, 231–233
translations, 232–233, 234–237
Translations
coordinates, 234–237
defined, 231–233
properties of, 247–253
symbolic representation, 234
verbal description of, 234
Transversal line, 208
Trapezoid, area of, 247, 289
Trend line
defined, 424
to make prediction, 459–463
scatter plot and, 440, 459–463

Triangles
angles of, 217–222
area of, 251, 284
exterior angles of, 223
hypotenuse of, 297–300
legs of, 298
Pythagorean Theorem, concept of,
297–300
remote interior angles, 224
similar, 136, 265–276
identify, 265–270
properties and conditions of, 271–276
proportions, 268
scale factor, 271–273
similarity statement, 268
sum of angles, 219–222
Triangular numbers, 114–115
Triangular prism
lateral and surface areas of, 330–331
volume of, 342
Truth in Lending Act, 490
Turn, 231–232
Two-way tables, 477–480, 485–486

V

Variables, categorical, 478
Vertical angles, 213
Volumes
composite solids, 348–350
cones, 343–347
cylinders, 343–347
prisms, 339–342
pyramids, 339–342
spheres, 343–347

W

Weak, association, 449
Wind power, 395
Writing Math, 9, 35, 36, 39, 135, 148,
269, 313

Y

y-intercept
finding, 137–138, 140–142
slope-intercept form, 155–158
writing, 148

Z

Zero, power of, 78–80, 88–89